THIRD FORM LATIN

TEACHER KEY
WORKBOOK, QUIZZES, & TESTS
Cheryl Lowe

THIRD FORM LATIN

TEACHER
WORKBOOK, QUIZZES
by Cheryl Lowe

Published by:
Memoria Press
www.memoriapress.com

First Edition © 2011 by Memoria Press Copyright 1216
All rights reserved
ISBN# 978-1-61538-146-3

Contents

Translation Checklist

As sentences become more complex, students are often insecure about their answers and want confirmation for every choice they make. Students need to learn how to evaluate their answers correctly, so they don't waste class time asking about every deviation from the key. Below is a checklist to help students distinguish between an error and legitimate choices in their answers. Go over this with your students thoroughly. These topics are listed in the order that students will encounter them, so you will have to refer to this checklist throughout the year. Latin word order is very flexible, so an answer that deviates from the norm is not wrong. However, the exercises stick with the usual word order *most of the time,* and so should the student.

1. **Word Choice.** There are two or more meanings for many vocabulary words. All choices are correct unless there are specific restrictions about certain meanings. The answer key doesn't always give each alternative meaning. Sometimes the key will give both choices for words with more than one meaning, but not on a consistent basis.

2. **Verb Tenses & Moods**

    a. There are three choices for the present tense.
        I call   *I do call*   *I am calling*

    b. There are three choices for the perfect tense.
        I called   *I did call*   *I have called*

    c. The English simple past is often a correct translation for the Latin imperfect tense. For a repeated action, *I called every day* sounds better in English than *I was calling every day.*

    d. The imperfect of **sum** can be *I was* or *I was being*; the perfect can be *I was* or *I have been.*

    e. Imperatives: When the number is unclear in English, the singular or plural may be used in Latin.

3. In Latin the indirect object usually precedes the verb, and can be translated two ways in English.
    I gave the dog a bone   or   *I gave a bone to the dog*

4. A possessive can be translated two ways—both are correct. In Latin the genitive usually precedes the noun, but it is not incorrect if it follows.
    Mary's house   or   *the house of Mary*

5. The location of prepositional phrases is variable in both Latin and English. Both sentences below are correct in English; likewise in the Latin, the prepositional phrase can be before or after the main clause.
    They made an altar to God at the foot of the mountain.
    At the foot of the mountain, they made an altar to God.

6. The location of an adverb is variable, although it usually precedes the verb in Latin.
    *We took the money **easily**.*   *We **easily** took the money.*

More Verb Tenses, Passive Voice
The present, imperfect, and perfect passive tenses can be translated with or without *being/been.*
    I am called   or   *I am being called*
    I was called   or   *I was being called*
    I was called   or   *I have been called*

7. For the sake of convenience, this text will use *you* for singular and *you all* for plural.

8. Possessive pronoun adjectives are frequently omitted in Latin but not in English.
    I love my father.   **Patrem amo.**

UNIT I

VERBS

1. Verb families are called _____conjugations_____, and noun families are called _____declensions_____.

2. Verbs have _____tense_____ and _____personal_____ endings, and nouns have _____case_____ endings.

3. Give the six attributes of verbs. _____conjugation, person, number, tense, voice, mood_____

4. Give the three moods of Latin verbs. _____indicative, imperative, subjunctive_____

5. All of the verb tenses you have learned have been in the _____indicative_____ mood.

6. The indicative mood is used for _____statements of fact_____ and _____questions_____.

7. The imperative mood is used for _____commands_____.

8. The subjunctive mood is used to express _____potential action, such as opinion, purpose, and wishes_____ and will be covered in Unit _____IV_____ of this text.

9. Give the two voices of Latin verbs. _____active and passive_____

10. Give the number of verbs you have learned in each conjugation.
    1st conj. _____50_____
    2nd conj. _____20_____
    3rd conj. _____10_____
    3rd conj. **io** _____5_____
    4th conj. _____10_____
    irregular verbs _____1_____

11. How many new verbs will you learn in this unit, and what conjugation are they?
    _____10 3rd-conjugation verbs_____

5

6

Lesson One

I. Word Study and Grammar

1. In the active voice, the subject __performs the action of the verb__ .

2. In the passive voice, the subject __receives the action of the verb__ .

3. The present passive system is formed by substituting __passive__ personal endings for __active__ personal endings.

4. Give the irregularity in the present system passive of the 1st and 2nd conjugations. (*Second Form* Grammar Question #65) __2nd person sing., future, is -beris instead of -biris__

5. The infinitive of all 1st conjugation verbs ends in __-are__ . The infinitive of all 2nd-conjugation verbs ends in __-ēre__ .

6. What does the (1) or (2) that follows a verb entry form mean? _____
   (1) means the verb is 1st conj. with regular principal parts
   (2) means 2nd conj. with regular p.p.

7. When the action of a passive verb is performed by a LIVING AGENT, the construction is called __ablative of agent__ and requires the preposition __ab__ .

II. Latin Sayings Review

1. always faithful __semper fidelis__

2. To err is human. __Errare est humanum.__

3. Now or never __Nunc aut numquam__

4. Fortune aids the brave. __Fortes fortuna juvat.__

5. Then we will fight in the shade. __In umbra, ígitur, pugnábimus.__

6. The mother was standing __Stabat Mater__

7. Let us recite together. __In choro recitemus.__

8. Pray and work. __Ora et labora.__

9. I am a Roman citizen. __Civis Romanus sum.__

10. I see and am silent. __Vídeo et táceo.__

11. I came, I saw, I conquered. __Veni, vidi, vici.__

12. Beware the dog. __Cave canem.__

13. To teach, to delight, to move __Docēre, delectare, movēre__

Lesson One

III. Vocabulary Review

Write 1 or 2 for the conjugation next to verbs with regular principal parts. Give the infinitive and the meaning. If the verb has irregular principal parts, write them out in full. Say all p.p. aloud and practice until perfect.

Latin		Infinitive	Meaning	Irregular Principal Parts	
accuso	1	accusare	to accuse		
adoro	1	adorare	to adore		
ámbulo	1	ambulare	to walk		
amo	1	amare	to love, like		
appáreo	2	apparēre	to appear		
appello	1	appellare	to address		
árdeo		ardēre	to burn, be on fire	arsi	arsus
aro	1	arare	to plow		
cáveo		cavēre	to beware of, guard against	cavi	cautus
celo	1	celare	to hide		
clamo	1	clamare	to shout		
creo	1	creare	to create		
culpo	1	culpare	to blame		
débeo	2	debēre	to owe, ought		
delecto	1	delectare	to delight, please		
demonstro	1	demonstrare	to show, point out		
do		dare	to give	dedi	datus
dóceo		docēre	to teach	dócui	doctus
dúbito	1	dubitare	to doubt		
erro	1	errare	to err, wander		
exploro	1	explorare	to explore		
exspecto	1	exspectare	to wait for, expect		
gáudeo		gaudēre	to rejoice	--	--
hábeo	2	habēre	to have		
hábito	1	habitare	to live in, dwell		
júbeo		jubēre	to order, command	jussi	jussus
júdico	1	judicare	to judge, consider		
juvo		juvare	to help	juvi	jutus
laboro	1	laborare	to work		
laudo	1	laudare	to praise		
lavo		lavare	to wash	lavi	lautus
líbero	1	liberare	to set free		
máneo		manēre	to remain, stay	mansi	mansus
móneo	2	monēre	to warn		

Latin		Infinitive	Meaning	Irregular Principal Parts	
móveo		movēre	to move	movi	motus
muto	1	mutare	to change		
narro	1	narrare	to tell		
nato	1	natare	to swim		
návigo	1	navigare	to sail		
nego	1	negare	to deny		
núntio	1	nuntiare	to report		
óccupo	1	occupare	to sieze		
oppugno	1	oppugnare	to attack		
opto	1	optare	to choose		
oro	1	orare	to speak, pray		
paro	1	parare	to prepare		
perturbo	1	perturbare	to disturb		
porto	1	portare	to carry		
prohíbeo	2	prohibēre	to prevent		
pugno	1	pugnare	to fight		
puto	1	putare	to think		
respóndeo		respondēre	to respond, answer	respondi	responsus
rogo	1	rogare	to ask		
saluto	1	salutare	to greet		
sédeo		sedēre	to sit	sedi	sessus
servo	1	servare	to guard, keep		
specto	1	spectare	to look at		
spero	1	sperare	to hope		
sto		stare	to stand	steti	status
sum		esse	to be	fui	futurus
súpero	1	superare	to overcome		
táceo	2	tacēre	to be silent		
tempto	1	temptare	to tempt		
téneo		tenēre	to hold	ténui	tentus
térreo	2	terrēre	to frighten		
tímeo		timēre	to fear, be afraid	tímui	--
váleo		valēre	to be strong, be well	válui	--
vídeo		vidēre	to see	vidi	visus
voco	1	vocare	to call		
volo	1	volare	to fly		
vúlnero	1	vulnerare	to wound		

IV. Active/Passive Voice Review

Give the voice of each sentence, A (active) or P (passive).
Rewrite each sentence in the opposite voice. Watch out for a trick sentence.

1. Hannibal invaded Italy. __(A)__ Italy was invaded by Hannibal.

2. Hannibal was feared by the Romans. __(P)__ The Romans feared Hannibal.

3. Hannibal defeated the Romans at the Battle of Cannae. __(A)__ The Romans were defeated by Hannibal at the Battle of Cannae.

4. Scipio finally defeated Hannibal. __(A)__ Hannibal was finally defeated by Scipio.

5. Hannibal was a great general. __(A)__ The "to be" verb cannot be written in the passive.

6. *De Bello Gallico* was written by Caesar. __(P)__ Caesar wrote *De Bello Gallico*.

7. Caesar formed the First Triumvirate. __(A)__ The First Triumvirate was formed by Caesar.

8. Caesar defeated Pompey in the Battle of Pharsalia. __(A)__ Pompey was defeated by Caesar in the Battle of Pharsalia.

9. The Julian Calendar was created by Caesar when he became emperor. __(P)__ Julius Caesar created the Julian Calendar when he became emperor.

10. The Senators stabbed Caesar in the Forum in 44 B.C. __(A)__ Caesar was stabbed by the Senators in the Forum in 44 B.C.

V. Conjugation

Give tense endings for the present system active of the 1st/2nd conjugations.

Person	Present		Imperfect		Future	
1st	o/m	mus	bam	bamus	bo	bimus
2nd	s	tis	bas	batis	bis	bitis
3rd	t	nt	bat	bant	bit	bunt

Lesson One   Worksheet 5

V. Conjugation (cont.)

Give the tense endings for the present system passive of the 1st/2nd conjugations.

Person	Present		Imperfect		Future	
1st	r/or	mur	bar	bamur	bor	bimur
2nd	ris	mini	baris	bámini	beris	bímini
3rd	tur	ntur	batur	bantur	bitur	buntur

Give the tense endings for the perfect system active, all conjugations.

Person	Perfect		Pluperfect		Future Perfect	
1st	i	imus	eram	eramus	ero	érimus
2nd	isti	istis	eras	eratis	eris	éritis
3rd	it	erunt	erat	erant	erit	erint

Make **four** copies of Drill/Test Form A in the Appendix. Conjugate each verb in the <u>indicative active</u> (6 tenses) and <u>indicative passive</u> (3 tenses). Make as many copies as necessary and practice these conjugations until you can do them from memory without error.

Copy 1) porto   **Copy 3)** dóceo (meanings, 1st P. sing. only)
Copy 2) dóceo   **Copy 4)** sum (active only)

VI. Form Drills
Drill A

1. errávimus ___we (have) erred___
2. putamus ___we think___
3. manserunt ___they remained___
4. delectavit ___hsi (has) delighted___
5. ambulabunt ___they will walk___
6. rogor ___I am (being) asked___

7. superabatur ___hsi was being overcome___
8. perturbabor ___I will be disturbed___
9. judicámini ___you all are (being) judged___
10. liberaris ___you are being set free___
11. vidébitur ___hsi will be seen___
12. speraveramus ___we had hoped___

Drill/Test Form A

Principal Parts: porto portare portavi portatus
Present System Stem: porta-

Present			
Indicative Active		Indicative Passive	
porto	portamus	portor	portamur
portas	portatis	portaris	portámini
portat	portant	portatur	portantur
Imperfect			
portabam	portabamus	portabar	portabamur
portabas	portabatis	portabaris	portabámini
portabat	portabant	portabatur	portabantur
Future			
portabo	portábimus	portabor	portábimur
portabis	portábitis	portáberis	portabímini
portabit	portabunt	portábitur	portabuntur

Perfect System Stem: portav-

Perfect			
Indicative Active		Indicative Passive	
portavi	portávimus		
portavisti	portavistis		
portavit	portaverunt		
Pluperfect			
portáveram	portaveramus		
portáveras	portaveratis		
portáverat	portáverant		
Future Perfect			
portávero	portavérimus		
portáveris	portavéritis		
portáverit	portáverint		

Principal Parts: dóceo docére dócui doctus
Present System Stem: doce-

Present			
Indicative Active		Indicative Passive	
dóceo	docemus	dóceor	docemur
doces	docetis	doceris	docémini
docet	docent	docetur	docentur
Imperfect			
docebam	docebamus	docebar	docebamur
docebas	docebatis	docebaris	docebámini
docebat	docebant	docebatur	docebantur
Future			
docebo	docébimus	docebor	docébimur
docebis	docébitis	docéberis	docebímini
docebit	docebunt	docébitur	docebuntur

Perfect System Stem: docu-

Perfect			
Indicative Active		Indicative Passive	
dócui	docúimus		
docuisti	docuistis		
dócuit	docuerunt		
Pluperfect			
docúeram	docueramus		
docúeras	docueratis		
docúerat	docúerant		
Future Perfect			
docúero	docúerimus		
docúeris	docuéritis		
docúerit	docúerint		

Principal Parts: sum esse fui futurus
Present System Stem: –   **Perfect System Stem:** fu-

Present		Perfect	
sum	sumus	fui	fúimus
es	estis	fuisti	fuistis
est	sunt	fuit	fuerunt
Imperfect		**Pluperfect**	
eram	eramus	fúeram	fueramus
eras	eratis	fúeras	fueratis
erat	erant	fúerat	fúerant
Future		**Future Perfect**	
ero	érimus	fúero	fuérimus
eris	éritis	fúeris	fuéritis
erit	erunt	fúerit	fuerunt

I teach
I was teaching
I will teach
I (have) taught
I had taught
I will have taught

I am (being) taught
I was (being) taught
I will be taught

Drill B

1. pugnavisti _you (have) fought_
2. creaverunt _they (have) created_
3. culpavi _I (have) blamed_
4. arávero _I will have plowed_
5. habitavistis _you all (have) dwelt_

6. accusatur _hsi is (being) accused_
7. mutáberis _you will be changed_
8. movébimur _we will be moved_
9. perturbatur _hsi is being disturbed_
10. prohibéberis _you will be prevented_

Saying
Say aloud and write 3X.

Latin	Cógito ergo sum
Latin	Cógito ergo sum
Latin	Cógito ergo sum
English	I think, therefore I am

VII. Translation
Underline the ablative of agent.

1. Nos a Deo non temptamur. _We are not tempted by God._
2. Pastor a lupo vulnerábitur. _The shepherd will be wounded by the wolf._
3. Lacus a piscatore videbatur. _The lake was being seen by the fisherman._
4. Libri a poetis creantur. _Books are being created by poets._
5. Senatores a pópulo culpabantur. _The senators were being blamed by the people._
6. Tu ab amicis juváberis. _You will be helped by friends._
7. Mark was being attacked by a bear. _Marcus ab ursā oppugnabatur._
8. Slaves are set free by good men. _Servi a viris bonis liberantur._
9. The soldiers will be wounded by the enemy. _Mílites ab hóstibus* vulnerabuntur._
10. The Gauls will be disturbed by the Romans. _Galli a Romanis perturbabuntur._

*Hostis is plural when it refers to a group.

I. Word Study and Grammar

1. The conjugation a verb belongs to is determined by the ___infinitive___ .
2. The infinitive of 3rd-conj. verbs ends in ___-ere___ , and 4th conj. in ___-ire___ .
3. Which conjugation does not have a model for regular principal parts? ___3rd___
4. The new 3rd-conj. verbs in this lesson form their 3rd principal part in ___s___ . The 3rd-conj. verbs in *Second Form* form their 3rd principal part in ___x___ .
5. When the action of a passive verb is performed by a NON-LIVING AGENT, the construction without a preposition is called the ___ablative of means___ .
6. Give the two kinds of direct questions.
   question words
   yes/no questions
7. What is the irregularity in the present passive tense of the 3rd and 3rd **io** conjugations? (*Second Form* Grammar Question #65) _2nd person sing., present tense is **-eris** instead of **-iris**_

Saying
Say aloud and write 3X.

Latin	Audi Ísrael!
Latin	Audi Ísrael!
Latin	Audi Ísrael!
English	Hear, O Israel!

Give the regular endings for the principal parts.

Conj.	1st	2nd	3rd	4th
1st	o	are	avi	atus
2nd	eo	ēre	ui	itus
4th	io	ire	ivi	itus

Conjugation Summary - Use model verbs.

Conj.	Dictionary entry (1st principal part)	Infinitive	Stem vowel
1st	amo	amare	a
2nd	móneo	monēre	ē
3rd	rego	régere	none (or weak e)
4th	áudio	audire	i
3rd io	cápio	cápere	i

II. Latin Sayings Review

1. Make haste slowly. _____ Festina lentē.

2. I shall either find a way or make one. _____ Aut viam invéniam aut fáciam.

3. Time flies _____ Tempus fugit

4. In this sign you will conquer. _____ In hoc signo vinces.

5. A friend is proven in time of necessity. _____ Amicus in necessitate probatur.

6. He is known by his companions. _____ Nóscitur ex sóciis.

7. Said and done _____ Dictum et factum

8. What's new? _____ Quid novi?

9. Iron is sharpened by iron. _____ Ferrum ferro exacúitur.

10. Repetition is the mother of learning. _____ Repetítio mater studiorum.

11. The city which captured the whole world is now captured. _____
 _____ Cápitur urbs quae totum cepit orbem.

12. From sea to sea _____ A mari usque ad mare

13. The master has spoken. _____ Magister dixit.

III. Question Review

1. Finiéntne? _____ Will they finish?

2. Quis es? _____ Who are you?

3. Quid das? _____ What are you giving?

4. Quando fúgies? _____ When will you flee?

5. Quómodo vivis? _____ How are you living?

6. Quam diu dórmies? _____ How long will you sleep?

7. Fecistíne cenam? _____ Did you make dinner?

8. Quot fratres habes? _____ How many brothers do you have?

IV. Vocabulary

Write 4 next to verbs with regular principal parts. Give the infinitive and the meaning. If the verb has irregular principal parts, write them out in full. Say all principal parts aloud. Practice until perfect.

Latin		Infinitive	Meaning	Irregular Principal Parts	
áudio	4	audire	to hear		
cápio		cápere	to take, capture	cepi	captus
cúpio		cúpere	to desire	cupivi	cupitus
dico		dícere	to say	dixi	dictus
duco		dúcere	to lead	duxi	ductus
dormio	4	dormire	to sleep		
fácio		fácere	to make, do	feci	factus
figo		fígere	to fix, fasten	fixi	fixus
finio	4	finire	to finish		
fúgio		fúgere	to flee	fūgi	fúgitus
impedio	4	impedire	to hinder, obstruct		
invénio		invenire	to discover, find out	invēni	inventus
jácio		jácere	to throw, hurl	jeci	jactus
jungo		júngere	to join, connect	junxi	junctus
munio	4	munire	to fortify, protect		
nescio	4	nescire	to not know		
rego		régere	to rule	rexi	rectus
scio	4	scire	to know		
séntio		sentire	to feel, perceive	sensi	sensus
struo		strúere	to build, construct	struxi	structus
traho		tráhere	to drag, haul	traxi	tractus
veho		véhere	to convey, transport	vexi	vectus
vénio		venire	to come	vēni	ventus
vinco		víncere	to conquer	vici	victus
vivo		vívere	to live, be alive	vixi	victus

V. Conjugation

Give tense endings for the **present system active** of the 3rd conjugation.

Person	Present		Imperfect		Future	
1st	o	imus	ebam	ebamus	am	emus
2nd	is	itis	ebas	ebatis	es	etis
3rd	it	unt	ebat	ebant	et	ent

V. Conjugation (cont.)

Give tense endings for the **present system active** of the 4th and 3rd **io** conjugations.

Person	Present		Imperfect		Future	
1st	o	mus	ebam	ebamus	am	emus
2nd	s	tis	ebas	ebatis	es	etis
3rd	t	unt	ebat	ebant	et	ent

Give tense endings for the **present system passive** of the 3rd conjugation.

Person	Present		Imperfect		Future	
1st	or	imur	ebar	ebamur	ar	emur
2nd	eris	ímini	ebaris	ebámini	ēris	émini
3rd	itur	untur	ebatur	ebantur	etur	entur

Give tense endings for the **present system passive** of the 3rd/4th and 3rd **io** conjugations.

Person	Present		Imperfect		Future	
1st	or	(i)mur*	ebar	ebamur	ar	emur
2nd	(e)ris*	(i)mini*	ebaris	ebámini	eris	émini
3rd	(i)tur*	untur	ebatur	ebantur	etur	entur

Conjugate in the active voice and then in the passive.

Present Active	
rego	régimus
regis	régitis
regit	regunt

Present Passive	
regor	régimur
régeris	regímini
régitur	reguntur

Imperfect Active	
regebam	regebamus
regebas	regebatis
regebat	regebant

Imperfect Passive	
regebar	regebamur
regebaris	regebámini
regebatur	regebantur

Future Active	
regam	regemus
reges	regetis
reget	regent

Future Passive	
regar	regemur
regēris	regémini
regetur	regentur

All 3rd-conjugation verbs (not **io**) have duplicate forms in the 2nd person singular passive, as shown in the highlighted boxes above. To help you distinguish these two forms, the present will have the regular accent mark, and the future will have a macron.

*Point out to the student that the present tense of the 3rd/4th and 3rd **io** conjugations have differing stem vowels.

16

Make **three** copies of Drill/Test Form A in the Appendix. Conjugate each verb in the <u>indicative active</u> (6 tenses) and <u>indicative passive</u> (3 tenses).

Copy 1) rego   **Copy 2)** áudio   **Copy 3)** rego (meanings, 1st P. sing. only)

VI. Form Drills
Drill A

1. capit _____ hsi takes
2. cepit _____ hsi took (has taken)
3. cupit _____ hsi desires
4. cupivit _____ hsi (has) desired
5. feci _____ I (have) made

6. cápitur _____ hsi is (being) taken
7. capiebantur _____ they were being taken
8. júngimur _____ we are (being) joined
9. vehuntur _____ they are (being) transported
10. vincímini _____ you all are (being) conquered

Drill B

1. fixerunt _____ they (have) fastened
2. vivit _____ hsi lives
3. régeris _____ you are being ruled
4. regēris _____ you will be ruled
5. regar _____ I will be ruled

6. figor _____ I am being fastened
7. struxit _____ hsi (has) built
8. vínceris _____ you are being conquered
9. vincēris _____ you will be conquered
10. vincebar _____ I was being conquered

Drill C

1. audívimus _____ we (have) heard
2. audimus _____ we hear
3. fugerunt _____ they (have) fled
4. fúgiunt _____ they flee
5. jacit _____ hsi throws

6. jecit _____ hsi threw (has thrown)
7. dicis _____ you say
8. dixit _____ hsi (has) said
9. duxit _____ hsi (has) led
10. ducit _____ hsi leads

17

Drill/Test Form A

Principal Parts: rego régere rexi rectus
Present System Stem: reg-

Present

Indicative Active		Indicative Passive	
rego	régimus	regor	régimur
regis	régitis	régeris	regímini
regit	regunt	régitur	reguntur

Imperfect

regebam	regebamus	regebar	regebamur
regebas	regebatis	regebaris	regebámini
regebat	regebant	regebatur	regebantur

Future

regam	regemus	regar	regemur
reges	regetis	regēris	regémini
reget	regent	regetur	regentur

Perfect System Stem: rex-

Perfect

Indicative Active		Indicative Passive	
rexi	réximus		
rexisti	rexistis		
rexit	rexerunt		

Pluperfect

réxeram	rexeramus		
réxeras	rexeratis		
réxerat	réxerant		

Future Perfect

réxero	rexérimus		
réxeris	rexéritis		
réxerit	réxerint		

I rule
I was ruling
I will rule
I (have) ruled
I had ruled
I will have ruled

I am (being) ruled
I was (being) ruled
I will be ruled

Principal Parts: áudio audire audivi auditus
Present System Stem: audi-

Present

Indicative Active		Indicative Passive	
áudio	audimus	áudior	audimur
audis	auditis	audiris	audímini
audit	áudiunt	auditur	audiuntur

Imperfect

audiebam	audiebamus	audiebar	audiebamur
audiebas	audiebatis	audiebaris	audiebámini
audiebat	audiebant	audiebatur	audiebantur

Future

áudiam	audiemus	áudiar	audiemur
áudies	audietis	audieris	audiémini
áudiet	áudient	audietur	audientur

Perfect System Stem: audiv-

Perfect

Indicative Active		Indicative Passive	
audivi	audívimus		
audivisti	audivistis		
audivit	audiverunt		

Pluperfect

audíveram	audiveramus		
audíveras	audiveratis		
audíverat	audíverant		

Future Perfect

audívero	audivérimus		
audíveris	audivéritis		
audíverit	audíverint		

VII. New Vocabulary

Give principal parts.

1st	2nd	3rd	4th	perfect stem
pono	pónere	pósui	pósitus	posu
mitto	míttere	misi	missus	mis
claudo	cláudere	clausi	clausus	claus
gero	gérere	gessi	gestus	gess
cedo	cédere	cessi	cessus	cess
premo	prémere	pressi	pressus	press
scribo	scríbere	scripsi	scriptus	scrips

Drill D

1. ponit ___hsi places___
2. pósuit ___hsi (has) placed___
3. mittam ___I will send___
4. misi ___I (have) sent___
5. geris ___you wage___
6. geres ___you will wage___

7. cedunt ___they yield___
8. cesserunt ___they (have) yielded___
9. scríbimus ___we write___
10. scrípsimus ___we wrote___
11. míserint ___they will have sent___
12. clausi ___I have closed___

Drill E

1. ponam ___I will place___
2. ponar ___I will be placed___
3. póneris ___you are being placed___
4. ponēris ___you will be placed___
5. géritur ___it is being waged___
6. premebam ___I was pressing___

7. premor ___I am being pressed___
8. premes ___you will press___
9. cedit ___hsi yields___
10. cessit ___hsi yielded___
11. posuerunt ___they have placed___
12. cesseramus ___we had yielded___

VIII. Translation
Underline the ablative of means.

1. Nos amore júngimur. _____We are joined by love._____

2. Óppidum vallo munietur. _____The town will be fortified by a wall._____

3. Piscatores vento bono vehuntur. _____The fishermen are being transported by a good wind._____

4. Libri magno labore finiuntur. _____Books are finished by great toil._____

5. Tu in próelio scuto munieris. _____You will be protected in battle by a shield._____

6. Nos auri amore non régimur. _____We are not ruled by the love of gold._____

7. The students were being hindered by mistakes. _____Discípuli peccatis impediebantur._____

8. You all are hindered by pain. _____Vos dolore impedímini._____

IX. Derivatives

1. In mathematics, an _____exponent_____ is placed above or outside the writing line of numbers and letters.

2. A weapon sent through the air over long distances is a _____missile_____ .

3. A _____missionary_____ is someone who is sent to bring the gospel to those in other lands.

4. A person who is afraid of closed spaces has _____claustrophobia_____ .

5. _____Belligerent_____ literally means someone who is waging or carrying on war.

6. A barometer measures air _____pressure_____ .

7. A _____scriptorium_____ is where the monks copied the Scriptures and other writings by hand.

8. The South _____seceded_____ from the Union.

I. Word Study and Grammar

1. Give the three moods of Latin verbs. 1)_____indicative_____ 2)_____imperative,_____ 3)_____subjunctive_____

2. The indicative mood is used for _____statements of fact_____ and _____questions_____ .

3. The imperative mood is used for _____commands_____ .

4. The subjunctive mood is used for _____potential action, such as opinion, purpose, and wishes_____ .

5. To form the singular imperative of all four conjugations, drop _____-re_____ from the infinitive.

6. To form the plural imperative of 1st, 2nd, and 4th conjugations, add _____-te_____ to the singular imperative.

7. The plural imperative of the 3rd conjugation and 3rd **io** verbs shows the variable stem vowel. Remember _____surge, súrgite_____ for the troublesome 3rd conjugation.

8. Give three irregular singular imperatives. 1)_____dic_____ 2)_____duc_____ 3)_____fac_____

9. Give the singular and plural imperatives of **sum**. _____es, este_____

Saying
Say aloud and write 3X.

Latin	Tolle, lege.
Latin	Tolle, lege.
Latin	Tolle, lege.
English	Take up and read.

Give principal parts.

1st	2nd	3rd	4th	perfect stem
ago	ágere	egi	actus	eg
cogo	cógere	coegi	coactus	coeg
tollo	tóllere	sústuli	sublatus	sustul

19   20

II A. 1st/2nd Conjugation Imperatives

Underline imperatives, give dictionary form of imperative verb, and translate.

Latin	Dictionary form	Translation
Da nobis hódie (panem)	do, dare	Give us this day (bread)
Dona nobis pacem	dono, donare	Grant us peace
Líbera nos a malo	líbero, liberare	Deliver us from evil
Ora et labora.	oro, orare; laboro, laborare	Pray and work.
Festina lente.	festino, festinare	Make haste slowly.
Gaude! Gaude! Emmánuel	gáudeo, gaudēre	Rejoice! Rejoice! Emmanuel
Gaudete, gaudete	gáudeo, gaudēre	Rejoice, rejoice
Salve, salvete	salveo, salvēre	Be well (hello)
Vale, valete	váleo, valēre	Be strong (goodbye)
Adeste fideles	adsum, adesse	(O) come (all ye) faithful

Form Drills
Drill A

Imperative mood. Indicate singular or plural by (you) or (you all).

1. State!____(you all) Stand!_____   6. Videte!____(you all) See!_____
2. Date!____(you all) Give!_____   7. Cave!____(you) Beware!_____
3. Para!____(you) Prepare!_____   8. Tacete!____(you all) Be silent!_____
4. Navigate!__(you all) Sail!_____   9. Vide!____(you) See!_____
5. Lava!____(you) Wash!_____   10. Docete!____(you all) Teach!_____

Drill B

Imperative mood. Give singular and plural for each.

1. Overcome.__Súpera. Superate.____   6. Ask.____Roga. Rogate._____
2. Work.____Labora. Laborate._____   7. Fight.____Pugna. Pugnate._____
3. Hold.____Tene. Tenete._____   8. Hide.____Cela. Celate._____
4. Deny.____Nega. Negate._____   9. Help.____Juva. Juvate._____
5. Move.____Move. Movete._____   10. Sit.____Sede. Sedete._____

II B. Translation

For 11-20, express imperatives in singular and plural forms.

1. Spectate puellas.____Look (pl.) at the girls.____
2. Pugnate fórtiter.____Fight (pl.) bravely.____
3. Appella mílites fortes.____Address the brave soldiers.____
4. Lava collum tuum.____Wash your neck.____
5. Portate aurum et argentum.____Carry (pl.) the gold and silver.____
6. Terre semper lupos malos.____Always frighten bad wolves.____
7. Tenete scuta et gládios.____Hold (pl.) the shields and swords.____
8. Vocate legatos et imperatorem.____Call (pl.) the lieutenants and general.____
9. Líbere oppugnate bárbaros.____Attack the barbarians freely.____
10. Mane saepe in horto.____Stay in the garden often.____
11. Free the Christians.____Líbera, liberate Christianos.____
12. Teach the lazy students.____Doce, docete discípulos pigros.____
13. Change the signs slowly.____Muta, mutate lentē signa.____
14. Guard the fishermen.____Serva, servate piscatores.____
15. Help the shepherds.____Juva, juvate pastores.____
16. Ask the senators.____Roga, rogate senatores.____
17. Be a man. Be men.____Es vir. Este viri.____
18. Plow the fields.____Ara, arate agros.____
19. Point out the wall.____Demonstra, demonstrate vallum.____
20. Seize the town roughly.____Óccupa, occupate áspere óppidum.____

III. 3rd/4th Conjugation Imperatives

<u>Underline</u> imperative endings, give dictionary form of imperative verb, and translate.

English	Dictionary form	Translation
Carp<u>e</u> diem.	carpo, cárpere	Seize the day.
Claud<u>e</u> jánuam.	claudo, cláudere	Close the door.
Dimitt<u>e</u> nobis débita nostra.	dimitto, dimíttere	Dismiss (forgive) our sins.
Surg<u>e</u>, súrg<u>ite</u>.	surgo, súrgere	Stand up.
Ven<u>i</u>, ven<u>i</u> Emmánuel	vénio, venire	Come, come Emmanuel
Ven<u>i</u> Creator Spíritus	vénio, venire	Come Creator Spirit
Bened<u>íc</u> Dómine nos	benedico, benedícere	Bless us O Lord
Aud<u>i</u> Ísrael!	audio, audire	Hear, O Israel
Toll<u>e</u>, leg<u>e</u>.	tollo, tollere lego, legere	Take up and read.

Drill C

Imperative mood. Indicate singular or plural by (you) or (you all).

1. Strue! (you) Build!
2. Cape! (you) Take!
3. Dic! (you) Say!
4. Fuge! (you) Flee!
5. Jácite! (you all) Throw!
6. Dúcite! (you all) Lead!
7. Fac! (you) Make, do!
8. Véhite! (you all) Transport!
9. Vive! (you) Live!
10. Fúgite! (you all) Flee!

Drill D

Imperative mood. Give singular and plural for each.

1. Come. Veni. Venite.
2. Hear. Audi. Audite.
3. Speak. Dic. Dícite.
4. Lead. Duc. Dúcite.
5. Flee. Fuge. Fúgite.
6. Sleep. Dormi. Dormite.
7. Know. Sci. Scite.
8. Finish. Fini. Finite.
9. Discover. Inveni. Invenite.
10. Rule. Rege. Régite.

IV. Translation

For 11-20, express imperatives in singular and plural forms.

1. Munite valla. Fortify (pl.) the walls.
2. Strúite lente óppida. Build (pl.) the towns slowly.
3. Júngite breviter manūs. Join (pl.) hands briefly.
4. Jace longē saxa. Throw the rocks far.
5. Cape pecúniam. Take the money.
6. Vince difficíliter peccata. Conquer sins with difficulty.
7. Impedite! Hinder! (pl.)
8. Rege fidéliter. Rule faithfully.
9. Oppugnate fácile bárbaros. Attack (pl.) the barbarians easily.
10. Trahe laete lignum et aquam. Haul the wood and water happily.
11. Live today. Vive, vivite hódie.
12. Find the money. Inveni, invenite pecúniam.
13. Come to the province. Veni, venite ad provínciam.
14. Transport the cows to town. Vehe, véhite ad óppidum vaccas.
15. Feel the pain. Senti, sentite dolorem.
16. Make a new door. Fac, fácite jánuam novam.
17. Sleep in the farmhouse. Dormi, dormite in villā.
18. Know the stars. Sci, scite stellas.
19. Always tell beautiful stories. Narra, narrate semper fábulas pulchras.
20. Fasten the windows. Fige, fígite fenestras.

Lesson Three

V. Verb Review
Give principal parts again.

1st	2nd	3rd	4th	perfect stem
ago	ágere	egi	actus	eg
cogo	cógere	coegi	coactus	coeg
tollo	tóllere	sústuli	sublatus	sustul

Make **three** copies of Drill/Test Form A in the Appendix. Conjugate each verb in the <u>indicative active</u> (6 tenses) and <u>indicative passive</u> (3 tenses). Make as many copies as necessary, and practice these conjugations until you can do them from memory without error.

Copy 1) tollo   **Copy 2)** ago   **Copy 3)** ago (meanings, 1st P. sing. only)

Drill E
Use **drive** and **force** for verb meanings.

1. agunt __they drive__
2. agit __hsi drives__
3. egit __hsi drove (has driven)__
4. cogo __I force__
5. coegi __I (have) forced__

6. aguntur __they are being driven__
7. ágimur __we are being driven__
8. cogetur __hsi will be forced__
9. cógitur __hsi is (being) forced__
10. cóegerat __hsi had forced__

Drill F

1. tollis __you lift up__
2. tollam __I will lift up__
3. sústuli __I (have) lifted up__
4. sustulerunt __they (have) lifted up__
5. sustúlerat __hsi had lifted up__

6. tólleris __you are lifted up__
7. tollēris __you will be lifted up__
8. tolles __you will lift up__
9. tollunt __they lift up__
10. tollent __they will lift up__

25

Drill/Test Form A

Principal Parts: tollo tóllere sústuli sublatus
Present System Stem: toll-

Present			
Indicative Active		Indicative Passive	
tollo	tóllimus	tollor	tóllimur
tollis	tóllitis	tólleris	tollímini
tollit	tollunt	tóllitur	tolluntur
Imperfect			
tollebam	tollebamus	tollebar	tollebamur
tollebas	tollebatis	tollebaris	tollebámini
tollebat	tollebant	tollebatur	tollebantur
Future			
tollam	tollemus	tollar	tollemur
tolles	tolletis	tollēris	tollémini
tollet	tollent	tolletur	tollentur

Perfect System Stem: sustul-

Perfect			
Indicative Active		Indicative Passive	
sústuli	sustúlimus		
sustulisti	sustulistis		
sústulit	sustulerunt		
Pluperfect			
sustúleram	sustuleramus		
sustúleras	sustuleratis		
sustúlerat	sustúlerant		
Future Perfect			
sustúlero	sustulérimus		
sustúleris	sustuléritis		
sustúlerit	sustúlerint		

Principal Parts: ago ágere egi actus
Present System Stem: ag-

Present			
Indicative Active		Indicative Passive	
ago	ágimus	agor	ágimur
agis	ágitis	ágeris	agímini
agit	agunt	ágitur	aguntur
Imperfect			
agebam	agebamus	agebar	agebamur
agebas	agebatis	agebaris	agebámini
agebat	agebant	agebatur	agebantur
Future			
agam	agemus	agar	agemur
ages	agetis	agēris	agémini
aget	agent	agetur	agentur

Perfect System Stem: eg-

Perfect			
Indicative Active		Indicative Passive	
egi	égimus		
egisti	egistis		
egit	egerunt		
Pluperfect			
égeram	egeramus		
égeras	egeratis		
égerat	égerant		
Future Perfect			
égero	egérimus		
égeris	egéritis		
égerit	egerint		

I drive
I was driving
I will drive
I drove (have driven)
I had driven
I will have driven

I am (being) driven
I was (being) driven
I will be driven

VI. Verb Review, Duplicate Forms

Conjugate vénio and fúgio in the present and perfect active.

Present Active	
venio	vénimus
venis	venitis
venit	véniunt

Perfect Active	
vēni	vēnimus
venisti	venistis
vēnit	venerunt

Present Active	
fugio	fúgimus
fugis	fugitis
fugit	fúgiunt

Perfect Active	
fūgi	fūgimus
fugisti	fugistis
fūgit	fugerunt

4th and 3rd-**io** verbs that have their perfect stem in the root, have identical forms in the 3rd person singular present and perfect, and the 1st person plural present and perfect, as shown in the highlighted boxes above. To help you distinguish these forms, the perfect forms will have macrons. The only such verbs in this text are **vénio**, **fúgio**, and **invénio**.

1. vēnit _____ hsi came _____
2. vénimus _____ we come _____
3. fūgit _____ hsi fled _____
4. invēnimus _____ we found _____
5. invenit _____ hsi finds _____
6. fugit _____ hsi flees _____
7. venit _____ hsi comes _____
8. fúgimus _____ we flee _____
9. fūgimus _____ we fled _____
10. invénimus _____ we find _____
11. vēnimus _____ we came _____
12. invēnit _____ hsi found _____

I. Word Study and Grammar

1. Give the two voices of Latin verbs. ___ active and passive ___
2. In the active voice, the subject ___ performs the action of the verb ___ .
3. In the passive voice, the subject ___ receives the action of the verb ___ .
4. The perfect passive is a ___ compound ___ tense consisting of ___ two ___ words.
5. The first word is a form of the ___ fourth principal part ___ and agrees with the subject in ___ gender, number, and case ___ .
6. The second word is a form of the verb ___ **sum** ___ and agrees with the subject in ___ person and number ___ .
7. The 4th principal part is a ___ participle ___ .
8. A participle is a ___ verbal adjective ___ .

Saying

Say aloud and write 3X.

Latin	Álea jacta est.
Latin	Álea jacta est.
Latin	Álea jacta est.
English	The die is cast.

For each verb, say the principal parts aloud, then write down the
4th principal part as a 1st/2nd-decl. adjective.

1. laudo ___ laudatus -a -um ___
2. vúlnero ___ vulneratus -a -um ___
3. do ___ datus -a -um ___
4. vídeo ___ visus -a -um ___
5. óccupo ___ occupatus -a -um ___
6. súpero ___ superatus -a -um ___
7. culpo ___ culpatus -a -um ___
8. aro ___ aratus -a -um ___
9. móneo ___ monitus -a -um ___
10. juvo ___ jutus -a -um ___
11. oppugno ___ oppugnatus -a -um ___
12. servo ___ servatus -a -um ___

II. Conjugation
Perfect Tense Passive Voice

Conjugate the perfect tense passive voice for **laudo** with a <u>masculine</u> subject.
You can use ditto marks.

Person	Singular	Plural
1st	laudatus sum	laudati sumus
2nd	" es	" estis
3rd	" est	" sunt

Conjugate the perfect tense passive voice for **laudo** with a <u>feminine</u> subject.

Person	Singular	Plural
1st	laudata sum	laudatae sumus
2nd	" es	" estis
3rd	" est	" sunt

Conjugate the perfect tense passive voice for **laudo** with a <u>neuter</u> subject.

Person	Singular	Plural
1st	laudatum sum	laudata sumus
2nd	" es	" estis
3rd	" est	" sunt

Give meanings for the perfect tense passive voice for **laudo**.

Person	Singular	Plural
1st	I was, have been praised	we were, have been praised
2nd	you were, "	you all "
3rd	hsi was, has been praised	they "

Now combine all three conjugations above into one conjugation. The singular is done for you.

Person	Singular		Plural	
1st	laudatus -a -um	sum	laudati -ae -a	sumus
2nd		es		estis
3rd		est		sunt

III. Form Drills
Drill A

Make each participle agree with its subject.

1. The slave has been praised. **Servus laudatus est.**
   The slaves have been praised. Servi laudati sunt.

2. The women have been tempted. **Feminae temptatae sunt.**
   The woman has been tempted. Fémina temptata est.

3. The gift has been given. **Donum datum est.**
   The gifts have been given. Dona data sunt.

4. The barbarians have been overcome. **Barbari superati sunt.**
   The barbarian has been overcome. Bárbarus superatus est.

5. The land has been plowed. **Terra arata est.**
   The lands have been plowed. Terrae aratae sunt.

6. The poet has been greeted. **Poeta salutatus est.**
   The poets have been greeted. Poetae salutati sunt.

Drill B

Circle the gender of each *italicized* 3rd-declension noun,
and make each participle and subject agree.

1. The law has been kept. ***Lex* servata est.**
   The laws have been kept. Leges servatae sunt. (M (F) N)

2. The hill has been seized. ***Collis* occupatus est.**
   The hills have been seized. Colles occupati sunt. ((M) F N)

3. The city has been attacked. ***Urbs* oppugnata est.**
   The cities have been attacked. Urbes oppugnatae sunt. (M (F) N)

4. The ship has been warned. ***Navis* mónita est.**
   The ships have been warned. Naves mónitae sunt. (M (F) N)

5. The river has been seen. ***Flumen* visum est.**
   The rivers have been seen. Flúmina visa sunt. (M F (N))

6. The fisherman has been helped. ***Piscator* jutus est.**
   The fishermen have been helped. Piscatores juti sunt. ((M) F N)

Drill C

Learn these steps to writing a verb in the perfect tense passive voice.

a. Identify the person, gender, and number of the subject.

b. Write the 4th principal part of the verb

c. Write the 4th principal part of the verb in the gender and number that agrees with the subject. It will always be in the nominative case.

d. Write the form of **sum** in the correct tense, and in the number and person that agrees with the subject.

Circle correct answers and then complete each sentence. All subjects are 3rd person.

Sentence	Gender of Subject	Number of Subject	Participle Ending	Form of sum
1. The slave has been wounded.	(M) F N	(s.) pl.	(us) i a ae um	(est) sunt

Serv___us__ **vulnerat**___us___ _____est_____ .

| 2. The lieutenants have been attacked. | (M) F N | s. (pl.) | us (i) a ae um | est (sunt) |

Legat_____i___ **oppugnat**___i___ _____sunt_____ .

| 3. The woman has been judged. | M (F) N | (s.) pl. | us i (a) ae um | (est) sunt |

Femin___a___ **judicat**___a___ _____est_____ .

| 4. The girls have been addressed. | M (F) N | s. (pl.) | us i a (ae) um | est (sunt) |

Puell___ae__ **appellat**___ae___ _____sunt_____ .

| 5. The kingdom has been overcome. | M F (N) | (s.) pl. | us i a ae (um) | (est) sunt |

Regn___um__ **superat**___um___ _____est_____ .

| 6. The temples have been explored. | M F (N) | s. (pl.) | us i (a) ae um | est (sunt) |

Templ___a___ **explorat**___a___ _____sunt_____ .

| 7. The sailor has been accused. | (M) F N. | (s.) pl. | (us) i a ae um | (est) sunt |

Naut___a___ **accusat**___us___ _____est_____ .

Drill D

<u>Underline</u> the mistake in the verb phrase, **X** the boxes, and correct each phrase below.

		Person			Number		Gender		
		1	2	3	Sing.	Pl.	M	F	N
1.	Puer laudatus <u>es</u>.	☐	☐	☒	☒	☐	☒	☐	☐
2.	Púeri laudat<u>um</u> est.	☐	☐	☒	☐	☒	☒	☐	☐
3.	Puella laudata <u>sunt</u>.	☐	☐	☒	☒	☐	☐	☒	☐
4.	Puellae laudat<u>us</u> est.	☐	☐	☒	☐	☒	☐	☒	☐
5.	Templum laudat<u>a</u> est.	☐	☐	☒	☒	☐	☐	☐	☒
6.	Templa laudata <u>est</u>.	☐	☐	☒	☐	☒	☐	☐	☒
7.	Tu laudat<u>a</u> est.	☐	☒	☐	☒	☐	☐	☒	☐
8.	Vos laudat<u>a</u> estis.	☐	☒	☐	☐	☒	☐	☒	☐
9.	Ego laudata <u>est</u>.	☒	☐	☐	☒	☐	☐	☒	☐
10.	Nos laudat<u>us</u> sumus.	☒	☐	☐	☐	☒	☒	☐	☐

1. **Puer laudatus est.** *The boy has been praised.*

2. ___Púeri laudati sunt.___   Boys have been praised. _____

3. ___Puella laudata est.___   The girl has been praised. _____

4. ___Puellae laudatae sunt.___   Girls have been praised. _____

5. ___Templum laudatum est.___   The temple has been praised. _____

6. ___Templa laudata sunt.___   Temples have been praised. _____

7. ___Tu laudata es.___   You have been praised. _____

8. ___Vos laudatae estis.___   You all have been praised. _____

9. ___Ego laudata sum.___   I have been praised. _____

10. ___Nos laudati sumus.___   We have been praised. _____

Drill E

Choose the correct form of **sum** and translate.

1. Legatus accusatus _____est_____ . The lieutenant has been accused.

2. Fenestrae motae _____sunt_____ . The windows have been moved.

3. Gallus mónitus_____est_____ . The Gaul has been warned.

4. Pecúnia celata _____est_____ . The money has been hidden.

5. Oppida oppugnata _____sunt_____ . The towns have been attacked.

6. Nómina clamata_____sunt_____ . The names have been shouted.

7. Arbor visa _____est_____ . The tree has been seen.

8. Pastores térriti _____sunt_____ . The shepherds have been frightened.

9. Res mutae _____sunt_____ . Things have been changed.

10. Adventus expectatus_____est_____ . The arrival has been expected.

Drill F

Choose the correct form of **sum** and translate. Give the gender of the pronoun subject.

1. Tu laudata _____es_____ . You have been praised.   F

2. Nos laudatae _____sumus_____ . We have been praised.   F

3. Vos culpati _____estis_____ . You all have been blamed.   M

4. Tu culpatus _____es_____ . You have been blamed.   M

5. Ego visus_____sum_____ . I have been seen.   M

6. Nos térritae_____sumus_____ . We have been frightened.   F

7. Tu servata _____es_____ . You have been guarded.   F

8. Ego perturbata _____sum_____ . I have been disturbed.   F

9. Vos liberati _____estis_____ . You all have been set free.   M

10. Nos vulnerati _____sumus_____ . We have been wounded.   M

IV. Verb Review

Give principal parts.

1st	2nd	3rd	4th	perfect stem
pono	pónere	pósui	pósitus	posu
mitto	míttere	misi	missus	mis
claudo	cláudere	clausi	clausus	claus
gero	gérere	gessi	gestus	gess
cedo	cédere	cessi	cessus	cess
premo	prémere	pressi	pressus	press
scribo	scríbere	scripsi	scriptus	scrips
ago	ágere	egi	actus	eg
cogo	cógere	coegi	coactus	coeg
tollo	tóllere	sústuli	sublatus	sustul

Make **three** copies of Drill/Test Form A in the Appendix. Conjugate each verb in the <u>indicative active</u> (6 tenses) and <u>indicative passive</u> (4 tenses). Make as many copies as necessary, and practice these conjugations until you can do them from memory without error.

Copy 1) mitto   **Copy 2)** paro   **Copy 3)** mitto (meanings, 1st P. sing. only)

V. Translation

<u>Underline</u> ablative of means or agent. Which two sentences do not have one?

1. Barbari a milítibus superati sunt. ___Barbarians have been overcome by the soldiers.___

2. Oppidum a bárbaris oppugnatum est.___The town has been attacked by the barbarians.___

3. Nos gáudio superatae sumus. ___We have been overcome by joy.___

4. Signum a discípulis positum est.___The sign has been placed by the students.___

5. Peccata a Christo sublata sunt. ___Sins have been lifted up (taken away) by Christ.___

6. Milites ab imperatore coacti sunt. ___Soldiers have been collected by the general.___

7. Vos gáudio et amore sublati estis. ___You all have been lifted up by joy and love.___

8. Missus es. ___You have been sent.___

9. Spes in Christo pósita est.___Hope has been placed in Christ.___

10. Multa verba a poetis scripta sunt. ___Many words have been written by poets.___

Drill/Test Form A

Principal Parts: mitto míttere misi missus
Present System Stem: mitt-

Present

Indicative Active		Indicative Passive	
mitto	míttimus	mittor	míttimur
mittis	míttitis	mítteris	mittímini
mittit	mittunt	míttitur	mittuntur

Imperfect

mittebam	mittebamus	mittebar	mittebamur
mittebas	mittebatis	mittebaris	mittebámini
mittebat	mittebant	mittebatur	mittebantur

Future

mittam	mittemus	mittar	mittemur
mittes	mittetis	mittēris	mittémini
mittet	mittent	mittetur	mittentur

Perfect System Stem: mis-

Perfect

Indicative Active		Indicative Passive	
misi	mísimus	missus sum	missi sumus
misisti	misistis	(a, um) es	(ae, a) estis
misit	miserunt	est	sunt

Pluperfect

míseram	miseramus		
míseras	miseratis		
míserat	míserant		

Future Perfect

mísero	misérimus		
míseris	miséritis		
míserit	míserint		

I send
I was sending
I will send
I (have) sent
I had sent
I will have sent

I am (being) sent
I was (being) sent
I will be sent
I have been sent

Principal Parts: paro parare paravi paratus
Present System Stem: para-

Present

Indicative Active		Indicative Passive	
paro	paramus	paror	paramur
paras	paratis	pararis	parámini
parat	parant	paratur	parantur

Imperfect

parabam	parabamus	parabar	parabamur
parabas	parabatis	parabaris	parabámini
parabat	parabant	parabatur	parabantur

Future

parabo	parábimus	parabor	parábimur
parabis	parábitis	paráberis	parabímini
parabit	parabunt	parábitur	parabuntur

Perfect System Stem: parav-

Perfect

Indicative Active		Indicative Passive	
paravi	parávimus	paratus sum	parati sumus
paravisti	paravistis	(a, um) es	(ae, a) estis
paravit	paraverunt	est	sunt

Pluperfect

paráveram	paraveramus		
paráveras	paraveratis		
paráverat	paráverant		

Future Perfect

parávero	paravérimus		
paráveris	paravéritis		
paráverit	paráverint		

I. Word Study and Grammar

1. Give the two voices of Latin verbs. _____ active and passive

2. In the active voice, the subject _____ performs the action of the verb _____.

3. In the passive voice, the subject _____ receives the action of the verb _____.

4. The perfect passive is a _____ compound _____ tense consisting of _____ two _____ words.

5. The first word is a form of the _____ fourth principal part
   and agrees with the subject in _____ gender, number, and case

6. The second word is a form of the verb _____ sum
   and agrees with the subject in _____ person and number _____.

7. The 4th principal part is a _____ participle

8. A participle is a _____ verbal adjective

Saying
Say aloud and write 3X.

Latin	Consummatum est.
Latin	Consummatum est.
Latin	Consummatum est.
English	It is finished.

Vocabulary
Say aloud and write with meanings. Use dictionary form.

Word	Meaning
aut	or
aut … aut	either … or
autem	however, moreover *(postpositive conj.)*
enim	for, in fact, truly *(postpositive conj.)*
et	and
et … et	both … and
ítaque	therefore, and so
olim	once (upon a time), of old, one day
-que	and *(enclitic conjunction)*
quod	because
sed	but
sicut	as *(conj.)*

II. Conjugation
Pluperfect Tense Passive Voice

Conjugate the pluperfect tense passive voice for **cápio** with a <u>masculine</u> subject.
You may use ditto marks.

Person	Singular	Plural
1st	captus eram	capti eramus
2nd	" eras	" eratis
3rd	" erat	" erant

Conjugate the pluperfect tense passive voice for **cápio** with a <u>feminine</u> subject.

Person	Singular	Plural
1st	capta eram	captae eramus
2nd	" eras	" eratis
3rd	" erat	" erant

Conjugate the pluperfect tense passive voice for **cápio** with a <u>neuter</u> subject.

Person	Singular	Plural
1st	captum eram	capta eramus
2nd	" eras	" eratis
3rd	" erat	" erant

Give meanings for the pluperfect tense passive voice for **cápio**.

Person	Singular	Plural
1st	I had been taken	we had been taken
2nd	you "	you all "
3rd	hsi "	they "

III. Form Drills
Drill A

1. capti eramus _we had been taken_
2. capta erat _she (it) had been taken_
3. captus eras _you had been taken_
4. captae erant _they had been taken_
5. capta erant _they had been taken_
6. captum erat _it had been taken_
7. captae eratis _you all had been taken_
8. capti erant _they had been taken_
9. captae eramus _we had been taken_
10. captus erat _he (it) had been taken_

Drill B

For each verb, say the principal parts aloud,
then write down the 4th principal part as a 1st/2nd-decl. adjective.

1. áudio _auditus -a -um_
2. cápio _captus -a -um_
3. cúpio _cúpitus -a -um_
4. duco _ductus -a -um_
5. figo _fixus -a -um_
6. fínio _finitus -a -um_
7. invénio _inventus -a -um_
8. jácio _jactus -a -um_
9. jungo _junctus -a -um_
10. múnio _múnitus -a -um_
11. rego _rectus -a -um_
12. traho _tractus -a -um_
13. vinco _victus -a -um_
14. struo _structus -a -um_
15. veho _vectus -a -um_
16. scio _scitus -a -um_

Drill C

Watch out for #5 and #6.

1. Labor finitus erat. _The work had been finished._
2. Telum jactum erat. _The missile had been thrown._
3. Tela jacta erant. _The missiles had been thrown._
4. Féminae inventae erant. _The women had been found._
5. Ab equo tractus erat. _He (it) had been dragged by a horse._
6. Ab equis tracti erant. _They had been dragged by horses._
7. Tu vectus eras. _You had been transported._
8. Vos vectae eratis. _You all had been transported._
9. Vallum structum erat. _The wall had been built._
10. Nos juncti eramus. _We had been joined._

Drill D
Perfect and Pluperfect Passive
Underline ablative of agent or means, if present.

1. Scutum a legato fixum erat. _____ The shield had been fastened by the lieutenant._____

2. Aurum ab imperatore cupítum est. _____ Gold was desired by the general._____

3. Lignum vectum erat._____ The wood had been transported._____

4. Frumenta vecta erant. _____ The grains had been transported._____

5. Campus vallo múnitus est. _____ The field has been fortified by a wall._____

6. Féminae dolore superatae erant._____ The women had been overcome by sorrow._____

7. Pecunia ab agricolis capta est. _____ The money has been taken by the farmers._____

8. Galli stúdio recti sunt._____ The Gauls were ruled by enthusiasm._____

9. Lupus a pastore captus erat. _____ The wolf had been captured by the shepherd._____

10. Hortus ab agrícola structus est. _____ The garden has been built by the farmer._____

Drill E
Underline ablative of agent or means, if present.

1. Frumenta ab agrícolis coacta sunt. _____ The grains (crops) have been collected by the farmers._____

2. Fólia ventis sublata sunt. _____ The leaves have been lifted by the winds._____

3. Fenestrae a discípulis in ludo clausae erant. _____
   The windows in school had been closed by the students._____

4. Romani a Gallis non victi sunt. _____ The Romans were not conquered by the Gauls._____

5. Lupi a pópulo numquam amati sunt. _____ Wolves have never been loved by the people._____

6. Senatus a sóciis non auditus erat. _____ The Senate had not been heard by the allies._____

7. Clamores a pópulo auditi erant. _____ Shouts had been heard by the people._____

8. Nimbi sublati sunt. _____ Clouds were raised (up)._____

9. Brácchia in mensas pósita sunt._____ The arms were placed onto the tables._____

10. Discípuli a magistro coacti erant. _____ The students had been collected by the teacher._____

Drill F
Match each noun with an opposite. For some there may be more than one answer.
The first one is done for you.

1. aut *(boys)* _____ **púeri** _____ aut _____ **puellae**

2. aut *(friends)* _____ amici _____ aut _____ hostes

3. aut *(sons)* _____ fílii _____ aut _____ fíliae

4. aut *(father)* _____ pater _____ aut _____ mater

5. aut *(men)* _____ viri _____ aut _____ féminae

6. et *(bread)* _____ panis _____ et _____ vinum or aqua

7. et *(heaven)* _____ caelum _____ et _____ terra

8. et *(war)* _____ bellum _____ et _____ pax

9. et *(hand)* _____ manus _____ et _____ pes

10. et *(silver)* _____ argentum _____ et _____ aurum

Drill G
Match each noun with an opposite or another noun that makes a natural pair.
For some there may be more than one answer. The first one is done for you.

1. Senate _____ **Senatus Populúsque**

2. shield _____ scutum gladiúsque

3. horses _____ equi vaccaéque

4. mountains _____ montes collésque *or* campíque *or* agríque

5. grief _____ dolor gaudiúmque

Lesson Five   Worksheet 6

Make **three** copies of Drill/Test Form A in the Appendix. Conjugate each verb in the <u>indicative active</u> (6 tenses) and <u>indicative passive</u> (5 tenses). Make as many copies as necessary, and practice these conjugations until you can do them from memory without error.

Copy 1) móveo   **Copy 2)** pono   **Copy 3)** móveo (meanings, 1st P. sing. only)

IV. Translation

1. The mountains, in fact, had been explored. Montes, enim, explorati erant.

2. And so, food has not been given to the people. Ítaque cibus pópulo datus non est.

3. Ánimus, autem, pópuli sublatus est. However, the spirit of the people has been lifted up.

4. Victóriae, enim, spes in deos pósita erat. For hope of victory had been placed in the gods.

5. The shouts of the people have been heard by the Senate. Pópuli clamores a Senatu auditi sunt.

6. Res bonae hódie actae sunt. Good things have been done today.

7. Grain has been carried into the town. Frumentum in óppidum portatum est. (vectum est)

8. Olim magni libri a Romanis scripti erant. Once, great books had been written by the Romans.

9. The way of the Lord is pleasant. Dómini via est dulcis.

10. Frumentum a Romanis captum est quod pópulus pacem perturbavit. The grain has been taken by the Romans because the people disturbed the peace.

Drill/Test Form A

Principal Parts: móveo movēre movi motus
Present System Stem: move-

Present			
Indicative Active		Indicative Passive	
móveo	movemus	móveor	movemur
moves	movetis	moveris	movémini
movet	movent	movetur	moventur
Imperfect			
movebam	movebamus	movebar	movebamur
movebas	movebatis	movebaris	movebámini
movebat	movebant	movebatur	movebantur
Future			
movebo	movébimus	movebor	movébimur
movebis	movébitis	movéberis	movebímini
movebit	movebunt	movébitur	movebuntur

Perfect System Stem: mov-

Perfect			
Indicative Active		Indicative Passive	
movi	móvimus	motus sum	moti sumus
movisti	movistis	(a, um) es	(ae, a) estis
movit	moverunt	est	sunt
Pluperfect			
móveram	moveramus	eram	eramus
móveras	moveratis	eras	eratis
móverat	móverant	erat	erant
Future Perfect			
móvero	movérimus		
móveris	movéritis		
móverit	móverint		

Principal Parts: pono pónere pósui pósitus
Present System Stem: pon-

Present			
Indicative Active		Indicative Passive	
pono	pónimus	ponor	pónimur
ponis	pónitis	póneris	ponímini
ponit	ponunt	pónitur	ponuntur
Imperfect			
ponebam	ponebamus	ponebar	ponebamur
ponebas	ponebatis	ponebaris	ponebámini
ponebat	ponebant	ponebatur	ponebantur
Future			
ponam	ponemus	ponar	ponemur
pones	ponetis	ponēris	ponémini
ponet	ponent	ponetur	ponentur

Perfect System Stem: posu-

Perfect			
Indicative Active		Indicative Passive	
pósui	posúimus	pósitus sum	pósiti sumus
posuisti	posuistis	(a, um) es	(ae, a) estis
pósuit	posuerunt	est	sunt
Pluperfect			
posúeram	posueramus	eram	eramus
posúeras	posueratis	eras	eratis
posúerat	posúerant	erat	erant
Future Perfect			
posúero	posuérimus		
posúeris	posuéritis		
posúerit	posúerint		

I move
I was moving
I will move
I (have) moved
I had moved
I will have moved

I am (being) moved
I was (being) moved
I will be moved
I have been moved
I had been moved

I. Word Study and Grammar

1. Verbs that take a direct object are called _____transitive verbs_____ .

2. Verbs that do not take a direct object are called _____intransitive verbs_____ .

3. In the passive voice, the subject _____receives the action of the verb_____ .

4. The perfect passive is a _____compound_____ tense consisting of _____two_____ words.

5. The first word is a form of the _____fourth principal part_____ and agrees with the subject in _____gender, number, and case_____ .

6. The second word is a form of the verb _____sum_____ and agrees with the subject in _____person and number_____ .

7. The 4th principal part is the _____perfect passive participle_____ .

8. A participle is a _____verbal adjective_____ .

Saying
Say aloud and write 3X.

Latin	Age quod agis.
Latin	Age quod agis.
Latin	Age quod agis.
English	Do what you're doing.

Vocabulary
Say aloud and write with meanings. Use dictionary form.

Word	Meaning
étiam	also
fere	almost
jam	already, now
ibi	there, in that place
ínterim	meanwhile
ita	yes, so
póstea	afterwards
súbito	suddenly
tamen	nevertheless

II. Conjugation
Future Perfect Tense Passive Voice

Conjugate the future perfect tense passive voice for **ago** with a **masculine** subject. You may use ditto marks.

Person	Singular	Plural
1st	actus ero	acti érimus
2nd	" eris	" éritis
3rd	" erit	" erunt

Conjugate the future perfect tense passive voice for **ago** with a **feminine** subject.

Person	Singular	Plural
1st	acta ero	actae érimus
2nd	" eris	" éritis
3rd	" erit	" erunt

Conjugate the future perfect tense passive voice for **ago** with a **neuter** subject.

Person	Singular	Plural
1st	actum ero	acta érimus
2nd	" eris	" éritis
3rd	" erit	" erunt

Give meanings for the future perfect tense passive voice for **ago**. Use *drive* for meaning.

Person	Singular	Plural
1st	I will have been driven	we will have been driven
2nd	you "	you "
3rd	hsi "	they "

III. Form Drills
Drill A
Use the meaning *drive* for **ago**. Use **whb** for *will have been*.

1. acti érimus _____we whb driven_____
2. actus ero _____I whb driven_____
3. acta eris _____you whb driven_____
4. actae erunt _____they whb driven_____
5. acti erunt _____they whb driven_____
6. actum erit _____it whb driven_____
7. acti éritis _____you all whb driven_____
8. acta erunt _____they whb driven_____
9. actae érimus _____we whb driven_____
10. acta erit _____she (it) whb driven_____

Lesson Six   Worksheet 3

Drill B

For each verb, say the principal parts aloud, then write down the
4th principal part as a 1st/2nd-decl. adjective.

1. pono ___pósitus -a -um___   6. premo ___pressus -a -um___

2. mitto ___missus -a -um___   7. scribo ___scriptus -a -um___

3. claudo ___clausus -a -um___   8. ago ___actus -a -um___

4. gero ___gestus -a -um___   9. cogo ___coactus -a -um___

5. cedo ___cessus -a -um___   10. tollo ___sublatus -a -um___

Make **three** copies of Drill/Test Form A in the Appendix. Conjugate each verb in the <u>indicative active</u> (6 tenses) and <u>indicative passive</u> (6 tenses). Make as many copies as necessary, and practice these conjugations until you can do them from memory without error.

Copy 1) laudo   **Copy 2)** jácio   **Copy 3)** laudo (meanings, 1st P. sing. only)

Drill C

Future Perfect Passive. Underline ablative of agent or means, if present.

1. Bellum gestum erit cum Gallis. ___War whb waged with the Gauls.___

2. Tu a Marco mónitus eris. ___You whb warned by Mark.___

3. Urbs fórtiter munita erit. ___The city whb strongly fortified.___

4. Bella gesta erunt cum bárbaris. ___Wars whb waged with the barbarians.___

5. Romani a forti imperatore ducti erunt. ___Romans whb led by a brave general.___

6. The enemy will have been captured. ___Hostes capti erunt.   (Hostis captus erit.)___

7. Many words will have been prayed. ___Multa verba orata erunt.___

8. You all will have been driven into the forest. ___Vos in silvas acti éritis. (in silvam)___

9. All things will have been prepared. ___Omnes res paratae erunt.___

10. Swords will have been given to the soldiers. ___Gládii milítibus dati erunt.___

Drill/Test Form A

Principal Parts: laudo laudare laudavi laudatus
Present System Stem: lauda-

Present			
Indicative Active		Indicative Passive	
laudo	laudamus	laudor	laudamur
laudas	laudatis	laudaris	laudámini
laudat	laudant	laudatur	laudantur
Imperfect			
laudabam	laudabamus	laudabar	laudabamur
laudabas	laudabatis	laudabaris	laudabámini
laudabat	laudabant	laudabatur	laudabantur
Future			
laudabo	laudábimus	laudabor	laudábimur
laudabis	laudábitis	laudáberis	laudabímini
laudabit	laudabunt	laudábitur	laudabuntur

Perfect System Stem: laudav-

Perfect			
Indicative Active		Indicative Passive	
laudavi	laudávimus	laudatus sum	laudati sumus
laudavisti	laudavistis	(a, um) es	(ae, a) estis
laudavit	laudaverunt	est	sunt
Pluperfect			
laudáveram	laudaveramus	eram	eramus
laudáveras	laudaveratis	eras	eratis
laudáverat	laudáverant	erat	erant
Future Perfect			
laudávero	laudavérimus	ero	érimus
laudáveris	laudavéritis	eris	éritis
laudáverit	laudáverint	erit	erunt

Principal Parts: jácio jácere jeci jactus
Present System Stem: jaci-

Present			
Indicative Active		Indicative Passive	
jácio	jácimus	jácior	jácimur
jacis	jácitis	jáceris	jacímini
jacit	jáciunt	jácitur	jaciuntur
Imperfect			
jacebam	jacebamus	jacebar	jacebamur
jacebas	jacebatis	jacebaris	jacebámini
jacebat	jacebant	jacebatur	jacebantur
Future			
jáciam	jaciemus	jáciar	jaciemur
jácies	jacietis	jacieris	jaciémini
jáciet	jácient	jacietur	jacientur

Perfect System Stem: jec-

Perfect			
Indicative Active		Indicative Passive	
jeci	jécimus	jactus sum	jacti sumus
jecisti	jecistis	(a, um) es	(ae, a) estis
jecit	jecerunt	est	sunt
Pluperfect			
jéceram	jeceramus	eram	eramus
jéceras	jeceratis	eras	eratis
jécerat	jécerant	erat	erant
Future Perfect			
jécero	jecérimus	ero	érimus
jéceris	jecéritis	eris	éritis
jécerit	jécerint	erit	erunt

I praise
I was praising
I will praise
I (have) praised
I had praised
I will have praised

I am (being) praised
I was (being) praised
I will be praised
I have been praised
I had been praised
I will have been praised

Drill D
Principal Parts Review

Recite aloud and then write from memory. Practice until you can write without errors.

1st	2nd	3rd	4th	perfect stem
pono	pónere	pósui	pósitus	posu-
mitto	míttere	misi	missus	mis-
claudo	cláudere	clausi	clausus	claus-
gero	gérere	gessi	gestus	gess-
cedo	cédere	cessi	cessus	cess-
premo	prémere	pressi	pressus	press-
scribo	scríbere	scripsi	scriptus	scrips-
ago	ágere	egi	actus	eg-
cogo	cógere	coegi	coactus	coeg-
tollo	tóllere	sústuli	sublatus	sustul-

Drill E

All perfect passive tenses. Underline ablative of agent or means, if present.

1. Tamen pax semper cupita est. Nevertheless, peace has always been desired.

2. Postea Deus appellatus erat. Afterwards, God was (had been) addressed. (called upon)

3. Fides ab homínibus sanctis ibi servata est. The faith has been kept there by holy men.

4. Província a milítibus fórtibus munita est .
    The province was (has been) protected by brave soldiers.

5. Mílites jam in pontem pósiti erant.
    The soldiers had already been placed on (onto) the bridge.

6. Pátria a viris fórtibus servata est. The fatherland has been guarded by brave men.

7. Ínterim et púeri et puellae ad ludum missi sunt.
    Meanwhile, both boys and girls were sent to school.

8. Lex fere servata est. The law has almost been kept.

Drill F

All passive tenses. Underline ablative of agent or means, if present.

1. Epístula a legato étiam mittetur. A letter will also be sent by the lieutenant.

2. Líberi a servis súbito cogebantur.
    Suddenly the children were being collected by the servants.

3. Vincenturne umquam a Gallis? Will they ever be conquered by the Gauls?

4. Vos vocati estis. You all have been called.

5. Tu étiam appellabaris. You also were being addressed.

6. Much food has already been prepared. Multus cibus jam paratus est.

7. Many letters have been written. Multae epístulae scriptae sunt.

8. Shameful wars have been waged. Bella túrpia gesta sunt.

9. Lazy boys have been accused. Púeri pigri accusati sunt.

10. Harsh words had often been heard. Verba áspera saepe audita erant.

Drill G

Meanings, 1st person singular only, *I love*, active and passive.

Present system	Active	Passive
Present	I love, do love, am loving	I am (being) loved
Imperfect	I was loving, I loved	I was (being) loved
Future	I will love	I will be loved

Perfect system	Active	Passive
Perfect	I loved, have loved, did love	I have been loved (was loved)
Pluperfect	I had loved	I had been loved
Future perfect	I will have loved	I will have been loved

I. Word Study and Grammar

1. Give the three moods of Latin verbs. 1) __indicative__ 2) __imperative__
   3) __subjunctive__

2. The indicative mood is used for __statements of fact__
   and __questions__ .

3. The imperative mood is used for __commands__ .

4. The subjunctive mood is used for __potential action, such as opinion, purpose, and wishes__ .

5. To form the singular imperative of all four conjugations, drop __-re__
   from the infinitive.

6. To form the plural imperative of 1st, 2nd, and 4th conjugation verbs, add __-te__
   to the singular imperative.

7. The plural imperative of the 3rd conjugation and 3rd **io** verbs shows the variable stem vowel.
   Remember __surge, súrgite__ for the troublesome 3rd conjugation.

8. Give three irregular singular imperatives. 1) __dic__ 2) __duc__ 3) __fac__

9. Give the singular and plural imperatives of **sum**. __es, este__

10. Give the two voices of Latin verbs. __active, passive__

11. In the active voice, the subject __performs the action of the verb__ .

12. In the passive voice, the subject __receives the action of the verb__ .

13. The perfect passive tenses are __compound__ tenses consisting of __two__ words.

14. The first word is a form of the __fourth principal part__
    and agrees with the subject in __gender, number, and case__ .

15. The second word is a form of the verb __sum__
    and agrees with the subject in __person and number__ .

16. The 4th principal part is a __participle__ .

17. A participle is a __verbal adjective__ .

II. Latin Sayings

1. The die is cast. __Álea jacta est.__

2. Do what you are doing. __Age quod agis.__

3. It is finished. __Consummatum est.__

4. Take up and read. __Tolle, lege.__

5. Hear, O Israel! __Audi Ísrael!__

6. I think, therefore I am. __Cógito ergo sum.__

III. Conjugation

Make **three** copies of Drill/Test Form A in the Appendix. Conjugate each verb in the <u>indicative active</u> (6 tenses) and <u>indicative passive</u> (6 tenses). Make as many copies as necessary, and practice these conjugations until you can do them from memory without error.

Copy 1) voco   **Copy 2)** rego   **Copy 3)** VOCO (meanings, 1st P. sing. only)

IV. Vocabulary

1st	2nd	3rd	4th	Meaning
pono	pónere	pósui	pósitus	to put, place
mitto	míttere	misi	missus	to send
claudo	cláudere	clausi	clausus	to close
gero	gérere	gessi	gestus	to wage, carry on
cedo	cédere	cessi	cessus	to yield, give way
premo	prémere	pressi	pressus	to press, push
scribo	scríbere	scripsi	scriptus	to write
ago	ágere	egi	actus	to do, drive, act
cogo	cógere	coegi	coactus	to collect, force
tollo	tóllere	sústuli	sublatus	to lift (up), raise

Drill/Test Form A

Principal Parts: voco vocare vocavi vocatus
Present System Stem: voca-

Present			
Indicative Active		Indicative Passive	
voco	vocamus	vocor	vocamur
vocas	vocatis	vocaris	vocámini
vocat	vocant	vocatur	vocantur
Imperfect			
vocabam	vocabamus	vocabar	vocabamur
vocabas	vocabatis	vocabaris	vocabámini
vocabat	vocabant	vocabatur	vocabantur
Future			
vocabo	vocábimus	vocabor	vocábimur
vocabis	vocábitis	vocáberis	vocabímini
vocabit	vocabunt	vocábitur	vocabuntur

Perfect System Stem: vocav-

Perfect			
Indicative Active		Indicative Passive	
vocavi	vocávimus	vocatus sum	vocati sumus
vocavisti	vocavistis	(a, um) es	(ae, a) estis
vocavit	vocaverunt	est	sunt
Pluperfect			
vocáveram	vocaveramus	eram	eramus
vocáveras	vocaveratis	eras	eratis
vocáverat	vocáverant	erat	erant
Future Perfect			
vocávero	vocavérimus	ero	érimus
vocáveris	vocavéritis	eris	éritis
vocáverit	vocáverint	erit	erunt

Principal Parts: rego régere rexi rectus
Present System Stem: reg-

Present			
Indicative Active		Indicative Passive	
rego	régimus	regor	régimur
regis	régitis	régeris	regímini
regit	regunt	régitur	reguntur
Imperfect			
regebam	regebamus	regebar	regebamur
regebas	regebatis	regebaris	regebámini
regebat	regebant	regebatur	regebantur
Future			
regam	regemus	regar	regemur
reges	regetis	regēris	regémini
reget	regent	regetur	regentur

Perfect System Stem: rex-

Perfect			
Indicative Active		Indicative Passive	
rexi	réximus	rectus sum	recti sumus
rexisti	rexistis	(a, um) es	(ae, a) estis
rexit	rexerunt	est	sunt
Pluperfect			
réxeram	rexeramus	eram	eramus
réxeras	rexeratis	eras	eratis
réxerat	réxerant	erat	erant
Future Perfect			
réxero	rexérimus	ero	érimus
réxeris	rexéritis	eris	éritis
réxerit	réxerint	erit	erunt

I call
I was calling
I will call
I (have) called
I had called
I will have called

I am (being) called
I was (being) called
I will be called
I have been called
I had been called
I will have been called

Unit I Review Worksheet 3

IV. Vocabulary (cont.)

aut	or	ítaque	therefore, and so
aut … aut	either … or	jam	already, now
autem	however, moreover	olim	once, of old, one day
enim	for, in fact, truly	póstea	afterwards
et	and	-que	and
et … et	both … and	quod	because
étiam	also	sed	but
fere	almost	sicut	as
ibi	there, in that place	súbito	suddenly
ínterim	meanwhile	tamen	nevertheless
ita	yes, so, thus		

Complete the chart for the model Conjugations and **sum**.

Model Verbs	Imperative Singular	Imperative Plural	Meaning
amo, amare	ama	amate	Love!
móneo, monēre	mone	monete	Warn!
rego, régere	rege	régite	Rule!
cápio, cápere	cape	cápite	Take!
áudio, audire	audi	audite	Hear!
sum, esse	es	este	Be!

Complete the chart for the three common Irregular Imperatives.

Verb	Imperative Singular	Imperative Plural	Meaning
dico, dícere	dic	dícite	Speak!
duco, dúcere	duc	dúcite	Lead!
fácio, fácere	fac	fácite	Make!

Unit I Review

Unit I Review

Translation A: Questions, Imperatives

1. Pray for us. _____ Ora pro nobis. _____
2. Make dinner now. _____ Fac nunc cenam. _____
3. Laborate fidéliter. _____ (you all) Work faithfully. _____
4. Lead the men bravely. _____ Duc fórtiter viros. _____
5. Speak (**dico**) your mind. _____ Dic ánimum tuum. _____
6. Orabátne pro me? _____ Was he praying for me? _____
7. Quid facis? _____ What are you doing? _____
8. Quid fecit? _____ What did he do? _____
9. Natásne latum flumen? _____ Are you swimming the wide river? _____
10. Pone pecúniam ibi. _____ Put the money there. _____

Translation B

1. Brave boys swim the wide river. _____ Púeri fortes flumen latum natant. _____
2. Puellae dulces domum laetam fáciunt. _____ Sweet girls make a happy home. _____
3. Sacred books have been written. _____ Libri sacri scripti sunt. _____
4. Serious matters have been treated. _____ Res graves actae sunt. _____
5. My faults are serious. _____ Culpae meae sunt graves. _____
6. Ferra teláque celata sunt. _____ Iron tools and missiles have been hidden. _____
7. The knife was hidden. _____ Culter celatus est. _____
8. Maris undae sunt pulchrae. _____ The waves of the sea are beautiful. _____
9. The neck of the horse is strong. _____ Equi collum est forte. _____
10. The wretched soldiers move slowly into battle. _____ Mílites míseri in próelium lentē movent. _____

Unit I Review

Translation C

1. The law has not often been kept. _____ Lex non saepe servata est. _____
2. Peace has not always been kept. _____ Pax non semper servata est. _____
3. The head sits on the neck. _____ Caput in collo sedet. _____
4. The bridge had been burned by a soldier. _____ Pons a mílite arsus erat. _____
5. Christ is the light of life. _____ Christus est vitae lux. _____
6. Christ is the lamp unto* my feet. _____ Christus est lumen in pedes. _____
7. The city was held by the enemy. _____ Urbs ab hóstibus tenta est (tenebatur). _____
8. The hill was held by the army. _____ Collis ab exércitu tentus est (tenebatur). _____
9. The bridge was seized by the sailors. _____ Pons a nautis occupatus est. _____
10. Both brothers and sisters rejoice in God. _____ Et fratres et sorores in Deo gaudent. _____

Translation D

1. Both sun and moon give light. _____ Et sol et luna lucem dant. _____
2. Men dwell either on land or on the sea. _____ Viri aut in terrā aut in mari hábitant. _____
3. Think with your head and heart. _____ Puta cápite cordéque. _____
4. Both sailors and soldiers protect our fatherland. _____ Et nautae et mílites pátriam nostram múniunt. _____
5. Make my day! _____ Fac diem meum! (A literal, if un-Roman translation.) _____
6. We have been created by God. _____ Nos a Deo creati sumus. _____
7. Guard against sin. _____ Cave peccatum. _____
8. We will be judged by God. _____ Nos a Deo judicábimur. _____
9. Lift up your hands. _____ Tolle manus tuas. _____
10. Lift up your heart. _____ Tolle cor tuum. _____

*Translate *unto* using **in** *w/acc.*

1. Verb families are called _____conjugations_____ ,
   and noun families are called _____declensions_____ .

2. Give **two** 4th-declension neuter nouns. _____1) **cornu** 2) **genu**_____

3. Give **two** indeclinable nouns. _____1) **satis** 2) **nihil**_____

4. What is the **vocative** case? _____case of direct address_____

5. Give the **Vocative Rule**. _____The vocative is identical to the nominative in all_____
   declensions except the singular masculine nouns of the 2nd declension
   ending in **-us** or **-ius**, where **-e** replaces **-us** and **-i** replaces **-ius**.

6. What are the **two** kinds of adjectives? _____1st/2nd declension and 3rd declension_____

7. Give the **three** kinds of 1st/2nd-declension adjectives.
   1) _____regular_____   2) _____**-er** adjectives_____   3) _____Naughty Nine_____

8. What are the Naughty Nine? _____1st/2nd-declension adjectives that have_____
   the genitive singular in **-ius** and the dative singular in **-i**

9. Which declensions have **er** adjectives? _____both 1st/2nd and 3rd declensions_____

10. Give the **three** kinds of 3rd-declension adjectives. _____
    one, two, and three terminations

11. Look at Lesson VII and give the numbers for how many nouns you know.
    1st declension _____51_____
    2nd declension masculine _____38_____
    2nd declension neuter _____30_____

I. Word Study and Grammar

1. The vocative case is the case of _____direct address_____ .

2. The vocative case is identical to the nominative in all declensions except in singular
   _____masculine_____ nouns of the _____second_____ declension ending in _____-us_____ or _____-ius_____ ,
   where _**-e**_ replaces _**-us**_ and _**-i**_ replaces _**-ius**_ .

3. Give three vocative expressions that illustrate this rule.
   Benedíc Dómine nos; **Et tu, Brute?**; **fili mi**; **serve**; **Claudi**; etc.

4. Give the **three** exceptions to the **Vocative Rule**.
   1) _____**meus = mi**_____   2) _____**deus = deus**_____   3) _____**Jesus = Jesu**_____

5. A vocative noun is often used with an _____imperative_____ verb and usually is not the
   _____first_____ word in the sentence.

6. Give the plural noun in the review vocabulary. _____**líberi liberorum** m._____

7. Give the nouns that have slightly different meanings in the singular and plural.
   grátia means *thanks* in the plural
   frumentum means *crops* in the plural

8. Give the dative and ablative plural of **filius** and **filia**. _____**fíliis**; **filiabus**_____

9. Give the dative and ablative plural of **deus** and **dea**. _____**deis**; **deabus**_____

II. Latin Sayings Review
Study until you can write these correctly from memory.

1. The Senate and the People of Rome _____Senatus Populúsque Romanus_____

2. Seize the day _____Carpe diem_____

3. In the year of our Lord _____Anno Dómini_____

4. before the war _____ante bellum_____

5. King of Kings _____Rex Regum_____

6. The Roman Peace _____Pax Romana_____

7. nurturing mother _____alma mater_____

8. Four seasons of the year _____Quattuor anni témpora_____

9. The mother of Italy—Rome _____Mater Itáliae—Roma_____

10. Eternal Rome _____Roma Aeterna_____

11. Head of the world _____Caput mundi_____

III. Vocabulary Drill

Say aloud and practice until perfect.

English	Latin (dictionary form)	English	Latin (dictionary form)
age	saéculum -i n.	field, plain	campus -i m.
ally	sócius -i m.	food	cibus -i m.
altar	ara -ae f.	forest	silva -ae f.
anger	ira -ae f.	fortune	fortuna -ae f.
arm	brácchium -i n.	forum	forum -i n.
back, rear	tergum -i n.	friend	amicus -i m.
barbarian	bárbarus -i m.	garden	hortus -i m.
battle	próelium -i n.	gate	porta -ae f.
bear	ursa -ae f.	Gaul	Gállia -ae f.
book	liber libri m.	a Gaul	Gallus -i m.
boy	puer púeri m.	gift	donum -i n.
children	líberi liberorum m.	girl	puella -ae f.
Christ	Christus -i m.	god	deus -i m.
a Christian	Christianus -i m.	grace, favor	grátia -ae f.
cow	vacca -ae f.	grain, crops	frumentum -i n.
crowd	turba -ae f.	green plant	herba -ae f.
crown	corona -ae f.	heaven, sky	caelum -i n
daughter	fília -ae f.	horse	equus -i m.
dawn	aurora -ae f.	iron	ferrum -i n.
debt, sin	débitum -i n.	island	ínsula -ae f.
dinner	cena -ae f.	Italy	Itália -ae f.
door	jánua -ae f.	joy	gáudium -i n.
eagle	áquila -ae f.	kingdom	regnum -i n.
earth, land	terra -ae f.	kitchen	culina -ae f.
evening	vesper vésperi m.	knife	culter cultri m.
eye	óculus -i m.	lamb	agnus -i m.
farmer	agrícola -ae m.	leaf	folium -i n.
farmhouse	villa -ae f.	letter	epístula -ae f.
fatherland	pátria -ae f.	lieutenant	legatus -i m.
fault, blame	culpa -ae f.	life	vita -ae f.
field, ground	ager agri m.		

III. Vocabulary Drill (cont.)

Say aloud and practice until perfect.

English	Latin (dictionary form)	English	Latin (dictionary form)
lord, master	dóminus -i m.	Spain	Hispánia -ae f.
Lucy	Lúcia -ae f.	star	stella -ae f.
man	vir viri m.	story, tale	fábula -ae f.
Mark	Marcus -i m.	student	discípulus -i m.
Mary	Maria -ae f.	sword	gládius -i m.
mind, spirit	ánimus -i m.	table	mensa -ae f.
missile	telum -i n.	tablet	tabella -ae f.
money	pecúnia -ae f.	teacher (f.)	magistra -ae f.
moon	luna -ae f.	teacher (m.)	magister magistri m.
neck	collum -i n.	temple	templum -i n.
people	pópulus -i m.	thanks	grátiae -arum f. (with **ago**)
place	locus -i m.	town	óppidum -i n.
poet	poeta -ae m.	victory	victória -ae f.
province	província -ae f.	war	bellum -i n.
queen	regina -ae f.	water	aqua -ae f.
raincloud	nimbus -i m.	wave	unda -ae f.
rampart	vallum -i n.	way, road	via -ae f.
reward	praémium -i n.	wind	ventus -i m.
rock	saxum -i n.	window	fenestra -ae f.
a Roman	Romanus -i m.	wine	vinum -i n.
Rome	Roma -ae f.	wolf	lupus -i m.
sailor	nauta -ae m.	woman	fémina -ae f.
school, game	ludus -i m.	wood	lignum -i n.
seat	sella -ae f.	word	verbum -i n.
servant	servus -i m.	world	mundus -i m.
shadow	umbra -ae f.	year	annus -i m.
shield	scutum -i n.	zeal	stúdium -i n.
sign	signum -i n.		
silver	argentum -i n.		
sin, mistake	peccatum -i n.		
son	fílius -i m.		

IV. Declensions

Decline model nouns.

Case	1st Declension		2nd Declension Masculine		2nd Declension Neuter	
nom.	mensa	mensae	servus	servi	bellum	bella
gen.	mensae	mensarum	servi	servorum	belli	bellorum
dat.	mensae	mensis	servo	servis	bello	bellis
acc.	mensam	mensas	servum	servos	bellum	bella
abl.	mensā	mensis	servo	servis	bello	bellis

Give case endings.

Case	1st Declension		2nd Declension Masculine		2nd Declension Neuter	
nom.	-a	-ae	-us	-i	-um	-a
gen.	-ae	-arum	-i	-orum	-i	-orum
dat.	-ae	-is	-o	-is	-o	-is
acc.	-am	-as	-um	-os	-um	-a
abl.	-ā	-is	-o	-is	-o	-is

Decline nouns.

Singular	Plural
puer	púeri
púeri	puerorum
púero	púeris
púerum	púeros
púero	púeris

Singular	Plural
vir	viri
viri	virorum
viro	viris
virum	viros
viro	viris

Singular	Plural
ager	agri
agri	agrorum
agro	agris
agrum	agros
agro	agris

Singular	Plural
vesper	vésperi
vésperi	vesperorum
véspero	vésperis
vésperum	vésperos
véspero	vésperis

V. Vocative Case
Drill A

Give the vocative singular for each noun.

1. deus _____ deus _____
2. dux _____ dux _____
3. dóminus _____ dómine _____
4. senator _____ senator _____
5. nauta _____ nauta _____

6. miles _____ miles _____
7. Marcus _____ Marce _____
8. Christus _____ Christe _____
9. Maria _____ Maria _____
10. fílius _____ fili _____

Drill B

Give the vocative singular for each noun. The O before each noun is to show the vocative case. O is not translated.

1. O God _____ Deus _____
2. O king _____ rex _____
3. O Lord _____ Dómine _____
4. O friend _____ amice _____
5. O Christian _____ Christiane _____

6. O my son _____ fili mi _____
7. O Mark _____ Marce _____
8. O Lucy _____ Lúcia _____
9. O lieutenant _____ legate _____
10. O student _____ discípule _____

Drill C

Give the vocative plural for each noun.

1. deus _____ dei _____
2. dux _____ duces _____
3. dominus _____ dómini _____
4. senator _____ senatores _____
5. nauta _____ nautae _____

6. miles _____ mílites _____
7. amicus _____ amici _____
8. barbarus _____ bárbari _____
9. filia _____ fíliae _____
10. filius _____ fílii _____

Lesson Seven

VI. Conjugation

Make copies of Drill/Test Form A in the Appendix. Conjugate **mitto** and **pono** in all 6 tenses, <u>active</u> and <u>passive</u>. Practice until perfect.

VII. Verb Drills
Drill D
Verb Review: **pono** (to put, place)

1. ponit ___hsi places___
2. ponet ___hsi will place___
3. pósuit ___hsi has placed___
4. posuerunt ___they have placed___
5. pósitus est ___he (it) has been placed___

6. pósiti sunt ___they have been placed___
7. pósitus erat ___he (it) had been placed___
8. pónitur ___it is (being) placed___
9. ponebantur ___they were (being) placed___
10. ponebámini ___you all were (being) placed___

Drill E
Verb Review: New Verbs in Unit I

1. mittar ___I will be sent___
2. missae sumus ___we have been sent___
3. mittebatis ___you all were sending___
4. mittent ___they will send___
5. misisti ___you have sent___

6. missum erit ___it will have been sent___
7. míttitur ___hsi is sent___
8. mittis ___you send___
9. miserunt ___they have sent___
10. mittetur ___hsi will be sent___

Drill F
Verb Review: Change from active to passive.

1. scripsit ___scriptus (-a -um) est___
2. mittam ___mittar___
3. cedunt ___ceduntur___
4. cessit ___cessus (-a -um) est___
5. geres ___gerēris___

6. gesserunt ___gesti (-ae -a) sunt___
7. prémimus ___premimur___
8. coegisti ___coactus (-a) es___
9. claudam ___claudar___
10. egerunt ___acti (-ae -a) sunt___

Drill/Test Form A

Principal Parts: mitto míttere misi misus
Present System Stem: mitt-

Present			
Indicative Active		Indicative Passive	
mitto	míttimus	mittor	míttimur
mittis	míttitis	mítteris	mittímini
mittit	mittunt	míttitur	mittuntur
Imperfect			
mittebam	mittebamus	mittebar	mittebamur
mittebas	mittebatis	mittebaris	mittebámini
mittebat	mittebant	mittebatur	mittebantur
Future			
mittam	mittemus	mittar	mittemur
mittes	mittetis	mittēris	mittémini
mittet	mittent	mittetur	mittentur

Perfect System Stem: mis-

Perfect				
Indicative Active		Indicative Passive		
misi	mísimus	misus	sum	misi sumus
misisti	misistis	(a, um)	es	(ae, a) estis
misit	miserunt		est	sunt
Pluperfect				
míseram	miseramus		eram	eramus
míseras	miseratis		eras	eratis
míserat	míserant		erat	erant
Future Perfect				
mísero	misérimus		ero	érimus
míseris	miséritis		eris	éritis
míserit	míserint		erit	erunt

Principal Parts: pono pónere pósui pósitus
Present System Stem: pon-

Present			
Indicative Active		Indicative Passive	
pono	pónimus	ponor	pónimur
ponis	pónitis	póneris	ponímini
ponit	ponunt	pónitur	ponuntur
Imperfect			
ponebam	ponebamus	ponebar	ponebamur
ponebas	ponebatis	ponebaris	ponebámini
ponebat	ponebant	ponebatur	ponebantur
Future			
ponam	ponemus	ponar	ponemur
pones	ponetis	ponēris	ponémini
ponet	ponent	ponetur	ponentur

Perfect System Stem: posu-

Perfect				
Indicative Active		Indicative Passive		
pósui	posúimus	pósitus	sum	pósiti sumus
posuisti	posuistis	(a, um)	es	(ae, a) estis
pósuit	posuerunt		est	sunt
Pluperfect				
posúeram	posueramus		eram	eramus
posúeras	posueratis		eras	eratis
posúerat	posúerant		erat	erant
Future Perfect				
posúero	posuérimus		ero	érimus
posúeris	posuéritis		eris	éritis
posúerit	posúerint		erit	erunt

VIII. Translation

*Remember, verbs of giving and telling take an indirect object in the dative case.

1. Scribe, legate, hostis imperatori epístulam. __Lieutenant, write a letter to the enemy's__
   __general.__

2. Cláudite, discípuli, libros vestros. __Students, close your books.__

3. Bellum contra Gallos omnes a Romanis gestum erat. _____
   __War had been waged by the Romans against all the Gauls.__

4. Tolle, serve, cultros post cenam. __Servant, pick up the knives after the dinner.__

5. Cláudite, mílites, óppidi portas. __Soldiers, close the gates of the town.__

6. The army has been placed on the hill. _____
   __Exércitus in collem pósitus est.__ (**Pono** implies movement, so it takes the acc.)

7. The soldiers have been driven from the province. __Mílites e provinciã acti sunt.__

8. *Lord, give us grace. __Da, Dómine, nobis grátiam.__

9. My son, lift up your heart. __Tolle, fili mi, cor tuum.__

10. *Jesus Christ, give me hope. __Da, Jesu Christe, mihi spem.__

I. Word Study and Grammar

1. Give **two** common **indeclinable** nouns and their meanings.
   1) __nihil - *nothing*__   2) __satis - *enough*__

2. Give **two** common **neuter** nouns of the 4th declension and their meanings.
   1) __cornu - *horn*__   2) __genu - *knee*__

3. Give the dative and ablative plural of **filius** and **filia**. __fíliis; filiabus__

4. Give the dative and ablative plural of **deus** and **dea**. __deis; deabus__

5. What is the **vocative** case? __case of direct address__

6. Give the **Vocative Rule**. __The vocative is the same as nom. except in 2nd decl. M sing.__
   __where -us changes to -e and -ius to -i.__

7. Give the **three** exceptions to the **Vocative Rule**.
   1) __meus = mi__   2) __deus = deus__   3) __Jesus = Jesu__

8. What is an appositive? _____
   __a noun that immediately follows another noun and renames it__

9. An appositive agrees with its noun or pronoun in __case__ , and usually
   but not necessarily in __gender and number__ .

10. What is the rule if the appositive refers to two persons of different genders? _____
    __Use the masculine form.__

II. Sayings

1. my fault __mea culpa__

2. You too, Brutus? __Et tu, Brute?__

3. Our Sea __Mare Nostrum__

4. Art is long and life is short. __Ars longa vita brevis.__

5. To the stars through difficulties __Ad astra per áspera__

6. I am the way, the truth, and the life. __Ego sum via et véritas et vita.__

7. Hannibal at the gates __Hannibal ad portas__

8. The Vatican Field __Ager Vaticanus__

9. From the founding of the city __Ab Urbe Cóndita__

III. Vocabulary Drill

Say aloud and write and practice until perfect.

English	Latin (dictionary form)	Give genitive pl. for **i-stems only**.
army	exércitus -ūs m.	
arrival	adventus -ūs m.	
bread	panis panis m.	
bridge	pons pontis m.	pontium
brother	frater fratris m.	
citizen	civis civis m./f.	civium
city	urbs urbis f.	urbium
cross	crux crucis f.	
custom	mos moris m.	
day	dies diei m.	
dog	canis canis m./f.	
enemy	hostis hostis m./f.	hostium
face	facies faciei f.	
faith, trust	fides fídei f.	
father	pater patris m.	
fear	metus -ūs m.	
fisherman	píscator -oris m.	
foot	pes pedis m.	
fruit	fructus -ūs m.	
general	imperator -oris m.	
grief, pain	dolor -oris m.	
hand	manus -ūs f.	
harbor	portus -ūs m.	
head	caput cápitis n	
heart	cor cordis n.	
hill	collis collis m.	collium
hope	spes spei f.	
house, home	domus -ūs f.	
king	rex regis m.	

III. Vocabulary Drill (cont.)

English	Latin (dictionary form)	
lake	lacus -ūs m.	
lamp	lumen lúminis n.	
law	lex legis f.	
leader	dux ducis m.	
light	lux lucis f.	
love, passion	amor amoris m.	
mother	mater matris f.	
mountain	mons montis m.	montium
name	nomen nóminis n.	
part, region	pars partis f.	partium
peace	pax pacis f.	
river	flumen flúminis n.	
sea	mare maris n.	marium
senate	senatus -ūs m.	
senator	senator -oris m.	
shepherd	pastor -oris m.	
ship	navis navis f.	navium
shout, cry	clamor -oris m.	
sister	soror sororis f.	
soldier	miles mílitis m.	
speaker, orator	órator -oris m.	
spirit	spíritus -ūs m.	
sun	sol solis m.	
thing	res rei f.	
tree	arbor árboris f.	
tribe	gens gentis f.	gentium
voice	vox vocis f.	
work, toil	labor -oris m.	

IV. Declensions

Give case endings.

Case	3rd Declension				4th Declension		5th Declension	
	M/F		N		M		F	
nom.	—	es	—	a	us	ūs	es	es
gen.	is	um	is	um	ūs	uum	ei	erum
dat.	i	ibus	i	ibus	ui	ibus	ei	ebus
acc.	em	es	—	a	um	ūs	em	es
abl.	e	ibus	e	ibus	u	ibus	e	ebus

Decline model nouns.

Case	3rd Declension			
	Masculine/Feminine		Neuter	
nom.	pater	patres	flumen	flúmina
gen.	patris	patrum	flúminis	flúminum
dat.	patri	pátribus	flúmini	flumínibus
acc.	patrem	patres	flumen	flúmina
abl.	patre	pátribus	flúmine	flumínibus

Case	4th Declension		5th Declension	
nom.	portus	portūs	res	res
gen.	portūs	pórtuum	rei	rerum
dat.	pórtui	pórtibus	rei	rebus
acc.	portum	portūs	rem	res
abl.	portu	pórtibus	re	rebus

Case	3rd Declension (i-stem)			
	Masculine/Feminine		Neuter	
nom.	pars	partes	mare	mária
gen.	partis	partium	maris	márium
dat.	parti	partibus	mari	máribus
acc.	partem	partes	mare	mária
abl.	parte	partibus	mari	máribus

Declensions Summary

Declension	Nominative Singular Ending(s)	Genitive Singular Ending(s)	Usual Gender
1st	a	ae	F
2nd	us, er, ir, um	i	M, N
3rd	—	is	M, F, N
4th	us, u	ūs	M, N
5th	es	ei	F

Decline **cornu** and **genu**.

Case	Singular	Plural	Singular	Plural
nom.	cornu	córnua	genu	génua
gen.	cornūs	córnuum	genūs	génuum
dat.	cornu	córnibus	genu	génibus
acc.	cornu	córnua	genu	génua
abl.	cornu	córnibus	genu	génibus

Decline.

Case	Jesus
nom.	Jesus
gen.	Jesu
dat.	Jesu
acc.	Jesum
abl.	Jesu

Draw the Gender Triangle.

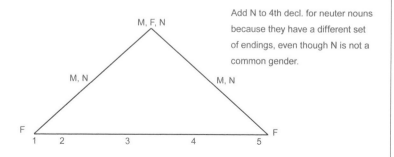

Add N to 4th decl. for neuter nouns because they have a different set of endings, even though N is not a common gender.

Lesson Eight   Worksheet 6

V. Conjugation

Make copies of Drill/Test Form A in the Appendix. Conjugate **ago** and **tollo** in all 6 tenses, <u>active</u> and <u>passive</u>. Practice until perfect.

VI. Verb Review Drills
Drill A

Use *drive* for **ago**.

1. agémini ___ you all will be driven ___
2. egit ___ hsi drove (has driven) ___
3. egi ___ I drove (have driven) ___
4. agunt ___ they drive ___
5. egerunt ___ they drove (have driven) ___

6. agam ___ I will drive ___
7. aget ___ hsi will drive ___
8. aguntur ___ they are driven ___
9. acti sumus ___ we have been driven ___
10. acta est ___ she (it) has been driven ___

Drill B

Use *lift* for **tollo**.

1. tollebatur ___ hsi was being lifted ___
2. tollit ___ hsi lifts ___
3. sústuli ___ I have lifted ___
4. tollam ___ I will lift ___
5. tollunt ___ they lift ___

6. sustulisti ___ you have lifted ___
7. tollemus ___ we will lift ___
8. sublatus est ___ he (it) has been lifted ___
9. sublati erunt ___ they will have been lifted ___
10. tollentur ___ they will be lifted ___

Drill C

1. we will press ___ prememus ___
2. she had been placed ___ pósita erat ___
3. he was closing ___ claudebat ___
4. it has been sent ___ missum est ___
5. you send ___ mittis ___

6. it is waged ___ géritur ___
7. he has driven ___ egit ___
8. we write ___ scríbimus ___
9. they have pressed ___ presserunt ___
10. you all have lifted ___ sustulistis ___

Drill/Test Form A

Principal Parts: ago ágere egi actus
Present System Stem: ag-

Present			
Indicative Active		Indicative Passive	
ago	ágimus	agor	ágimur
agis	ágitis	ágeris	agímini
agit	agunt	ágitur	aguntur
Imperfect			
agebam	agebamus	agebar	agebamur
agebas	agebatis	agebaris	agebámini
agebat	agebant	agebatur	agebantur
Future			
agam	agemus	agar	agemur
ages	agetis	agēris	agémini
aget	agent	agetur	agentur

Perfect System Stem: eg-

Perfect			
Indicative Active		Indicative Passive	
egi	égimus	actus sum	acti sumus
egisti	egistis	(a, um) es	(ae, a) estis
egit	egerunt	est	sunt
Pluperfect			
égeram	egeramus	eram	eramus
égeras	egeratis	eras	eratis
égerat	égerant	erat	erant
Future Perfect			
égero	egérimus	ero	érimus
égeris	egéritis	eris	éritis
égerit	égerint	erit	erunt

Principal Parts: tollo tóllere sústuli sublatus
Present System Stem: toll-

Present			
Indicative Active		Indicative Passive	
tollo	tóllimus	tollor	tóllimur
tollis	tóllitis	tólleris	tollímini
tollit	tollunt	tóllitur	tolluntur
Imperfect			
tollebam	tollebamus	tollebar	tollebamur
tollebas	tollebatis	tollebaris	tollebámini
tollebat	tollebant	tollebatur	tollebantur
Future			
tollam	tollemus	tollar	tollemur
tolles	tolletis	tollēris	tollémini
tollet	tollent	tolletur	tollentur

Perfect System Stem: sustul-

Perfect			
Indicative Active		Indicative Passive	
sústuli	sustúlimus	sublatus sum	-lati sumus
sustulisti	sustulistis	(a, um) es	(ae, a) estis
sústulit	sustulerunt	est	sunt
Pluperfect			
sustúleram	sustuleramus	eram	eramus
sustúleras	sustuleratis	eras	eratis
sustúlerat	sustúlerant	erat	erant
Future Perfect			
sustúlero	sustulérimus	ero	érimus
sustúleris	sustuléritis	eris	éritis
sustúlerit	sustúlerint	erit	erunt

VII. Translation

Appositives are set off with commas.

1. Epístulam brevem Lúciae, Marci fíliae, scripsi. _____
   I wrote a short letter to Marcus' daughter Lucy.

2. Ob belli metum mílites coacti erant. _____
   Soldiers had been collected because of fear of war.

3. Nihil a rege cedetur. _____
   Nothing will be yielded by the king.

4. Mater canes e culinā premebat. _____
   Mother was pushing the dogs out of the kitchen.

5. Interim, portae Óstiae*, Romae portūs, clausae sunt. _____
   Meanwhile, the gates of Óstia, port of Rome, have been closed.

   *Óstia -ae f. is a proper noun.

6. Pónite aurum, victóriae práemium, in templum. _____
   Put the gold, the reward of victory, in the temple.

7. Naves Cáesari, exércitūs imperatori, mittentur. _____
   Ships will be sent to Caesar, the general of the army.

8. Gallus aquilam, exércitūs Romani signum, sustulit. _____
   A Gaul raised the eagle, the standard of the Roman army.

9. Mark, a farmer and shepherd, was driving a lamb into the field. _____
   Marcus agrícola et pastor agnum in agrum agebat.

10. Close the door with your foot. _____
    Cláudite (claude) pede jánuam.

I. Word Study and Grammar

1. Give two common **indeclinable** nouns and their meanings.
   1) _____**nihil** - *nothing*_____   2) _____**satis** - *enough*_____

2. Give two common **neuter** nouns of the 4th declension and their meanings.
   1) _____**cornu** - *horn*_____   2) _____**genu** - *knee*_____

3. Give the **Vocative Rule**. The vocative is the same as nom. except in 2nd decl. M sing. where **-us** changes to **-e** and **-ius** to **-i**.

4. Give the **three** exceptions to the **Vocative Rule**.
   1) _____**meus = mi**_____   2) _____**deus = deus**_____   3) _____**Jesus = Jesu**_____

5. Give the **two** kinds of Latin adjectives. _____1st/2nd-declension; 3rd-declension_____

6. The new adjectives in this lesson are what kind? _____1st/2nd-declension_____

7. Adjectives agree with their nouns in _____gender, number, and case_____ .

8. Adjectives of _____quantity_____ usually precede their nouns, and adjectives of _____quality_____ usually follow their nouns.

9. Give **two** examples of adjectives used as nouns in English. _____1) the rich 2) the poor, etc._____

10. English has _____the article_____ , but Latin has no way to signal when an adjective is being used as a noun.

11. Latin uses the _____masculine or neuter plural adjective_____ as a noun to describe a group of people or things.

12. Give two examples of the above.
    1) **Fortes fortuna juvat.**   2) **Multi pecúniam cúpiunt. Multa cupit.**

Saying

Say aloud and write 3X.

Latin	Amor vincit ómnia.
Latin	Amor vincit ómnia.
Latin	Amor vincit ómnia.
English	Love conquers all things.

II. Vocabulary Drill

Write and say aloud and practice until perfect.

English	Latin (dictionary form)
bad	malus -a -um
beautiful	pulcher, pulchra, pulchrum
certain	certus -a -um
difficult	difficilis -e
each, every, all	omnis -e
easy	fácilis -e
eternal	aeternus -a -um
faithful	fidelis -e
free	liber, líbera, líberum
good	bonus -a -um
great, large	magnus -a -um
happy	laetus -a -um
heavy, serious	gravis -e
high, deep	altus -a -um
lazy	piger, pigra, pigrum
left, left-hand	sinister, sinistra, sinistrum
long	longus -a -um
many, much	multus -a -um
new	novus -a -um
noble	nóbilis -e
right, right-handed	dexter, dextra, dextrum
sacred	sacer, sacra, sacrum
holy, saint	sanctus -a -um
shameful	turpis -e
harsh, rough	asper, áspera, ásperum
short, brief	brevis -e
sick, ill	aeger, aegra, aegrum
slow, sluggish	lentus -a -um
small	parvus -a -um
strong, brave	fortis -e
sweet, pleasant	dulcis -e
whole, uninjured	ínteger, íntegra, íntegrum
wide, broad	latus -a -um
wretched	miser, mísera, míserum

III. New Vocabulary

Say aloud and write with dictionary form, meaning, and derivative.

Latin (dictionary form)	Meaning	Derivative
albus -a -um	white	albino
almus -a -um	nurturing	alma mater
cálidus -a -um	warm, hot	calorie, cauldron, calidarium
defessus -a -um	tired, weary	
excelsus -a -um	on high, lofty	excelsis, excel
ferus -a -um	wild, fierce	feral
foedus -a -um	foul, ugly, hideous	
frígidus -a -um	cold	refrigerate, frigid
nefárius -a -um	wicked	nefarious
stultus -a -um	foolish, stupid	stultify, stolid

IV. Declensions

Decline **piger**, **pigra**, **pigrum**.

Singular			Plural		
M	F	N	M	F	N
piger	pigra	pigrum	pigri	pigrae	pigra
pigri	pigrae	pigri	pigrorum	pigrarum	pigrorum
pigro	pigrae	pigro	pigris	pigris	pigris
pigrum	pigram	pigrum	pigros	pigras	pigra
pigro	pigrã	pigro	pigris	pigris	pigris

Decline **fácilis -e**.

Case	Masculine/Feminine		Neuter	
nom.	fácilis	fáciles	fácile	facília
gen.	fácilis	facílium	fácilis	facílium
dat.	fácili	facílibus	fácili	facílibus
acc.	fácilem	fáciles	fácile	facília
abl.	fácili	facílibus	fácili	facílibus

V. Form Drills
Drill A

1. ugly bridge ___pons foedus___
2. tired cows ___vaccae defessae___
3. hot water ___aqua cálida___
4. the stupid king ___rex stultus___
5. wild dogs ___canes feri___

6. white hills ___colles albi___
7. the wicked brother ___frater nefárius___
8. nurturing cities ___urbes almae___
9. a lofty love ___amor excelsus___
10. cold wind ___ventus frígidus___

Drill B

1. the tired sailor ___nauta defessus___
2. wicked customs ___mores nefárii___
3. cold rivers ___flúmina frígida___
4. a nurturing leader ___dux almus___
5. foolish senators ___senatores stulti___

6. lofty work ___labor excelsus___
7. wild spirits ___spíritūs feri___
8. the foul river ___flumen foedum___
9. warm hands ___manūs cálidae___
10. white ships ___naves albae___

Drill C

1. mater defessa ___tired mother___
2. mores stulti ___foolish customs___
3. lúmina foeda ___ugly lamps___
4. cives almi ___nurturing citizens___
5. lacus frígidus ___cold lake___

6. miles nefárius ___wicked soldier___
7. lux alba ___white light___
8. spíritus excelsus ___lofty spirit___
9. mare cálidum ___warm sea___
10. dux ferus ___fierce leader___

VI. Conjugation

Make copies of Drill/Test Form A in the Appendix. Conjugate **cogo** and **gero** in all 6 tenses, <u>active</u> and <u>passive</u>. Practice until perfect.

VII. Verb Review Drills
Drill D

1. coactum est ___it has been collected___
2. coegit ___hsi has collected___
3. cogis ___you collect___
4. coget ___hsi will collect___
5. coegerunt ___they have collected___

6. coegerit ___hsi will have collected___
7. cogemur ___we will be collected___
8. coacta erat ___she (it) had been collected___
9. cogam ___I will collect___
10. coacti sunt ___they have been collected___

Drill E

11. gerebat ___hsi was waging___
12. gessisti ___you have waged___
13. gestum est ___it has been waged___
14. gerit ___hsi wages___
15. geretis ___you all will wage___

16. gerunt ___they wage___
17. gesta erant ___they had been waged___
18. gésserit ___hsi will have waged___
19. géritur ___it is waged___
20. gerent ___they will wage___

Drill F

21. he will send ___mittet___
22. it has been pressed ___pressum (-us -a) est___
23. they will close ___claudent___
24. I was lifting up ___tollebam___
25. we have written ___scrípsimus___

26. she is being driven ___ágitur___
27. they had been collected ___coacti (-ae -a) erant___
28. you have placed ___posuisti___
29. it will be waged ___geretur___
30. you all yield ___céditis___

Drill/Test Form A

Principal Parts: cogo cógere coegi coactus
Present System Stem: cog-

Present			
Indicative Active		Indicative Passive	
cogo	cógimus	cogor	cógimur
cogis	cógitis	cógeris	cogímini
cogit	cogunt	cógitur	coguntur
Imperfect			
cogebam	cogebamus	cogebar	cogebamur
cogebas	cogebatis	cogebaris	cogebámini
cogebat	cogebant	cogebatur	cogebantur
Future			
cogam	cogemus	cogar	cogemur
coges	cogetis	cogēris	cogémini
coget	cogent	cogetur	cogentur

Perfect System Stem: coeg-

Perfect			
Indicative Active		Indicative Passive	
coegi	coégimus	coactus sum	coacti sumus
coegisti	coegistis	(a, um) es	(ae, a) estis
coegit	coegerunt	est	sunt
Pluperfect			
coégeram	coegeramus	eram	eramus
coégeras	coegeratis	eras	eratis
coégerat	coégerant	erat	erant
Future Perfect			
coégero	coegérimus	ero	érimus
coégeris	coegéritis	eris	éritis
coégerit	coégerint	erit	erunt

Principal Parts: gero gérere gessi gestus
Present System Stem: ger-

Present			
Indicative Active		Indicative Passive	
gero	gérimus	geror	gérimur
geris	géritis	géreris	gerímini
gerit	gerunt	géritur	geruntur
Imperfect			
gerebam	gerebamus	gerebar	gerebamur
gerebas	gerebatis	gerebaris	gerebámini
gerebat	gerebant	gerebatur	gerebantur
Future			
geram	geremus	gerar	geremur
geres	geretis	gerēris	gerémini
geret	gerent	geretur	gerentur

Perfect System Stem: gess-

Perfect			
Indicative Active		Indicative Passive	
gessi	géssimus	gestus sum	gesti sumus
gessisti	gessistis	(a, um) es	(ae, a) estis
gessit	gesserunt	est	sunt
Pluperfect			
gésseram	gesseramus	eram	eramus
gésseras	gesseratis	eras	eratis
gésserat	gésserant	erat	erant
Future Perfect			
géssero	gessérimus	ero	érimus
gésseris	gesséritis	eris	éritis
gésserit	gésserint	erit	erunt

VIII. Translation
Underline the adjective used as a noun.

1. <u>Defessi</u> bellum non gerunt. _____ The tired do not wage war. _____

2. <u>Feri</u> in silvā hábitant. _____ The wild (ones) live in the forest. _____

3. Oppidum a <u>nostris</u> oppugnatum est. _____ The town was attacked by our men. _____

4. <u>Pigri</u> lente laborant. _____ The lazy work slowly. _____

5. Imperator praemia <u>fórtibus</u> dedit. _____ The general gave rewards to the brave. _____

6. <u>Ours (our men)</u> were collecting rocks. _____ Nostri saxa cogebant. _____

7. <u>The sick</u> often have pain. _____ Aegri dolorem saepe habent. _____

8. <u>Many (things)</u> had been sent to the city. _____ Multa ad urbem missa erant. _____

9. <u>Many (people)</u> have remained in the province. _____ Multi in província manserunt. _____

10. We do not desire the <u>shameful (things)</u>. _____ Túrpia non cúpimus. _____

IX. Derivatives

1. The senators were _____ stultified _____ by the complexity of the problem.

2. The unpopular teacher has an unfriendly, _____ frigid _____ personality.

3. The white bear was polar, not _____ albino _____ .

4. _____ Feral _____ dogs run in packs.

I. Word Study and Grammar

1. Give **two** common **indeclinable** nouns and their meanings.
   1) **nihil** - *nothing*   2) **satis** - *enough*

2. Give **two** common **neuter** nouns of the 4th declension and their meanings.
   1) **cornu** - *horn*   2) **genu** - *knee*

3. Give the **Vocative Rule**. The vocative is the same as nom. except in 2nd decl. M sing. where **-us** changes to **-e** and **-ius** to **-i**.

4. Give the **three** exceptions to the **Vocative Rule**.
   1) **meus = mi**   2) **deus = deus**   3) **Jesus = Jesu**

5. Give **two** examples of adjectives used as nouns in English.
   1) the rich   the poor   2) the good   the bad

6. Latin uses the __masculine or neuter plural adjective__ as a noun to describe a group of people or things.

7. Give **two** examples of the above.
   1) **Fortes fortuna juvat.**   2) **Multi pecúniam cúpiunt. Multa cupit.**

8. English has __the article__, but Latin has no way to signal when an adjective is being used as a noun.

9. Give the **two** kinds of Latin adjectives.
   1) 1st/2nd-declension   2) 3rd-declension

10. Give the **three** kinds of 1st/2nd-declension adjectives.
    1) regular (**bonus**)   2) **-er**   3) Naughty Nine

11. The new adjectives in this lesson are what kind? __1st/2nd-declension__

12. Nine adjectives that have irregularities in the __genitive__, and __dative__ cases are sometimes called __the Naughty Nine__.

Saying
Say aloud and write 3X.

Latin	alter ego
Latin	alter ego
Latin	alter ego
English	another self

New Vocabulary
Say aloud and write with dictionary form, meaning, and derivative.

Latin (dictionary form)	Meaning	Derivative
unus una unum	one	unity
solus sola solum	alone, only, sole	solo
totus tota totum	whole, entire	total
ullus ulla ullum	any (at all)	
nullus nulla nullum	no, not any	
álius ália áliud	other, another	alias
alter áltera álterum	the other, the second (of two)	alternative
neuter neutra neutrum	neither (of two)	neutral
uter utra utrum	which (of two)	

II. Declensions
álius ália áliud

	Singular			Plural	
M	F	N	M	F	N
álius	ália	áliud	álii	áliae	ália
alíus	alíus	alíus	aliorum	aliarum	aliorum
álii	álii	álii	áliis	áliis	áliis
álium	áliam	áliud	álios	álias	ália
álio	áliã	álio	áliis	áliis	áliis

unus

Singular		
M	F	N
unus	una	unum
uníus	uníus	uníus
uni	uni	uni
unum	unam	unum
uno	unã	uno

III. Adjective Form Drills
Drill A

1. only way ___sola via___
2. other words ___ália verba___
3. neither boy ___neuter puer___
4. any cows ___ullae vaccae___
5. one book ___unus liber___
6. no money ___nulla pecúnia___
7. the whole tree ___tota arbor___
8. the other hand ___áltera manus___
9. which law ___utra lex___
10. any day ___ullus dies___

Drill B

1. other battle ___áliud proélium___
2. only house ___sola domus___
3. another life ___ália vita___
4. neither man ___neuter vir___
5. one dog ___unus (una) canis___
6. any name ___ullum nomen___
7. no ships ___nullae naves___
8. the other foot ___alter pes___
9. a whole city ___tota urbs___
10. which eye ___uter óculus___

Drill C

1. áltera urbs ___the other city___
2. utra soror ___which sister___
3. unum bellum ___one war___
4. totus mons ___the whole mountain___
5. ulla porta ___any gate___
6. áliae fenestrae ___other windows___
7. neutra via ___neither way___
8. nullae naves ___no ships___
9. solus exércitus ___the only army___
10. áliud praémium ___other reward___

IV. Conjugation

> Make copies of Drill/Test Form A in the Appendix. Conjugate **premo** and **struo** in all 6 tenses, <u>active</u> and <u>passive</u>. Practice until perfect.

V. Verb Drills
Drill D

1. premit ___hsi presses___
2. préssimus ___we have pressed___
3. prement ___they will press___
4. pressa erant ___they had been pressed___
5. prémitis ___you all press___
6. pressus erit ___he (it) whb pressed___
7. premuntur ___they are pressed___
8. premam ___I will press___
9. premebant ___they were pressing___
10. pressae sumus ___we have been pressed___

Drill E

1. strúitur ___it is being built___
2. struxerunt ___they have built___
3. structus est ___it has been built___
4. struit ___hsi builds___
5. strúxerant ___they had built___
6. structa erat ___she (it) had been built___
7. struxit ___hsi has built___
8. struebat ___hsi was building___
9. struent ___they will build___
10. structi sunt ___they have been built___

Drill F

1. it has been written ___scriptum (-us -a) est___
2. they were lifting ___tollebant___
3. she has placed ___pósuit___
4. I will close ___claudam___
5. you had driven ___égeras___
6. it will be collected ___cogetur___
7. they have pressed ___presserunt___
8. we will wage ___geremus___
9. they have been put ___pósiti (-ae -a) sunt___
10. I have sent ___misi___

Drill/Test Form A

Principal Parts: premo prémere pressi pressus
Present System Stem: prem-

Present

Indicative Active		Indicative Passive	
premo	prémimus	premor	prémimur
premis	prémitis	prémeris	premímini
premit	premunt	prémitur	premuntur

Imperfect

premebam	premebamus	premebar	premebamur
premebas	premebatis	premebaris	premebámini
premebat	premebant	premebatur	premebantur

Future

premam	prememus	premar	prememur
premes	premetis	prémēris	premémini
premet	prement	premetur	prementur

Perfect System Stem: press-

Perfect

Indicative Active		Indicative Passive	
pressi	préssimus	pressus sum	pressi sumus
pressisti	pressistis	(a, um) es	(ae, a) estis
pressit	presserunt	est	sunt

Pluperfect

présseram	présseramus	eram	eramus
présseras	présseratis	eras	eratis
présserat	présserant	erat	erant

Future Perfect

préssero	présserimus	ero	érimus
présseris	présséritis	eris	éritis
présserit	présserint	erit	erunt

Principal Parts: struo strúere struxi structus
Present System Stem: stru-

Present

Indicative Active		Indicative Passive	
struo	strúimus	struor	strúimur
struis	strúitis	strúeris	struímini
struit	struunt	strúitur	struuntur

Imperfect

struebam	struebamus	struebar	struebamur
struebas	struebatis	struebaris	struebámini
struebat	struebant	struebatur	struebantur

Future

struam	struemus	struar	struemur
strues	struetis	strúēris	struémini
struet	struent	struetur	struentur

Perfect System Stem: strux-

Perfect

Indicative Active		Indicative Passive	
struxi	strúximus	structus sum	structi sumus
struxisti	struxistis	(a, um) es	(ae, a) estis
struxit	struxerunt	est	sunt

Pluperfect

strúxeram	struxeramus	eram	eramus
strúxeras	struxeratis	eras	eratis
strúxerat	strúxerant	erat	erant

Future Perfect

strúxero	struxérimus	ero	érimus
strúxeris	struxéritis	eris	éritis
strúxerit	strúxerint	erit	erunt

VI. Translation

1. Terra unam lunam habet.
   Earth has one moon.

2. Alter imperator est in Itáliā et alter est in Gálliā.
   One general is in Italy and the other is in Gaul.

3. Neuter ex senatóribus est in Itáliā.
   Neither of the senators is in Italy.

4. Nulla domus in viā fenestras habet.
   No house on the road has windows.

5. Utrā manu scribis?
   Which hand do you write with?

6. Exércitus ullum frumentum non habet.
   The army does not have any grain.

7. Tota Roma est laeta.
   All Rome is happy.

8. Gállia a Cáesare solo superata est.
   Gaul was conquered by Caesar alone.

9. Exércitum ad áliam urbem mittemus.
   We will send the army to another city.

10. Tolle álterum pedum.
    Lift the other foot.

VII. Derivatives

1. The producer wants to cut the drum _____solo_____ .

2. Fuel is ninety percent of the _____total_____ weight of the rocket.

3. The _____alternative_____ to buying a house is renting.

4. A writer has a pen name, but a criminal has an _____alias_____ .

5. A referee must favor neither side; he must be _____neutral_____ .

Lesson Eleven   Worksheet 1

I. Word Study and Grammar

1. Give the **Vocative Rule**. _____The vocative is the same as nom. except in 2nd decl. M_
   sing. where **-us** changes to **-e** and **-ius** to **-i**.

2. Give the **three** exceptions to the **Vocative Rule**.
   1) **meus = mi**   2) **deus = deus**   3) **Jesus = Jesu**

3. Give **two** examples of adjectives used as nouns in English.
   1) the rich   the poor   2) the good   the bad

4. Latin uses the _masculine or neuter plural adjective_
   as a noun to describe a group of people or things.

5. Give **two** examples of the above.
   1) **Fortes fortuna juvat**   2) **Multi pecúniam cúpiunt. Multa cupit.**

6. English has_____the article_____, but Latin has no way to signal when an adjective is
   being used as a noun.

7. Give the **two** kinds of Latin adjectives.
   1) 1st/2nd-declension   2) 3rd-declension

8. Give the **three** kinds of 1st/2nd-declension adjectives.
   1) regular   2) **-er**   3) Naughty Nine

9. Give the three kinds of 3rd-declension adjectives. _1, 2, 3 terminations_

10. The new adjectives in this lesson are what kind? _1 and 3 terminations_

Saying
Say aloud and write 3X.

Latin	Homo sápiens
Latin	Homo sápiens
Latin	Homo sápiens
English	Rational man

Lesson Eleven   Worksheet 2

New Vocabulary
Say aloud and write with dictionary form, meaning, and derivative.

Latin (dictionary form)	Meaning	Derivative
acer acris acre	sharp, bitter	acrid
céleber célebris célebre	famous	celebrity, celebrate
celer céleris célere	fast, swift	accelerate
álacer álacris álacre	lively, spirited	alacrity
audax audacis	bold, rash	audacious
diligens diligentis	careful, diligent	diligent
felix felicis	fortunate, lucky	felicity
ingens ingentis	huge	
potens potentis	powerful	potent, potential
sápiens sapientis	wise, rational	
senex senis	aged, old	senile

II. Decline
Decline **celer** and **diligens**.

S.	M/F		N	M/F	N
nom.	celer	céleris	célere	díligens	díligens
gen.	céleris		céleris	diligentis	diligentis
dat.	céleri		céleri	diligenti	diligenti
acc.	célerem		célere	diligentem	diligens
abl.	céleri		céleri	diligenti	diligenti

Pl.	M/F	N	M/F	N
nom.	céleres	celéria	diligentes	diligéntia
gen.	celérium	celérium	diligéntium	diligéntium
dat.	celéribus	celéribus	diligéntibus	diligéntibus
acc.	céleres	celéria	diligentes	diligéntia
abl.	celéribus	celéribus	diligéntibus	diligéntibus

Identify the dictionary forms, and give the number of terminations.

álacer	álacris	álacre	
M nom. sing.	F nom. sing.	N nom. sing.	3

ingens	ingentis		
M/F/N nom. sing	gen. sing		1

celer	céleris	célere	
M nom. sing.	F nom. sing.	N nom. sing.	3

fortis	-e		
M/F nom. sing	N nom. sing		2

senex	senis		
M/F/N nom. sing	gen. sing		1

céleber	célebris	célebre	
M nom. sing.	F nom. sing.	N nom. sing.	3

dulcis	-e		
M/F nom. sing	N nom. sing		2

potens	potentis		
M/F/N nom. sing	gen. sing		1

III. Derivatives

1. _____Felicity_____ means good fortune and is sometimes used as a girl's name.

2. When I step on the gas, the car _____accelerates_____ .

3. She mastered the difficult composition through _____diligent_____ effort.

4. Burning plastic has an _____acrid_____ odor.

5. The _____potential_____ risk outweighs the advantage.

6. One general was too timid, the other too_____audacious_____.

IV. Form Drills
Drill A

1. saxa ingéntia _____huge rocks_____   6. navis potens _____powerful ship_____
2. bellum célebre _____famous war_____   7. discípuli álacres _____lively students_____
3. matres sapientes _____wise mothers_____   8. hortus ingens _____huge garden_____
4. pastores senes _____old shepherds_____   9. Romani audaces _____bold Romans_____
5. urbes ingentes _____huge cities_____   10. undae ingentes _____huge waves_____

Drill B

1. huge farmhouse _____villa ingens_____   6. lucky girl _____puella felix_____
2. fast horse _____equus celer_____   7. bitter wine _____vinum acre_____
3. famous orator _____orator céleber_____   8. an old senator _____senator senex_____
4. wise general _____imperator sápiens_____   9. a diligent boy _____puer díligens_____
5. powerful army _____exércitus potens_____   10. bold soldier _____miles audax_____

Drill C

1. lively citizens _____cives álacres_____   6. old trees _____árbores senes_____
2. huge fruits _____fructus ingentes_____   7. fortunate tribes _____gentes félices_____
3. fast dogs _____canes céleres_____   8. wise leaders _____duces sapientes_____
4. rash barbarians _____bárbari audaces_____   9. huge temples _____templa ingéntia_____
5. famous women _____féminae célebres_____   10. the sharp words _____verba ácria_____

Lesson Eleven

V. Conjugation

Make copies of Drill/Test Form A in the Appendix. Conjugate **claudo** and **scribo** in all 6 tenses, <u>active</u> and <u>passive</u>. Practice until perfect.

VI. Verb Drills
Drill D

1. clausa erant _they had been closed_
2. claudis _you close_
3. clauserunt _they have closed_
4. claudam _I will close_
5. cláuditur _it is closed_

6. cláudimus _we close_
7. clausum est _it has been closed_
8. cláusimus _we have closed_
9. clausae erunt _they whb closed_
10. claudent _they will close_

Drill E

1. scripsi _I have written_
2. scribet _hsi will write_
3. scriptum erit _it whb written_
4. scribo _I write_
5. scribuntur _they are written_
   b is part of stem, not a future ending

6. scrípseris _you will have written_
7. scribetur _it will be written_
8. scribis _you write_
9. scrípsimus _we have written_
10. scripta sunt _they have been written_

Drill F

1. it will be placed _ponetur_
2. they have lifted _sustulerunt_
3. he will be sent _mittetur_
4. I had pressed _présseram_
5. we are being driven _ágimur_

6. you wage _geris_
7. they are collected _coguntur_
8. you will write _scribes_
9. we are closing _cláudimus_
10. I have put _pósui_

Drill/Test Form A

Principal Parts: claudo cláudere clausi clausus
Present System Stem: claud-

Present

Indicative Active		Indicative Passive	
claudo	cláudimus	claudor	cláudimur
claudis	cláuditis	cláuderis	claudímini
claudit	claudunt	cláuditur	clauduntur

Imperfect

claudebam	claudebamus	claudebar	claudebamur
claudebas	claudebatis	claudebaris	claudebámini
claudebat	claudebant	claudebatur	claudebantur

Future

claudam	claudemus	claudar	claudemur
claudes	claudetis	claudēris	claudémini
claudet	claudent	claudetur	claudentur

Perfect System Stem: claus-

Perfect

Indicative Active		Indicative Passive	
clausi	cláusimus	clausus sum	clausi sumus
clausisti	clausistis	(a, um) es	(ae, a) estis
clausit	clauserunt	est	sunt

Pluperfect

cláuseram	clauseramus	eram	eramus
cláuseras	clauseratis	eras	eratis
cláuserat	cláuserant	erat	erant

Future Perfect

cláusero	clausérimus	ero	érimus
cláuseris	clauséritis	eris	éritis
cláuserit	cláuserint	erit	erunt

Principal Parts: scribo scríbere scripsi scriptus
Present System Stem: scrib-

Present

Indicative Active		Indicative Passive	
scribo	scríbimus	scribor	scríbimur
scribis	scríbitis	scríberis	scribímini
scribit	scribunt	scríbitur	scribuntur

Imperfect

scribebam	scribebamus	scribebar	scribebamur
scribebas	scribebatis	scribebaris	scribebámini
scribebat	scribebant	scribebatur	scribebantur

Future

scribam	scribemus	scribar	scribemur
scribes	scribetis	scribēris	scribémini
scribet	scribent	scribetur	scribentur

Perfect System Stem: scrips-

Perfect

Indicative Active		Indicative Passive	
scripsi	scrípsimus	scriptus sum	-pti sumus
scripsisti	scripsistis	(a, um) es	(ae, a) estis
scripsit	scripserunt	est	sunt

Pluperfect

scrípseram	scripseramus	eram	eramus
scrípseras	scripseratis	eras	eratis
scrípserat	scrípserant	erat	erant

Future Perfect

scrípsero	scripsérimus	ero	érimus
scrípseris	scripséritis	eris	éritis
scrípserit	scrípserint	erit	erunt

VII. Translation

1. Urbs a rege potenti régitur. _____
   The city is ruled by a powerful king.

2. Milites novi sunt audaces. ____The new soldiers are bold._____

3. Circum urbem vallum ingens fécerunt. _____
   They made a huge rampart around the city.

4. Navem célerem tibi mittam.____I will send you a fast ship._____

5. Totus exércitus in provínciam mittetur. _____
   The whole army will be sent into the province.

6. Urbs felix ullos hostes non habet. _____
   The lucky city does not have any enemies.

7. Senator senex voce acri orabat. _____
   The old senator was speaking with a sharp voice.

8. The book was written by a famous poet. _____
   Liber a poetā célebri scriptus est.

9. The letter was written by a wise king. _____
   Epístula a rege sapienti scripta est.

10. Mark, lift up the huge rocks. ___Tolle, Marce, saxa ingéntia._____

I. Word Study and Grammar

1. Give **two** examples of adjectives used as nouns in English.
   1) _the rich   the poor_____ 2) ___the good   the bad____

2. Latin uses the _____masculine or neuter plural adjective_____
   as a noun to describe a group of people or things.

3. Give the **two** kinds of Latin adjectives.
   1) _1st/2nd-declension_____ 2) ____3rd-declension_____

4. Give the **three** kinds of 1st/2nd-declension adjectives.
   1) _regular_____ 2)_____-er_____ 3) ____Naughty Nine___

5. Give the three kinds of 3rd-declension adjectives. _1, 2, 3 terminations____

6. Nine adjectives that have irregularities in the ____genitive_____ and _____
   _____dative_____ cases are sometimes called ___the Naughty Nine____

7. How many of this lesson's adjectives are 1st/2nd declension adjectives?_____8_____
   How many are 3rd-declension adjectives? Name them. ____2; **útilis**, **símilis**____
   What kind of 3rd-declension adjectives are they? ___2-termination____

8. The prepositions ___in___ and ___sub____ take the ___accusative_____ when motion
   is indicated, and ___ablative_____when location is indicated.

9. In English, some adjectives require a ___prepositional phrase_____ to complete their thought.

10. The three ways in Latin to express this prepositional phrase is by _____
    _____a case, infinitive, preposition_____ .

II. New Vocabulary
Say aloud and write with dictionary form, meaning, and derivative.

Latin (dictionary form)	Meaning	Derivative
cúpidus -a -um	eager, desirous	cupidity
plenus -a -um	full	plenty
carus -a -um	dear	care
finítimus -a -um	neighboring, close	finite
idóneus -a -um	suitable, fit, proper	
símilis -e	similar	similar
paratus -a -um	prepared	
útilis -e	useful	utility
tutus -a -um	safe	tutor
vácuus -a -um	empty	vacuum

Lesson Twelve   Worksheet 2

Derivatives

1. Anything that has a distinct beginning and end is _____ finite _____ .

2. I have a _____ tutor _____ to help me with math.

3. Space is a near but not perfect _____ vacuum _____ .

4. I keep my old car for its _____ utility _____ , not its beauty.

5. These two pictures are _____ similar _____ , but not identical.

6. Wanting more than you need is _____ cupidity _____ .

III. Preposition Review

Give the correct Latin preposition and the case it governs.

English	Latin	Case
1. across	trans	accusative
2. after, behind	post	accusative
3. against	contra	accusative
4. among	apud	accusative
5. around	circum	accusative
6. because of	ob	accusative
7. on account of	propter	accusative
8. before	ante	accusative
9. between	inter	accusative
10. about, down from	de	ablative
11. for, on behalf of, in front of	pro	ablative
12. by, from	a, ab	ablative
13. at the head of	prae	ablative
14. in the presence of	coram	ablative
15. in, on	in	ablative
16. into, onto	in	accusative
17. near	juxta	accusative
18. out of, out from	e, ex	ablative
19. through	per	accusative
20. to, toward, at	ad	accusative
21. to the foot of	sub	accusative
22. under, at the foot of	sub	ablative
23. with	cum	ablative
24. without	sine	ablative
25. as far as	tenus	ablative

Lesson Twelve   Worksheet 3

IV. Form Drills - Adjectives and Prepositions
Drill A

1. into the kitchen _____ in culinam _____   6. toward the river _____ ad flumen _____

2. through the field _____ per agrum _____   7. against enemies _____ contra hostes _____

3. without hope _____ sine spe _____   8. between the towns _____ inter óppida _____

4. around the city _____ circum urbem _____   9. for the province _____ pro provínciã _____

5. under a rock _____ sub saxo _____   10. with friends _____ cum amicis _____

Drill B

Use nominative singular masculine form for adjectives.

1. full of water _____ plenus aquae _____   6. close to the mountain _____ finítimus monti _____

2. safe from danger _____ tutus perículo _____   7. fit for work _____ idóneus labori _____

3. empty of grain _____ vácuus frumento _____   8. prepared to flee _____ paratus fúgere _____

4. desirous of money _____ cúpidus pecúniae _____   9. similar to iron _____ símilis ferro _____

5. dear to me _____ carus mihi _____   10. useful for war _____ útilis ad bellum _____

Drill C

1. pro senatu _____ for the senate _____   6. cúpidus victóriae _____ desirous of victory _____

2. trans flumen _____ across the river _____   7. sine cibo _____ without food _____

3. cum sóciis _____ with allies _____   8. carus milítibus _____ dear to the soldiers _____

4. in hortum _____ into the garden _____   9. ad domum _____ to the house _____

5. plenus saxorum _____ full of rocks _____   10. símilis telo _____ similar to a missile _____

V. Adjective Review (Lesson XI)

Drill D: Nominative Case

1. huge brother __frater ingens__
2. fast eagle __áquila céleris__
3. famous battle __proélium célebre__
4. wise sister __soror sápiens__
5. powerful father __pater potens__

6. lucky sailor __nauta felix__
7. bitter queen __regina acris__
8. an old cow __vacca senex__
9. a diligent teacher __magister díligens__
10. bold leader __dux audax__

Drill E: Nominative Case

1. lively voices __voces álacres__
2. huge mountains __montes ingentes__
3. fast dogs __canes céleres__
4. bold laws __leges audaces__
5. famous senators __senatores célebres__

6. old trees __árbores senes__
7. fortunate tribes __gentes felices__
8. wise customs __mores sapientes__
9. huge hearts __corda ingéntia__
10. bitter pains __dolores acres__

VI. Conjugation

> Make copies of Drill/Test Form A in the Appendix. Conjugate **vénio** and **cedo** in all 6 tenses, __active__ only. Practice until perfect.

VII. Verb Drills
Drill F

1. véniam __I will come__
2. veni __I came__
3. vénies __you will come__
4. véniunt __they come__
5. vénient __they will come__

6. vēnit __hsi came__
7. venit __hsi comes__
8. vēnimus __we came__
9. veniemus __we will come__
10. venerunt __they came__

Drill G

1. préssimus __we have pressed__
2. geret __hsi will wage__
3. scriptum erat __it had been written__
4. cogímini __you all are collected__
5. césserit __hsi will have given up__

6. claudam __I will close__
7. posúimus __we have placed__
8. mittetur __hsi will be sent__
9. actum est __it has been driven__
10. sustulisti __you have lifted__

Drill H

1. we were placing __ponebamus__
2. they have been sent __missi (-ae -a) sunt__
3. you all will give way __cedetis__
4. it is waged __géritur__
5. you will write __scribes__

6. she will have driven __égerit__
7. they will be collected __cogentur__
8. he lifts up __tollit__
9. they will press __prement__
10. it will be closed __claudetur__

Drill/Test Form A

Principal Parts: vénio venire vēni ventus
Present System Stem: veni-

Present

Indicative Active		Indicative Passive	
vénio	venimus		
venis	venitis		
venit	véniunt		

Imperfect

veniebam	veniebamus		
veniebas	veniebatis		
veniebat	veniebant		

Future

véniam	veniemus		
vénies	venietis		
véniet	vénient		

Perfect System Stem: vēn-

Perfect

Indicative Active		Indicative Passive	
veni	vēnimus		
venisti	venistis		
vēnit	venerunt		

Pluperfect

véneram	veneramus		
véneras	veneratis		
vénerat	vénerant		

Future Perfect

vénero	venérimus		
véneris	venéritis		
vénerit	vénerint		

Principal Parts: cedo cédere cessi cessus
Present System Stem: ced-

Present

Indicative Active		Indicative Passive	
cedo	cédimus		
cedis	céditis		
cedit	cedunt		

Imperfect

cedebam	cedebamus		
cedebas	cedebatis		
cedebat	cedebant		

Future

cedam	cedemus		
cedes	cedetis		
cedet	cedent		

Perfect System Stem: cess-

Perfect

Indicative Active		Indicative Passive	
cessi	céssimus		
cessisti	cessistis		
cessit	cesserunt		

Pluperfect

césseram	cesseramus		
césseras	cesseratis		
césserat	césserant		

Future Perfect

céssero	cessérimus		
césseris	cesséritis		
césserit	césserint		

VIII. Translation

1. Agrícolae vaccas sub collem agebant. _____
   The farmers were driving the cows to the foot of the hill. _____

2. Silva plena ferorum erat. _____
   The forest was full of wild (animals).

3. Cives cúpidi pecúniae pro urbe sunt. _____
   The citizens are desirous of money for the city.

4. Mílites pugnare parati trans flumen missi sunt. _____
   Soldiers prepared to fight have been sent across the river.

5. Urbs regi cara ab exércitu cessa est. _____
   A city dear to the king has been given up by the army.

6. Grain will be put into the ships. _____
   Frumentum in naves ponetur.

7. Cives in província sunt tuti bello. _____
   The citizens in the province are safe from war.

8. The windows will have been closed on account of the wind. _____
   Fenestrae propter ventum clausae erunt.

9. Ferrum idóneum telis a nostris coactum est. _____
   Iron suitable for missiles was collected by our men.

10. Post próelium óppidum erat vácuum homínibus. _____
    After the battle the town was empty of men.

I. Word Study and Grammar

1. Latin uses the ___masculine or neuter plural adjective___ ___ as a noun to describe a group of people or things.

2. Give **two** examples of the above.
   1) **Fortes fortuna juvat**   2) **Multi pecúniam cúpiunt. Multa cupit.**

3. Give the **two** kinds of Latin adjectives.
   1) 1st/2nd-declension   2) 3rd-declension

4. Give the **three** kinds of 1st/2nd-declension adjectives.
   1) regular   2) **-er**   3) Naughty Nine

5. Give the **three** kinds of 3rd-declension adjectives. 1, 2, 3 terminations

6. Nine adjectives that have irregularities in the ___genitive___ and ___dative___ singular are sometimes called ___the Naughty Nine___.

7. Many 1st/2nd-declension adjectives can be changed into adverbs by adding ___-ē___ to the adjective stem.

8. Many 3rd-declension adjectives can be changed into adverbs by adding ___-iter___ to the adjective stem.

9. The prepositions ___in___ and ___sub___ take the ___accusative___ when motion is indicated, and ___ablative___ when location is indicated.

10. The three ways in Latin to express the prepositional phrase is by ___ ___case, infinitive, and preposition___.

11. Which cardinal numbers are declined and how? ___ **unus** - like the Naughty Nine; **duo** - only in the plural; **tres** - like the plural of **brevis**

Saying
Say aloud and write 3X.

Latin	O témpora, O mores
Latin	O témpora, O mores
Latin	O témpora, O mores
English	O the times, O the customs

II. New Vocabulary
Give the Arabic numerals and cardinal numbers from 11-20.

Ar. Numerals	Cardinal Numbers
11	úndecim
12	duódecim
13	trédecim
14	quattuórdecim
15	quíndecim
16	sédecim
17	septéndecim
18	duodeviginti
19	undeviginti
20	viginti

III. Declensions
Decline **unus**.

Singular		
M	F	N
unus	una	unum
uníus	uníus	uníus
uni	uni	uni
unum	unam	unum
uno	unā	uno

Decline **duo**.

Plural	
M/N	F
duo	duae
duorum	duarum
duobus	duabus
duo, duos (m.)	duas
duobus	duabus

Decline **tres, tria** (like plural of **brevis**).

Plural	
M/F	N
tres	tria
trium	trium
tribus	tribus
tres	tria
tribus	tribus

Lesson Thirteen   Worksheet 3

IV. Form Drills
Drill A

1. in two cities _____ in duabus úrbibus
2. three days _____ tres dies
3. out of two houses _____ e duabus dómibus
4. behind three ships _____ post tres naves
5. under one foot _____ sub uno pede

6. with two friends _____ cum duobus amicis
7. of one enemy _____ unius hostis
8. into one town _____ in unum óppidum
9. for two provinces _____ pro duabus provínciis
10. against three kings _____ contra tres reges

Drill B

1. twenty days _____ viginti dies
2. thirteen horses _____ trédecim equi
3. eleven sisters _____ úndecim sorores
4. fifteen years _____ quíndecim anni
5. seventeen soldiers _____ septéndecim mílites

6. nineteen lakes _____ undeviginti lacūs
7. eighteen ships _____ duodeviginti naves
8. twelve cities _____ duódecim urbes
9. fourteen missiles _____ quattuórdecim tela
10. sixteen trees _____ sédecim arbores

Drill C

1. trium virorum _____ of three men
2. uníus senatoris _____ of one senator
3. cum tribus cánibus _____ with three dogs
4. in unā provínciā _____ in one province
5. per duas portas _____ through two gates

6. uni sorori _____ to one sister
7. tria fólia _____ three leaves
8. sub uno saxo _____ under one rock
9. ad duo montes _____ toward two mountains
10. duarum matrum _____ of two mothers

Lesson Thirteen   Worksheet 4

V. Review Vocabulary
Adverbs made from adjectives

highly, deeply	altē	happily	laetē
roughly	ásperē	widely	latē
shortly, briefly	bréviter	slowly	lentē
certainly	certē	freely	líberē
with difficulty	difficíliter	far, by far	longē
easily	fácile	unhappily	míserē
faithfully	fidéliter	much	multum
bravely	fórtiter	beautifully	pulchrē
heavily	gráviter	shamefully	túrpiter

Numbers

Roman Numerals	Cardinal		Ordinal	
I	unus -a -um	one	primus -a -um	first
II	duo -ae -o	two	secundus -a -um	second
III	tres tria	three	tértius -a -um	third
IV	quattuor	four	quartus -a -um	fourth
V	quinque	five	quintus -a -um	fifth
VI	sex	six	sextus -a -um	sixth
VII	septem	seven	séptimus -a -um	seventh
VIII	octo	eight	octavus -a -um	eighth
IX	novem	nine	nonus -a -um	ninth
X	decem	ten	décimus -a -um	tenth

VI. Conjugation

Make copies of Drill/Test Form A in the Appendix. Conjugate **dórmio** and **fácio** in all 6 tenses, active only. Practice until perfect.

VII. Verb Drills
Drill D

1. tolletur _____ hsi will be lifted
2. egisti _____ you have driven
3. premebamus _____ we were pressing
4. gesta sunt _____ they have been waged
5. cessi _____ I yielded

6. claudit _____ hsi closes
7. missi erant _____ they had been sent
8. pósitae erunt _____ they will have been placed
9. scribet _____ hsi will write
10. cogebantur _____ they were being collected

Drill E

1. fáciunt _____ they make
2. scribunt _____ they write
3. dórmient _____ they will sleep
4. facit _____ hsi makes
5. fáciam _____ I will make

6. fecit _____ hsi (has) made
7. fécerat _____ hsi had made
8. dormiebat _____ hsi was sleeping
9. dormiverunt _____ they slept
10. míserit _____ hsi will have sent

Drill F

1. you all have placed _____ posuistis
2. they will be sent _____ mittentur
3. it had been waged _____ gestum (-us -a) erat
4. I will press _____ premam
5. it will be written _____ scribetur

6. we have lifted up _____ sustúlimus
7. you will give up _____ cedes
8. they are driving _____ agunt
9. they will be collected _____ cogentur
10. it will close _____ claudet

Drill/Test Form A

Principal Parts: dórmio dormire dormivi dormitus
Present System Stem: dormi-

Present		Present	
Indicative Active		Indicative Passive	
dórmio	dormimus		
dormis	dormitis		
dormit	dórmiunt		

Imperfect			
dormiebam	dormiebamus		
dormiebas	dormiebatis		
dormiebat	dormiebant		

Future			
dórmiam	dormiemus		
dórmies	dormietis		
dórmiet	dórmient		

Perfect System Stem: dormiv-

Perfect		Perfect	
Indicative Active		Indicative Passive	
dormivi	dormívimus		
dormivisti	dormivistis		
dormivit	dormiverunt		

Pluperfect			
dormíveram	dormiveramus		
dormíveras	dormiveratis		
dormíverat	dormíverant		

Future Perfect			
dormívero	dormivérimus		
dormíveris	dormivéritis		
dormíverit	dormíverint		

Principal Parts: fácio fácere feci factus
Present System Stem: faci-

Present		Present	
Indicative Active		Indicative Passive	
fácio	fácimus		
facis	fácitis		
facit	faciunt		

Imperfect			
faciebam	faciebamus		
faciebas	faciebatis		
faciebat	faciebant		

Future			
fáciam	faciemus		
fácies	facietis		
fáciet	fácient		

Perfect System Stem: fec-

Perfect		Perfect	
Indicative Active		Indicative Passive	
feci	fécimus		
fecisti	fecistis		
fecit	fecerunt		

Pluperfect			
féceram	feceramus		
féceras	feceratis		
fécerat	fécerant		

Future Perfect			
fécero	fecérimus		
féceris	fecéritis		
fécerit	fécerint		

Lesson Thirteen   Worksheet 6

Conjugation Meanings

amo 1st person singular only

Present system	Active	Passive
Present	I love, do love, am loving	I am (being) loved
Imperfect	I was loving	I was (being) loved
Future	I will love	I will be loved
Perfect System		
Perfect	I loved, have loved, did love	I have been loved
Pluperfect	I had loved	I had been loved
Future perfect	I will have loved	I will have been loved

VIII. Translation

1. Vacca duo córnua habet. _The cow has two horns._

2. Rex contra duos exércitūs bellum diffíciliter gerebat. _____
   The king was waging war with difficulty against two armies.

3. Epístulam scripsi sed numquam misi. _____
   I wrote but never sent the letter.

4. Duae naves frumenti plenae cras mittentur. _____
   Tomorrow two ships full of grain will be sent.

5. Cives duas urbis portas certe clauserunt. _____
   The citizens have certainly closed two gates of the city.

6. My son, put twenty huge rocks around the garden. _____
   Pone, fili mi, viginti ingéntia saxa circum hortum.

7. Quintum librum celériter* scribet. _____
   He will quickly write the fifth book.

8. Senatus centum mílites ad provínciam líbere misit. _____
   The Senate freely sent one hundred soldiers to the province.

9. The leaves of the trees are being pushed (**premo**) by a strong wind. _____
   Arborum fólia vento forti premuntur.

10. Urbis portae contra hostes potentes clausae sunt. _____
    The gates of the city have been closed against powerful enemies.

*celériter *adv.* swiftly

I. Word Study and Grammar

1. The vocative case is the case of _____direct address_____ .

2. The vocative case is identical to the nominative in all declensions except in singular _____
   _____masculine_____ nouns of the _____second_____ declension ending in
   _-us_ or _-ius_ , where _-e_ replaces _-us_ and _-i_ replaces _-ius_ .

3. A vocative noun is often used with an _____imperative_____ verb and usually is not the _____first_____
   word in the sentence.

4. Give **two** common **indeclinable** nouns and their meanings.
   1) **nihil** - *nothing*   2) **satis** - *enough*

5. Give **two** common **neuter** nouns of the 4th declension and their meanings.
   1) **cornu** - *horn*   2) **genu** - *knee*

6. What is an appositive? _____
   a noun that immediately follows another noun and renames it _____

7. An appositive agrees with its noun or pronoun in_____case_____ , and usually
   but not necessarily in _____gender and number_____ .

8. What is the rule if the appositive refers to two persons of different genders?_____
   Use the masculine form. _____

9. English has _____the article_____ , but Latin has no way to signal when an adjective is being used as
   a noun.

10. Latin uses the _____masculine or neuter plural adjective_____
    as a noun to describe a group of people or things.

11. Nine adjectives that have irregularities in the _____genitive_____ and _____
    _____dative_____ cases are sometimes called _____the Naughty Nine_____ .

12. Give the **three** kinds of 1st/2nd-declension adjectives.
    1) regular   2) -er   3) Naughty Nine

13. Give the three kinds of 3rd-declension adjectives. _____1, 2, 3 terminations_____

14. In English some adjectives require a _____prepositional phrase_____ to complete their thought.

15. The three ways in Latin to express this prepositional phrase is by _____
    a case, infinitive, and preposition _____ .

16. Which cardinal numbers are declined and how? _____
    unus - like the Naughty Nine; **duo** - only in the plural; **tres** - like the plural of **brevis**

II. Latin Sayings

1. Rational man _____Homo sápiens_____

2. Love conquers all (things). _____Amor vincit ómnia._____

3. Another self _____alter ego_____

4. O the times, O the customs _____O témpora, O mores_____

III. Conjugation

> Make copies of Drill/Test Form A in the Appendix. Conjugate **pono** and **tollo** in all 6 tenses,
> active and passive. Practice until perfect.

IV. Declensions

Decline **álius ália áliud**.

	Singular			Plural	
M	F	N	M	F	N
álius	ália	áliud	álii	áliae	ália
alíus	alíus	alíus	aliorum	aliarum	aliorum
álii	álii	álii	áliis	áliis	áliis
álium	áliam	áliud	álios	álias	ália
álio	áliā	álio	áliis	áliis	áliis

Decline **duo**.

Plural	
M/N	F
duo	duae
duorum	duarum
duobus	duabus
duo, duos (m.)	duas
duobus	duabus

Decline **tres**.

Plural	
M/F	N
tres	tria
trium	trium
tribus	tribus
tres	tria
tribus	tribus

Drill/Test Form A

Principal Parts: pono pónere pósui pósitus
Present System Stem: pon-

Present			
Indicative Active		Indicative Passive	
pono	pónimus	ponor	pónimur
ponis	ponitis	póneris	ponímini
ponit	ponunt	pónitur	ponuntur
Imperfect			
ponebam	ponebamus	ponebar	ponebamur
ponebas	ponebatis	ponebaris	ponebámini
ponebat	ponebant	ponebatur	ponebantur
Future			
ponam	ponemus	ponar	ponemur
pones	ponetis	ponēris	ponémini
ponet	ponent	ponetur	ponentur

Perfect System Stem: posu-

Perfect			
Indicative Active		Indicative Passive	
pósui	posúimus	pósitus sum	pósiti sumus
posuisti	posuistis	(a, um) es	(ae, a) estis
pósuit	posuerunt	est	sunt
Pluperfect			
posúeram	posueramus	eram	eramus
posúeras	posueratis	eras	eratis
posúerat	posúerant	erat	erant
Future Perfect			
posúero	posúerimus	ero	érimus
posúeris	posúeritis	eris	éritis
posúerit	posúerint	erit	erunt

Principal Parts: tollo tóllere sústuli sublatus
Present System Stem: toll-

Present			
Indicative Active		Indicative Passive	
tollo	tóllimus	tollor	tóllimur
tollis	tóllitis	tólleris	tollímini
tollit	tollunt	tóllitur	tolluntur
Imperfect			
tollebam	tollebamus	tollebar	tollebamur
tollebas	tollebatis	tollebaris	tollebámini
tollebat	tollebant	tollebatur	tollebantur
Future			
tollam	tollemus	tollar	tollemur
tolles	tolletis	tollēris	tollémini
tollet	tollent	tolletur	tolluntur

Perfect System Stem: sustul-

Perfect			
Indicative Active		Indicative Passive	
sústuli	sustúlimus	sublatus sum	-lati sumus
sustulisti	sustulistis	(a, um) es	(ae, a) estis
sústulit	sustulerunt	est	sunt
Pluperfect			
sustúleram	sustuleramus	eram	eramus
sustúleras	sustuleratis	eras	eratis
sustúlerat	sustúlerant	erat	erant
Future Perfect			
sustúlero	sustulérimus	ero	érimus
sustúleris	sustuléritis	eris	éritis
sustúlerit	sustúlerint	erit	erunt

Decline **unus**.

Singular		
M	F	N
unus	una	unum
uníus	uníus	uníus
uni	uni	uni
unum	unam	unum
uno	unā	uno

Decline **celer céleris célere**.

Singular			Plural	
M/F		N	M/F	N
celer	céleris	célere	céleres	celéria
céleris		céleris	celérium	celérium
céleri		céleri	celéribus	celéribus
célerem		célere	céleres	celéria
céleri		céleri	celéribus	celéribus

Decline **potens potentis**.

M/F		N	
S.	Pl.	S.	Pl.
potens	potentes	potens	poténtia
potentis	poténtium	potentis	poténtium
potenti	poténtibus	potenti	poténtibus
potentem	potentes	potens	poténtia
potenti	poténtibus	potenti	poténtibus

Decline **cornu** and **genu**.

Case	S.	Pl.	S.	Pl.
nom.	cornu	córnua	genu	génua
gen.	cornūs	córnuum	genūs	génuum
dat.	cornu	córnibus	genu	génibus
acc.	cornu	córnua	genu	génua
abl.	cornu	córnibus	genu	génibus

V. Vocabulary
Give the dictionary form.

careful	díligens -entis	fortunate	felix, felicis
only	solus -a -um	nurturing	almus -a -um
knee	genu -ūs n.	wicked	nefárius -a -um
eager	cúpidus -a -um	enough	satis
white	albus -a -um	lofty, on high	excelsus -a -um
huge	ingens -entis	powerful	potens -entis
full	plenus -a -um	whole, entire	totus -a -um
fast, swift	celer céleris célere	empty	vácuus -a -um
wild	ferus -a -um	suitable	idóneus -a -um
aged	senex senis	famous	céleber -bris -bre
which (of two)	uter -tra -trum	prepared	paratus -a -um
ugly	foedus -a -um	safe	tutus -a -um
sharp, bitter	acer -cris -cre	neighboring	finítimus -a -um
not any	nullus -a -um	nothing	nihil (nil)
tired	defessus -a -um	foolish	stultus -a -um
hot	cálidus -a -um	the one ... the other	alter ... alter
Jesus	Jesus -u m.	horn	cornu -ūs n.
the other	alter áltera álterum	bold	audax, audacis
similar	símilis -e	wise	sápiens -entis
cold	frígidus -a -um	one	unus -a -um
neither	neuter -tra -trum	useful	útilis -e
dear	carus -a -um	lively	álacer -cris -cre
another	álius ália áliud	any	ullus -a -um

Give the case or preposition that completes the adjective.

1. símilis -e _____ dative
2. vácuus -a -um _____ ablative
3. carus -a -um _____ dative
4. cúpidus -a -um _____ genitive
5. útilis -e _____ ad + accusative
6. tutus -a -um _____ ablative
7. idóneus -a -um _____ dative
8. finítimus -a -um _____ dative
9. paratus -a -um _____ ad + accusative, infinitive
10. plenus -a -um _____ genitive

Give the Latin name and Roman numeral.

	Latin Name	Roman Numeral
11	úndecim	XI
12	duódecim	XII
13	trédecim	XIII
14	quattuórdecim	XIV
15	quíndecim	XV
16	sédecim	XVI
17	septéndecim	XVII
18	duodeviginti	XVIII
19	undeviginti	XIX
20	viginti	XX

Unit II Review

VI. Translation A
Vocative, apposition, adjective as noun

1. My friend, write me a letter. _Scribe, amice mi, epístulam mihi._

2. Son, shut the door. _Claude, fili, jánuam._

3. Gállia a Caésare imperatore superata est. _Gaul was overcome by Caesar, the general._

4. My sister, Mary, will prepare dinner. _Mária soror cenam parabit._

5. Felices urbem Romam hábitant. _The lucky ones live in the city (of) Rome._

6. Give water to the weary. _Da defessis aquam._

7. Imperator multa nostris dedit. _The general gave many things to our men._

VI. Translation B
Adjectives

1. The big door is the only door of the whole house. _Magna jánua est totíus domūs jánua sola._

2. Put the horn in your other hand. _Pone cornu in álteram manum._

3. The huge ship will be full of grain and wine. _Navis ingens erit frumenti viníque (et vini) plena._

4. Libri sunt senis sapientis libri. _The books are the books of a wise old man._

5. Urbs célebris ab imperatóribus audácibus duobus oppugnata erat. _The famous city had been attacked by two bold generals._

6. Saxa sunt vallis idónea. _The rocks are suitable for ramparts._

7. The lake is full of water. _Lacus est aquae plenus._

8. The dogs are dear to my brother, but they are not dear to me. _Canes sunt fratri cari sed non sunt mihi cari._

9. Find a table similar to my table. _Inveni mensam mensae meae símilem._

Unit III
Introduction

1. Define pronoun. _A pronoun takes the place of a noun._

2. Give the eight kinds of pronouns in pairs. _personal and possessive; reflexive and intensive; relative and interrogative; demonstrative and indefinite_

3. Why are pronouns confusing? _There are many kinds; they have attributes of verbs (person) and nouns (case and gender); they have antecedents with which they must agree; some can also function as adjectives._

4. Give the Pronoun Agreement Rule. _A pronoun agrees with its antecedent in gender and number, but its case is determined by its function in its own clause._

5. Give the Adjective Agreement Rule. _An adjective agrees with its noun in gender, number, and case._

6. Demonstrative pronouns _point to something_ .

7. Give the names of the four demonstrative pronouns in Latin. _is ea id   hic haec hoc   ille illa illud   iste ista istud_

8. Which two kinds of pronouns have the same forms in English but different forms in Latin? _intensive and reflexive_

9. Reflexive pronouns refer to the _subject_ of the clause or sentence.

10. Intensive pronouns give _emphasis_ to another word in the sentence.

I. Word Study and Grammar

1. Give three reasons for using a personal pronoun in the nominative case (as a subject). _____
   clarity, contrast, emphasis

2. The preposition **cum** takes the _____ablative_____ case, and when combined with 1st/2nd-personal pronouns results in these forms:_____ **mecum, tecum, nobiscum, vobiscum** _____

3. To show possession in the 1st and 2nd persons use the possessive pronoun adjectives _____
   meus, tuus, noster, vester ,
   which usually ___follow___ the noun, and are usually omitted when referring to ____
   parts of one's own body or members of one's own family
   .

4. The genitive of 1st/2nd-declension pronouns is used for ___of___
   expressions that do not show ___possession___ .

5. What is the objective genitive? Give examples. _____ A noun that implies action may be
   followed by a noun or pronoun in the genitive case.
   metus Dei = *fear of God*   **metus nostr**i = *fear of us*

6. What is the partitive genitive? Give examples._____ A noun that implies part or
   division may be followed by a noun or pronoun in the genitive case.
   pars legionis part of the legion   pars nostrum part of us

7. Nostri and vestri are used for the ____objective____ genitive.

8. Nostrum and vestrum are used for the ____partitive____ genitive.

9. Third-declension nouns that end in **o** are usually what gender?____feminine____

10. Give three exceptions from the vocabulary list and an explanation for each. _____
    homo, leo, centúrio—natural gender

11. Why is **légio, legionis** feminine? _____
    Groups are usually feminine, even when made up of men.

II. New Vocabulary

Say aloud and write with dictionary form, meaning, and derivative.

Latin (dictionary form)	Meaning	Derivative
virgo vírginis f.	virgin, maiden	virgin
homo hóminis m.	man, human being	homicide, homo sapiens
ordo órdinis m.	order, rank, line, row	ordinal
leo leonis m.	lion	leonine
oratio orationis f.	speech	oration
centúrio centurionis m.	centurion	centurion
pássio passionis f.	suffering	passion
tentátio tentationis f.	temptation	temptation
léctio lectionis f.	lesson	lecture
légio legionis f.	legion	legionary

III. Declensions

Complete charts from memory.

First Person Pronouns				
Case	S.	Meaning	Pl.	Meaning
nom.	ego	I	nos	we
gen.	mei	of me	nostri, nostrum	of us
dat.	mihi	to/for me	nobis	to/for us
acc.	me	me	nos	us
abl.	me	ibwf me	nobis	ibwf us

Second Person Pronouns				
Case	S.	Meaning	Pl.	Meaning
nom.	tu	you	vos	you all
gen.	tui	of you	vestri, vestrum	of you all
dat.	tibi	to/for you	vobis	to/for you all
acc.	te	you	vos	you all
abl.	te	ibwf you	vobis	ibwf you all

1st/2nd Person Possessive Pronoun Adjectives				
Person	S.	Meaning	Pl.	Meaning
1st	meus mea meum	my	noster nostra nostrum	our
2nd	tuus tua tuum	your	vester vestra vestrum	your (pl.)

IV. Form Drills
Drill A
Partitive and Objective Genitive

1. pars orationis _part of the speech_
2. amor vestri _love of you all_
3. pars nostrum _part of us_
4. lectionis pars áltera _second part of the lesson_
5. metus tui _fear of you_

6. nullus mílitum _none of the soldiers_
7. unus canum _one of the dogs_
8. memória nostri _memory of us_
9. fori pars dextra _right part of the forum_
10. metus leonum _fear of lions_

Drill B
Possessive Pronoun Adjectives

1. leo meus _my lion_
2. legio nostra _our legion_
3. órdines vestri _your (pl.) ranks_
4. pássio tua _your suffering_
5. tentationes meae _my temptations_

6. centúrio noster _our centurion_
7. lectiones tuae _your lessons_
8. ordo meus _my rank_
9. hómines vestri _your (pl.) men_
10. leones nostri _our lions_

Drill C
Possessive Pronoun Adjectives

1. my good city _urbs bona mea_
2. our fast dogs _canes céleres nostri_
3. your whole house _domus tota tua_
4. my noble name _nomen nóbile meum_
5. your (pl.) shadows _umbrae vestrae_

6. our brave soldiers _mílites fortes nostri_
7. your small town _óppidum parvum tuum_
8. your (pl.) senators _senatores vestri_
9. my weary face _fácies defessa mea_
10. your two horns _córnua duo tua_

Drill D
Express the *italicized* pronoun or prepositional phrase in Latin.

1. Give *us* a horse. _nobis_
2. They see *you all*. _vos_
3. I am working *for (on behalf of) you*. _pro te_
4. She is walking *with me*. _mecum_
5. I will give *you* a shield. _tibi_
6. Tell *me* a story. _mihi_
7. He has sent *you* to the army. _te_
8. He has sent *you* a letter. _tibi_
9. The dogs came *with us*. _nobiscum_
10. She has given *me* a prize. _mihi_
11. The Gauls fear *us*. _nos_
12. We have no fear *of you*. _tui_
13. They have come *for (on behalf of) us*. _pro nobis_
14. Why are they fighting *for (on behalf of) me*? _pro me_
15. They are close *to me*. _mihi_
16. The house is full *of us*. _nostrum_
17. The city is dear *to us*. _nobis_
18. I was expecting *you all*. _vos_
19. *You* are correct. _tu_
20. It has tempted *me*. _me_
21. She will greet *you*. _te_
22. We have been rescued *by you all*. _a vobis_

V. Translation

Personal Pronouns

1. Puellae me audiverunt. _The girls heard me._

2. Magister longam fábulam nobis narravit. _The teacher told us a long story._

3. Centúrio nos in silvā invēnit. _The centurion found us in the forest._

4. Agrícola ad flumen me misit. _The farmer sent me to the river._

5. Argentum a me celábitur. _The silver will be hidden by me._

6. Canem post te vídeo. _I see a dog behind you._

7. Epístula nobis missa est. _A letter has been sent to us._

8. Vos ad provínciam mittet. _He will send you all to the province._

9. Donum tibi miserunt. _They have sent you a gift._

10. Sine me fugerunt. _They fled without me._

11. I wrote you a letter. _Epístulam tibi scripsi._

12. You all will see us in the water. _Nos in aquā vidébis._

13. You have wounded me with a sword. _Gládio me vulneravisti._

14. We had blamed you all after the battle. _Post proélium vos culpaveramus._

15. I did not help you. _Non te juvi._

16. We hid you all. _Vos celávimus._

17. I have put the shield behind you. _Scutum post te pósui._

18. We will walk with you. _Tecum ambulábimus._

VI. Conjugation

> Make copies of Drill/Test Form A in the Appendix. Conjugate **múnio** and **do** in all 6 tenses, <u>active</u> and <u>passive</u>. Give the meanings for **do** (1st P. sing. only). Practice until perfect.

Drill/Test Form A

Principal Parts: múnio munire munivi munitus
Present System Stem: muni-

Present			
Indicative Active		Indicative Passive	
múnio	múnimus	múnior	munimur
munis	munitis	muniris	munímini
munit	múniunt	munitur	muniuntur
Imperfect			
muniebam	muniebamus	muniebar	muniebamur
muniebas	muniebatis	muniebaris	muniebámini
muniebat	muniebant	muniebatur	muniebantur
Future			
múniam	muniemus	múniar	muniemur
múnies	munietis	munierís	muniémini
múniet	múnient	munietur	munientur

Perfect System Stem: muniv-

Perfect			
Indicative Active		Indicative Passive	
munivi	munívimus	munitus sum	-iti sumus
munivisti	munivistis	(a, um) es	(ae, a) estis
munivit	muniverunt	est	sunt
Pluperfect			
muníveram	muniveramus	eram	eramus
muníveras	muniveratis	eras	eratis
muníverat	muníverant	erat	erant
Future Perfect			
munívero	munivérimus	ero	érimus
muníveris	munivéritis	eris	éritis
muníverit	muníverint	erit	erunt

Principal Parts: do dare dedi datus
Present System Stem: da-

Present			
Indicative Active		Indicative Passive	
do	damus	dor*	damur
das	datis	daris	dámini
dat	dant	datur	dantur
Imperfect			
dabam	dabamus	dabar	dabamur
dabas	dabatis	dabaris	dabámini
dabat	dabant	dabatur	dabantur
Future			
dabo	dábimus	dabor	dábimur
dabis	dábitis	dáberis	dabímini
dabit	dabunt	dábitur	dabuntur

Perfect System Stem: ded-

Perfect			
Indicative Active		Indicative Passive	
dedi	dédimus	datus sum	dati sumus
dedisti	dedistis	(a, um) es	(ae, a) estis
dedit	dederunt	est	sunt
Pluperfect			
déderam	dederamus	eram	eramus
déderas	dederatis	eras	eratis
déderat	déderant	erat	erant
Future Perfect			
dédero	dedérimus	ero	érimus
déderis	dedéritis	eris	éritis
déderit	déderint	erit	erunt

I give
I was giving
I will give
I gave (have given)
I had given
I will have given

I am (being) given
I was (being) given
I will be given
I have been given
I had been given
I will have been given

*This form is not found in Latin literature. However, do not mark students wrong if they include it.

VII. Translation

1. Pars legionis décimae barbarorum órdines habet.
   Part of the tenth legion has ranks of barbarians.

2. Cives metu belli acti erant.
   The citizens had been driven by the fear of war.

3. Centurio noster legionis partem sinistram oppugnavit.
   Our centurion attacked the left part of the legion.

4. Pro nobis senatus legem novam fáciet.
   The senate will make a new law for us (on our behalf).

5. Tres leones e provínciā vestrā nobiscum vehentur.
   Three lions will be transported with us from your province.

6. Pars una nostrum dórmiet et pars áltera nostrum laborabit.
   One part of us will sleep and the other part of us will work.

7. The general hid us behind a long row of trees.
   Imperator post longum órdinem árborum nos celavit.

8. Wine will protect me against the fear of battle.
   Vinum contra metum proélii me múniet.

9. Da mihi equum labori gravi idóneum.
   Give me a horse suitable for heavy work.

10. Agrícola vaccas in partem áliam agri misit.
    The farmer sent the cows into another part of the field.

VIII. Derivatives

1. *Eleventh* is what kind of number? ___ordinal___

2. With its long mane, my cat has a ___leonine___ appearance.

3. A Roman legion contained four or five thousand ___legionaries___.

4. ___Homicide___ is a capital crime.

5. A short, plain speech is not an ___oration___.

IX. Reading
Translate the reading in the space below.

JÚLII DIES MALUS

Amicus: *Juli*, mi amice! Dic mihi, quómodo vulneratus es?

Július: Cum duobus telis in manu heri ambulabam. Defessus, parvam villam vidi et eram cibi viníque cúpidus. Villa erat vácua, et panis dulcis in mensā in culinā sedebat. Per fenestram uno telo panem sústuli, sed canem non audivi. Canis me oppugnavit et áltero telo vulneratus sum.

Amicus: Audax es, Juli mi, sed stultus.

JULIUS' BAD DAY.

Friend: Julius, my friend! Speak to (tell) me, how were you wounded?

Julius: Yesterday I was walking with two spears in my hand. Tired, I saw a small

farmhouse and I wanted (was desirous of) food and wine. The farmhouse was empty,

and a sweet bread was sitting on a table in the kitchen. Through the window, I lifted

up the bread with one spear, but I didn't hear the dog. The dog attacked me and I was

wounded by the other spear.

Friend: You are bold, my Julius, but foolish.

Július -i *m.* Julius

I. Word Study and Grammar

1. All but two of the 3rd person pronoun forms have the letter _____ e- _____ as a stem. Give these two forms. _____ is, id _____

2. The genitive and dative forms of the 3rd-person personal pronouns are similar to the same forms in _____ the Naughty Nine _____ .

3. When do you use the English pronoun **it** to translate *m.* and *f.* forms of **is** and **ea**? _____ when the antecedent is a non-living thing with grammatical gender _____

4. The 3rd person possessive pronoun adjective is _____ suus sua suum _____ .

5. The genitive forms of 1st/2nd-person pronouns do not show _____ possession _____ .

6. The genitive forms of **is ea id** DO show non-reflexive possession, but they function as _____ pronouns _____ , not _____ adjectives _____ .

7. Give the Pronoun Agreement Rule. _____ A pronoun agrees with its antecedent in gender and number. Its case is determined by its function in its own clause. _____

8. Most vocabulary words are what declension? _____ 1st _____
   Which vocabulary word is a plural noun? _____ Athenae _____
   Which is a 3rd-declension noun? _____ Carthago _____

9. Third-declension nouns that end in **o** are usually what gender? _____ feminine _____

II. New Vocabulary

Say aloud and write with dictionary form, meaning, and derivative.

Latin (dictionary form)	Meaning	Derivative
Athenae -arum f.	Athens	
Británnia -ae f.	Britain	
Caledónia -ae f.	Scotland	
Carthago -inis f.	Carthage	
Europa -ae f.	Europe	
Germánia -ae f.	Germany	
Gráecia -ae f.	Greece	
Helvétia -ae f.	Switzerland	
Hibérnia -ae f.	Ireland	

112

III. Declensions

Study the **3rd Person Pronouns** and complete the chart from memory.

Singular						
Case	Masculine	Meaning	Feminine	Meaning	Neuter	Meaning
nom.	is	he	ea	she	id	it
gen.	ejus	his, its	ejus	her, its	ejus	its
dat.	ei	to/for him	ei	to/for her	ei	to/for it
acc.	eum	him (it)	eam	her (it)	id	it
abl.	eo	ibwf him (it)	eā	ibwf her (it)	eo	ibwf it

Plural						
Case	Masculine	Meaning	Feminine	Meaning	Neuter	Meaning
nom.	ei	they	eae	they	ea	they
gen.	eorum	their	earum	their	eorum	their
dat.	eis	to/for them	eis	to/for them	eis	to/for them
acc.	eos	them	eas	them	ea	them
abl.	eis	ibwf them	eis	ibwf them	eis	ibwf them

IV. Form Drills
Drill A

Translate the *italicized* pronouns.

Britain is part of Europe, but *it*[1] is not connected to Europe. The Channel separates *it*[2] from Europe. Caesar invaded Britain because *its*[3] people were related to the Gauls and helped *them*[4] in *their*[5] wars. *He*[6] also invaded Germany. The Germans were not related to the Gauls, but *he*[7] found that some Germans lived among *them*[8] and fought against *him*[9].

Spain is connected to Europe and at the same time outside of *it*[10], cut off by mountains. *They*[11] form a natural barrier. Spain also has a culture different from the rest of Europe. Arabs ruled *it*[12] for centuries and gave *it*[13] some of their Arabic culture.

1. ea
2. eam
3. ejus
4. eos
5. eorum
6. Is
7. is
8. eos
9. eum
10. eā
11. Ei
12. eam
13. ei

113

Lesson Fifteen   Worksheet 3

Drill B

1. eas ___them (f.)___
2. id ___it___
3. eā ___ibwf her (it)___
4. eorum ___of them, their (m., n.)___
5. is ___he (it)___

6. ejus ___his, her, its (of him, her, it)___
7. eae ___they (f.)___
8. eo ___ibwf him (it)___
9. eis ___to/for, ibwf them___
10. eos ___them (m.)___

Drill C

1. its ___ejus___
2. their (f.) ___earum___
3. to them ___eis___
4. she ___ea___
5. it ___id, is, ea, eum, eam___

6. him ___eum___
7. with her ___eā___
8. by them ___eis___
9. their (n.) ___eorum___
10. in him ___eo___

Drill D

In the second sentence, give the correct form of the pronoun **is ea id** and its meaning. <u>Underline</u> the noun in the first sentence to which it refers, and give its meaning. The first one is done for you.

1. <u>Amicos</u> hábeo duos. <u>Eorum</u> nómina sunt Marcus et Caesar. ___their___
2. Epístulam <u>matri</u> scribo. Epístulam ___ei___ mittam. ___to her___
3. <u>Flumen</u> videmus. In ___eo___ sunt hóstium naves. ___it___
4. <u>Mílites</u> fórtiter pugnaverunt. Imperator ___eis___ práemium dedit. ___(to) them___
5. <u>Imperator</u> venit. ___eum___ salutabo. ___him___
6. Caesar contra <u>Gallos</u> pugnavit. Caesar ___eos___ superavit. ___them___
7. Bárbari <u>óppidum</u> oppugnaverunt. Cives ___ejus___ portas clauserunt. ___its___
8. Milites ad <u>flumen</u> venerunt. Pontem trans ___id___ fecerunt. ___it___
9. Exércitus in <u>próvinciā</u> pugnavit. Post bellum in ___eā___ mansit. ___it___
10. Naves frumentum portant. ___Eae___ sunt magnae et graves. ___they___
11. <u>Portus</u> est tutus. In ___eum___ navigemus. ___it___
12. Specta <u>Marcum</u>. Videsne ___ejus___ equum parvum? ___his___

Lesson Fifteen   Worksheet 4

13. <u>Saxa</u> sunt multa. Óppidum ___eis___ oppugnábimus. ___with them___
14. <u>Cibus</u> paratus est. E culinā ___eum___ portábimus. ___it___
15. <u>Puellae</u> e ludo veniunt. Cum ___eis___ ambulábimus. ___them___
16. <u>Mensa</u> est vácua. In ___eam___ libros ponemus. ___it___
17. Non est <u>canis</u> meus. ___Ei___ cibum non dabo. ___(to) it (him)___
18. Caesar <u>Gallos</u> audaces vincit. ___Eorum___ exércitus fortis non erat. ___their___

3rd Person Possessive Pronoun Adjectives (reflexive)	
Latin Meaning	English Meaning
suus sua, suum	his, her, its, their (own)

Drill E

Use genitive of **is ea id**.

1. his dog ___ejus canis___
2. his dogs ___ejus canes___
3. her dog ___ejus canis___
4. her dogs ___ejus canes___
5. to her dog ___ejus cani___

6. to its land ___ejus terrae___
7. their land ___eorum (earum) terra___
8. of his dogs ___ejus canum___
9. of their dogs ___eorum (earum) canum___
10. of her dogs ___ejus canum___

Drill F

Use **suus -a -um**.

1. his lion ___leo suus___
2. his lions ___leones sui___
3. her lion ___leo suus___
4. her lions ___leones sui___
5. to her lion ___leoni suo___

6. to its land ___terrae suae___
7. their land ___terra sua___
8. of his lions ___leonum suorum___
9. of their lions ___leonum suorum___
10. of her lions ___leonum suorum___

Drill G
His, Her, and Their: Reflexive or Non-Reflexive
Use **suus -a -um** or genitive of **is ea id**.

1. *The poet does not like his work.* (his own)
   Poeta opus __suum__ non amat.

2. *The poet does not like his work.* (another's work)
   Poeta __ejus__ opus non amat.

3. *The soldier threw his spear.* (his own)
   Miles hastam __suam__ jecit.

4. *The soldier threw his spear.* (another soldier's spear)
   Miles __ejus__ hastam jecit.

5. *The king gave the crown to his son.* (his own)
   Rex coronam fílio __suo__ dedit.

6. *The king gave the crown to his son.* (another's)
   Rex coronam __ejus__ fílio dedit.

7. *Julia has a horse. Her horse is fast.*
   Equus __ejus__ est celer.

8. *The Romans won many battles. Their victories were not easy.*
   __Eorum__ victóriae non erant fáciles.

9. *A free state has its own laws.*
   Cívitas líbera leges __suas__ habet.

10. *The teacher wrote his own books.*
    Magister libros __suos__ scripsit.

11. *The students like his lessons.*
    Discípuli __ejus__ lectiones amant.

12. *The teacher likes their enthusiasm.*
    Magister __eorum__ stúdium amat.

V. Translation

1. Galli suos milites impediverunt. __The Gauls hindered their own soldiers.__

2. Romani eorum milites impediverunt. __The Romans hindered their soldiers.__

3. The Gauls sailed into their own harbor. __Galli in portum suum navigaverunt.__

4. The Gauls sailed into their (the Romans') harbor. __Galli in eorum portum navigaverunt.__

5. Caesar addressed his own soldiers. __Caesar mílites suos appellavit.__

6. Caesar addressed his (Marcus') soldiers __Caesar ejus mílites appellavit.__

VI. Reading
Translate the reading in the space below.

JÚLIUS AGRÍCOLA*, BRITTÁNIAE PROCONSUL

Július Agrícola erat vir sápiens civitatum rebus. Británnia a Romanis victa erat, et Agrícola ejus *procónsulem* factus est. Quando pars *equitatūs* Romani a Caledóniae bárbaris superata est, Agrícola contra eos bellum gessit. *História* ejus vitae a Tácito *género* scripta est.

__JULIUS AGRICOLA, GOVERNOR OF BRITAIN.__

Julius Agricola was a man wise in the affairs of states. Britain had been conquered by

the Romans, and Agricola was made its governor. When part of the Roman cavalry was

overcome by Scottish barbarians, Agricola waged war against them. The history of his life

was written by his son-in-law Tacitus.

* Julius Agricola is the name of a real Roman. Agricola is his name, not an appositive. He is not a farmer.

proconsul -is *m.* proconsul, governor of a province
equitatus -ūs *m.* cavalry
história -ae *f.* history, story
gener géneri *m.* son-in-law

VII. Conjugation

Make copies of Drill/Test Form A in the Appendix. Conjugate **duco** and **cúpio** in all 6 tenses, <u>active</u> and <u>passive</u>. Give the meanings for **duco** (1st P. sing. only). Practice until perfect.

Drill/Test Form A

Principal Parts: duco dúcere duxi ductus
Present System Stem: duc-

Present			
Indicative Active		Indicative Passive	
duco	dúcimus	ducor	dúcimur
ducis	dúcitis	dúceris	ducímini
ducit	ducunt	dúcitur	ducuntur
Imperfect			
ducebam	ducebamus	ducebar	ducebamur
ducebas	ducebatis	ducebaris	ducebámini
ducebat	ducebant	ducebatur	ducebántur
Future			
ducam	ducemus	ducar	ducemur
duces	ducetis	ducēris	ducémini
ducet	ducent	ducetur	ducentur

Perfect System Stem: dux-

Perfect			
Indicative Active		Indicative Passive	
duxi	dúximus	ductus sum	ducti sumus
duxisti	duxistis	(a, um) es	(ae, a) estis
duxit	duxerunt	est	sunt
Pluperfect			
dúxeram	duxeramus	eram	eramus
dúxeras	duxeratis	eras	eratis
dúxerat	dúxerant	erat	erant
Future Perfect			
dúxero	duxérimus	ero	érimus
dúxeris	duxéritis	eris	éritis
dúxerit	dúxerint	erit	erunt

I lead
I was leading
I will lead
I (have) led
I had led
I will have led

I am (being) led
I was (being) led
I will be led
I have been led
I had been led
I will have been led

Principal Parts: cúpio cúpere cupivi cupitus
Present System Stem: cupi-

Present			
Indicative Active		Indicative Passive	
cúpio	cúpimus	cúpior	cúpimur
cupis	cúpitis	cúperis	cupímini
cupit	cúpiunt	cúpitur	cupiuntur
Imperfect			
cupiebam	cupiebamus	cupiebar	cupiebamur
cupiebas	cupiebatis	cupiebaris	cupiebámini
cupiebat	cupiebant	cupiebatur	cupiebantur
Future			
cúpiam	cupiemus	cúpiar	cupiemur
cúpies	cupietis	cupieris	cupiémini
cúpiet	cúpient	cupietur	cupientur

Perfect System Stem: cupiv-

Perfect			
Indicative Active		Indicative Passive	
cupivi	cupívimus	cupitus sum	cupiti sumus
cupivisti	cupivistis	(a, um) es	(ae, a) estis
cupivit	cupiverunt	est	sunt
Pluperfect			
cupíveram	cupiveramus	eram	eramus
cupíveras	cupiveratis	eras	eratis
cupíverat	cupíverant	erat	erant
Future Perfect			
cupívero	cupivérimus	ero	érimus
cupíveris	cupivéritis	eris	éritis
cupíverit	cupíverint	erit	erunt

Lesson Sixteen

I. Word Study and Grammar

1. Give three reasons for using a personal pronoun in the nominative case (as a subject). _____
   clarity, contrast, emphasis

2. The genitive of 1st/2nd-person pronouns is used for _____ objective or partitive
   expressions that do not show possession .

3. To show possession in the 1st and 2nd person, use the possessive pronoun adjectives_____
   meus, tuus, noster, vester ,
   which observe the ___Adjective___ Agreement Rule.

4. Give the eight kinds of pronouns.___ personal, possessive, reflexive, intensive,
   relative, interrogative, demonstrative, indefinite

5. What kind of pronouns point out persons or things? demonstrative

6. Give the etymology of *demonstrative*. **demonstro -are** *(to point out)*

7. When demonstrative pronouns function as ___adjectives___ ,
   they observe the Adjective Agreement Rule.

8. When demonstrative pronouns function as ___pronouns___ ,
   they observe the Pronoun Agreement Rule.

9. In what three respects does **hic** refer to something close to the speaker? _____
   time, place, thought

10. Third-declension nouns ending in ___-tas, -tatis___ are always feminine.

Saying
Say aloud and write 3X.

Latin	Fides, spes, cáritas, tria haec
Latin	Fides, spes, cáritas, tria haec
Latin	Fides, spes, cáritas, tria haec
English	Faith, hope, and love, these three

II. New Vocabulary

Say aloud and write with dictionary form, meaning, and derivative.

Latin (dictionary form)	Meaning	Derivative
aestas aestatis f.	summer	estival
auctóritas auctoritatis f.	authority	
cáritas caritatis f.	charity, love	charitable
celéritas celeritatis f.	quickness, speed	celerity
cívitas civitatis f.	state	civic
libertas libertatis f.	liberty, freedom	liberty
píetas pietatis f.	piety, duty	piety
tempestas tempestatis f.	thunderstorm	tempest
véritas veritatis f.	truth	veritable, verity
voluntas voluntatis f.	will	voluntary

III. Declensions

Study the chart and complete from memory.

hic haec hoc

Demonstrative Adjective and Pronoun

Singular			
Case	Masculine	Feminine	Neuter
nom.	hic	haec	hoc
gen.	hujus	hujus	hujus
dat.	huic	huic	huic
acc.	hunc	hanc	hoc
abl.	hoc	hac	hoc

Plural			
Case	Masculine	Feminine	Neuter
nom.	hi	hae	haec
gen.	horum	harum	horum
dat.	his	his	his
acc.	hos	has	haec
abl.	his	his	his

119

IV. Form Drills
Drill A

1. hujus ___of this___
2. horum ___of these (m./n.)___
3. huic ___to this___
4. hic ___this (m.)___
5. harum ___of these (f.)___
6. has ___these (f.)___
7. hanc ___this (f.)___
8. his ___to/for these, ibwf these___
9. hoc ___ibwf this (m./n.), this (n.)___
10. hos ___these (m.)___

Drill B

1. hac veritate ___by this truth___
2. hujus aestatis ___of this summer___
3. horum leonum ___of these lions___
4. his lectiónibus ___by (to/for) these lessons___
5. huic hómini ___to this man___
6. hujus legionis ___of this legion___
7. hoc verbo ___by this word___
8. has orationes ___these speeches___
9. hi centuriones ___these centurions___
10. hae auctoritates ___these authorities___

Drill C

1. to these states ___his civitátibus___
2. of this storm ___hujus tempestatis___
3. this sea ___hoc mare___
4. of these sailors ___horum nautarum___
5. these stars ___hae stellae___
6. of this year ___hujus anni___
7. by this authority ___hac auctoritate___
8. to this city ___huic urbi___
9. these words ___haec verba___
10. of this land ___hujus terrae___

Drill D

Put these phrases into the genitive and dative.

1. haec manus ___hujus manūs___ ___huic manui___
2. hoc mare ___hujus maris___ ___huic mari___
3. hic pons ___hujus pontis___ ___huic ponti___
4. hae lectiones ___harum lectionum___ ___his lectiónibus___
5. hi mores ___horum morum___ ___his móribus___
6. haec regna ___horum regnorum___ ___his regnis___

120

Lesson Sixteen

Drill E

Give the correct form of **hic haec hoc** and translate.

1. in ___hanc___ provínciam ___into this province___
2. ___horum___ agricolarum ___of these farmers___
3. trans ___hoc___ flumen ___across this river___
4. circum ___hunc___ montem ___around this mountain___
5. cum ___his___ féminis ___with these women___
6. inter ___has___ vias ___between these roads___
7. cúpidus ___horum___ equorum ___desirous of these horses___
8. idónei ___his___ návibus ___suitable for these ships___
9. ex ___hac___ domu ___out of this house___
10. in ___his___ agris ___in these fields___

Drill F

Translate the *italicized* words and identify them as either adjectives or pronouns.

At the time of the first Punic War, the Romans were not good sailors and their ships were not good. The Romans built ships. *These*[1] were destroyed by the Carthaginians. The Romans built more ships. *These*[2] ships were also destroyed. The Roman state had no more money. But rich Roman nobles did have money, and the state needed the help of *these*[3] men. The Roman nobles gave money for a third navy, and *this*[4] money saved the state.

The Roman sailors finally learned how to fight at sea, and *these*[5] were able to defeat the Carthaginians. Because of *this*[6] war, Rome became a major power in the Mediterranean Sea and gained control of Sicily. *This*[7] victory, however, led to another war. *This*[8] was the second Punic War.

1. ___hae___ pronoun   5. ___hi___ pronoun
2. ___hae___ adjective   6. ___hoc___ adjective
3. ___horum___ adjective   7. ___haec___ adjective
4. ___haec___ adjective   8. ___hoc___ pronoun

Lesson Sixteen

V. Translation

hic haec hoc as adjective

1. De his tentatiónibus scribo.
   I am writing about these temptations.

2. Hanc urbem oppugnábimus.
   We will attack this city.

3. Árbores sunt huic dómui finítimae.
   The trees are close to this house.

4. Da, miles, huic centurioni telum tuum.
   Soldier, give your weapon (missile) to this centurion.

5. Exércitus ab hoc imperatore victus est.
   The army has been conquered by this general.

6. By this charity you have guarded the state.
   Civitatem hac caritate servavisti.

7. After this summer I will be famous.
   Post hanc aestatem ero céleber (célebris).

8. We see the temples of this city.
   Templa hujus urbis videmus.

9. These ships will remain in this river.
   Hae naves in hoc flúmine manebunt.

10. The harbor is full of these ships.
    Portus est harum navium plenus.

VI. Derivatives

1. Although attendance is ___voluntary___ , payment is compulsory.

2. ___Celerity___ is not a fast vegetable.

3. The ___Tempest___ is a drama by Shakespeare.

4. Baseball is an ___estival___ sport.

5. If a bank were ___charitable___ , it would be a ___veritable___ miracle.

VII. Translation
hic haec hoc as pronoun

Translate, then identify the reference of the underlined pronoun.

1. Caesar naves novas in Gálliā struxit. <u>His</u> Brittániam oppugnavit. _____
   Caesar built new ships in Gaul. With these he attacked Britain.
   His = naves

2. Canes duos hábeo. <u>Horum</u> nómina sunt Ferus et Audax._____
   I have two dogs. The names of these are Fierce and Bold.
   Horum = canes

3. Marcus et Lúcia sunt amici mei. <u>Haec</u> est senatoris soror. _____
   Mark and Lucy are my friends. She (this one, the latter) is the sister of a senator.
   Haec = Lúcia

4. Post aestatem tempestates vénient. Nautae <u>has</u> timent. _____
   After the summer the storms will come. Sailors fear these.
   has = tempestates

5. Légio nona in Hispániā pugnat. Imperator novus <u>huic</u> mittetur. _____
   The ninth legion is fighting in Spain. A new general will be sent to this one.
   huic = legio

6. Cívitas duobus flumínibus muniebatur. Romani pontes trans <u>haec</u> fecerunt. _____
   The state was protected by two rivers. The Romans built (made) bridges across
   these. haec = fluminibus

7. Caesar bellum contra Gallos gessit. De <u>hoc</u> septem libros scripsit. _____
   Caesar waged a war against the Gauls. He wrote seven books about this.
   hoc = bellum

8. Hómines libertatem amant. Sine <u>hac</u> non sunt laeti. _____
   Men love liberty. Without this they are not happy.
   hac = libertatem

VIII. Conjugation

> Make copies of Drill/Test Form A in the Appendix. Conjugate **veho** and **gero** in all 6 tenses, <u>active</u> and <u>passive</u>. Give the meanings for **veho** (1st P. sing. only). Practice until perfect.

Drill/Test Form A

Principal Parts: veho véhere vexi vectus
Present System Stem: veh-

Present			
Indicative Active		Indicative Passive	
veho	véhimus	vehor	véhimur
vehis	véhitis	véheris	vehímini
vehit	vehunt	véhitur	vehuntur
Imperfect			
vehebam	vehebamus	vehebar	vehebamur
vehebas	vehebatis	vehebaris	vehebámini
vehebat	vehebant	vehebatur	vehebantur
Future			
veham	vehemus	vehar	vehemur
vehes	vehetis	vehēris	vehémini
vehet	vehent	vehetur	vehentur

Perfect System Stem: vex-

Perfect			
Indicative Active		Indicative Passive	
vexi	véximus	ductus sum	ducti sumus
vexisti	vexistis	(a, um) es	(ae, a) estis
vexit	vexerunt	est	sunt
Pluperfect			
véxeram	vexeramus	eram	eramus
véxeras	vexeratis	eras	eratis
véxerat	véxerant	erat	erant
Future Perfect			
véxero	vexérimus	ero	érimus
véxeris	vexéritis	eris	éritis
véxerit	véxerint	erit	erunt

Principal Parts: gero gérere gessi gestus
Present System Stem: ger-

Present			
Indicative Active		Indicative Passive	
gero	gérimus	geror	gérimur
geris	géritis	géreris	gerímini
gerit	gerunt	géritur	geruntur
Imperfect			
gerebam	gerebamus	gerebar	gerebamur
gerebas	gerebatis	gerebaris	gerebámini
gerebat	gerebant	gerebatur	gerebantur
Future			
geram	geremus	gerar	geremur
geres	geretis	gerēris	gerémini
geret	gerent	geretur	gerentur

Perfect System Stem: gess-

Perfect			
Indicative Active		Indicative Passive	
gessi	géssimus	gestus sum	gesti sumus
gessisti	gessistis	(a, um) es	(ae, a) estis
gessit	gesserunt	est	sunt
Pluperfect			
gésseram	gesseramus	eram	eramus
gésseras	gesseratis	eras	eratis
gésserat	gésserant	erat	erant
Future Perfect			
géssero	gessérimus	ero	érimus
gésseris	gesséritis	eris	éritis
gésserit	gésserint	erit	erunt

I convey
I was conveying
I will convey
I (have) conveyed
I had conveyed
I will have conveyed

I am (being) conveyed
I was (being) conveyed
I will be conveyed
I have been conveyed
I had been conveyed
I will have been conveyed

Lesson Sixteen — Worksheet 7

IX. Reading

Translate the reading in the space below.

LEO

Metus hóminum a leónibus néscitus est. Hi sunt fortes contra álios leones, contra hómines, contra vaccas, contra canes, contra omnes. Ingens, audax, potens, leo est semper paratus ad próelium. Nihil leone est *tutum*. Pro fugā homo satis celeritatem non habet. Et in campo vácuo et in silvā leo plenam auctoritatem habet. Regit. Leo solam rem unam timet—tempestatem. Sub tempestate leo est símilis *muri*.

THE LION

Fear of men has not been known by lions. They [lions] are brave against other lions,

against men, against cows, against dogs, against everything. Huge, bold, powerful,

the lion is always prepared for battle. Nothing is safe from the lion. A man does not

have enough speed for escape. Both in the open field and in the forest, the lion has full

authority. He rules. The lion is afraid of only one thing—a storm. Under a storm, the lion

is like a mouse.

ablative with **tutus** = *safe from*
mus muris *m./f.* mouse

Lesson Seventeen — Worksheet 1

I. Word Study and Grammar

1. Give the four Latin demonstrative pronouns. _____
   hic haec hoc   **is ea id**   **ille illa illud**   **iste ista istud**

2. Demonstrative pronouns can function as _____pronouns_____ or _____adjectives_____ .

3. Give the etymology of *demonstrative*. _____**demonstro -are** (*to point out*)_____

4. When demonstrative pronouns function as _____adjectives_____ , they observe the Adjective Agreement Rule.

5. When demonstrative pronouns function as _____pronouns_____ , they observe the Pronoun Agreement Rule.

6. When **hic** and **ille** are used in contrast, **hic** refers to the _____latter_____ , and **ille** refers to the _____former_____ .

7. Which demonstrative is often used in contempt? _____**iste ista istud**_____

8. Which demonstrative is also used as the 3rd person personal pronoun?_____**is ea id**_____

9. Which demonstrative means *the famous* when it follows a noun? _____**ille illa illud**_____

Saying

Say aloud and write 3X.

Latin	Dies irae, dies illa
Latin	Dies irae, dies illa
Latin	Dies irae, dies illa
English	Day of wrath, that day

II. Conjugation

Make copies of Drill/Test Form A in the Appendix. Conjugate **téneo** and **puto** in all 6 tenses, <u>active</u> and <u>passive</u>. Give the meanings for **téneo** (1st P. sing. only). Practice until perfect.

Drill/Test Form A

Principal Parts: téneo tenére ténui tentus
Present System Stem: tene-

Present

Indicative Active		Indicative Passive	
téneo	tenemus	téneor	tenemur
tenes	tenetis	teneris	tenémini
tenet	tenent	tenetur	tenentur

Imperfect

tenebam	tenebamus	tenebar	tenebamur
tenebas	tenebatis	tenebaris	tenebámini
tenebat	tenebant	tenebatur	tenebantur

Future

tenebo	tenébimus	tenebor	tenébimur
tenebis	tenébitis	tenéberis	tenebímini
tenebit	tenebunt	tenébitur	tenebuntur

Perfect System Stem: tenu-

Perfect

Indicative Active		Indicative Passive	
ténui	tenúimus	tentus sum	tenti sumus
tenuisti	tenuistis	(a, um) es	(ae, a) estis
ténuit	tenuerunt	est	sunt

Pluperfect

tenúeram	tenueramus	eram	eramus
tenúeras	tenueratis	eras	eratis
tenúerat	tenúerant	erat	erant

Future Perfect

tenúero	tenúerimus	ero	érimus
tenúeris	tenuéritis	eris	éritis
tenúerit	tenúerint	erit	erunt

Principal Parts: puto putare putavi putatus
Present System Stem: puta-

Present

Indicative Active		Indicative Passive	
puto	putamus	putor	putamur
putas	putatis	putaris	putámini
putat	putant	putatur	putantur

Imperfect

putabam	putabamus	putabar	putabamur
putabas	putabatis	putabaris	putabámini
putabat	putabant	putabatur	putabantur

Future

putabo	putábimus	putabor	putábimur
putabis	putábitis	putáberis	putabímini
putabit	putabunt	putábitur	putabuntur

Perfect System Stem: putav-

Perfect

Indicative Active		Indicative Passive	
putavi	putávimus	putatus sum	putati sumus
putavisti	putavistis	(a, um) es	(ae, a) estis
putavit	putaverunt	est	sunt

Pluperfect

putáveram	putaveramus	eram	eramus
putáveras	putaveratis	eras	eratis
putáverat	putáverant	erat	erant

Future Perfect

putávero	putavérimus	ero	érimus
putáveris	putavéritis	eris	éritis
putáverit	putáverint	erit	erunt

I hold
I was holding
I will hold
I (have) held
I had held
I will have held

I am (being) held
I was (being) held
I will be held
I have been held
I had been held
I will have been held

III. New Vocabulary

Say aloud and write with dictionary form, meaning, and derivative.

Latin (dictionary form)	Meaning	Derivative
amicítia -ae f.	friendship	
fossa -ae f.	ditch, trench	fossil
fuga -ae f.	flight, escape	fugitive
hasta -ae f.	spear	
injúria -ae f.	injury, injustice, wrong	injurious
inópia -ae f.	lack, scarcity, shortage	
memória -ae f.	memory	memorable
sagitta -ae f.	arrow	Sagittarius
sapiéntia -ae f.	wisdom	
sciéntia -ae f.	knowledge	science

IV. Declensions

Study the chart and complete from memory.

ille illa illud
Demonstrative Adjective and Pronoun

Singular			
Case	Masculine	Feminine	Neuter
nom.	ille	illa	illud
gen.	illíus	illíus	illíus
dat.	illi	illi	illi
acc.	illum	illam	illud
abl.	illo	illā	illo

Plural			
Case	Masculine	Feminine	Neuter
nom.	illi	illae	illa
gen.	illorum	illarum	illorum
dat.	illis	illis	illis
acc.	illos	illas	illa
abl.	illis	illis	illis

Lesson Seventeen   Worksheet 3

V. Form Drills
Drill A

1. illi ___to/for that, those (m.)___
2. illíus ___of that___
3. illā ___ibwf that (f.)___
4. illis ___to/for, ibwf those___
5. illarum ___of those (f.)___

6. illo ___ibwf that (m./n.)___
7. illae ___those (f.)___
8. illam ___that (f.)___
9. illa ___that (f.), those (n.)___
10. illos ___those (m.)___

Drill B

1. illa fossa ___that ditch___
2. illíus hastae ___of that spear___
3. illam memóriam ___that memory___
4. illis sagittis ___by those arrows___
5. illo verbo ___by that word___

6. illi sciéntiae ___to/for that knowledge___
7. illos equos ___those horses___
8. illarum injuriarum ___of those wrongs___
9. illud scutum ___that shield___
10. illa bella ___those wars___

Drill C

1. of that ditch ___illíus fossae___
2. for that scarcity ___illi inópiae___
3. by that knowledge ___illā sciéntiā___
4. those spears ___illae hastae___
5. of those arrows ___illarum sagittarum___

6. those memories ___illae memóriae___
7. for that wisdom ___illi sapiéntiae___
8. by those wrongs ___illis injúriis___
9. of that flight ___illíus fugae___
10. that temple ___illud templum___

Lesson Seventeen   Worksheet 4

Drill D
Give the correct form of **ille illa illud** and translate.

1. in ___illud___ flumen ___into that river___
2. pro ___illā___ reginā ___for that queen___
3. ab ___illis___ milítibus ___by those soldiers___
4. sine ___illo___ nautā ___without that sailor___
5. ___Illa___ nómina ___those names___
6. de ___illis___ lectionibus ___about those lessons___
7. símilis ___illi___ árbori ___similar to that tree___
8. ___Illud___ mare ___that sea___
9. carus ___illis___ viris ___dear to those men___
10. ___Illarum___ pártium ___of those parts___

Drill E
Translate the *italicized* words and identify them as either adjectives or pronouns.

Hannibal was the son of Hamlicar Barca, Carthaginian general in the first Punic War. In *that*[1] war, Carthage lost control of Sicily. Hannibal commanded the Carthaginian troops in the second Punic War. *Those*[2] soldiers crossed the Alps into Italy. The journey across *those*[3] mountains in winter was difficult. After entering Italy by *that*[4] way, Hannibal began to attack the Romans. In *those*[5] two battles, the Romans lost almost 100,000 men. *Those*[6] were Hannibal's greatest victories.

Because of *those*[7] battles, the Romans would no longer fight Hannibal directly. *That*[8] was a problem for Hannibal. Italy was not Hannibal's country, and in *that*[9] country, it was hard for him to obtain supplies and fresh troops. Because of *that*[10], he eventually had to return to his country. *That*[11] is the place where he was finally defeated.

1. ___illo___ adjective
2. ___illi___ adjective
3. ___illos___ adjective
4. ___illā___ adjective
5. ___illis___ adjective
6. ___illa___ pronoun (battles)

7. ___illa___ adjective
8. ___illud___ pronoun (indefinite)
9. ___illā___ adjective
10. ___illud___ pronoun (indefinite)
11. ___illa___ pronoun (country)

VI. Translation

1. Propter fugam illas hastas céssimus. _____
   On account of flight, we gave up those spears.

2. Illorum dierum memória mihi est cara. _____
   The memory of those days is dear to me.

3. Cur aquae plena illa fossa?_____
   Why is that ditch full of water?

4. Sciéntia et sapiéntia. Illa fácilis, haec difficilis. _____
   Knowledge and wisdom. The former is easy, the latter hard.

5. Illi Romani trans flumen fúgerant. _____
   Those Romans had fled across the river.

6. Illíus viae sciéntia tuam fugam juvabit. _____
   Knowledge of that road will help your escape.

7. Domus nostra est plena istorum canum. _____
   Our house is full of those dogs of yours.

8. I will write about the injustice of those laws. _____
   De injúriã illarum legum scribam.

9. Istae sagittae non debent esse in illā fossā. _____
   Those arrows of yours ought not to be in that ditch.

10. Because of the storm, I do not see those hills._____
    Ob tempestatem illos colles non vídeo.

VII. Derivatives

1. He was a _____ fugitive _____ from justice.

2. All _____ science _____ begins with observation.

3. Eating broccoli is not_____ injurious _____to your health.

VIII. Reading
Translate the reading in the space below.

FUGA

Fuga sub hastis et sagittis erat céleris alacrísque. Romani a Gallis ad flumen pressi sunt, et illi propter ligni inópiam pontem non fecerunt. Illi propter aquae celeritatem *diligenter* nataverunt. Hi Galli natare non amaverunt, et Romani fugerunt. Romani póstea illíus fugae *históriam* saepe narrabant—históriam fugae non turpis sed nóbilis. Galli vícerant, Romani fúgerant, sed in Romanorum fábulis hi erant fortes, illi stulti quod natare non amáverant.

FLIGHT

The flight beneath spears and arrows was swift and lively. The Romans were pressed

toward the river by the Gauls, and they [the Romans] did not build a bridge on account of

a lack of wood. Those [Romans] swam carefully on account of the swiftness of the water.

These Gauls did not like to swim, and the Romans escaped. Afterwards the Romans often

told the story of that escape—the story of a noble escape, not a shameful one. The Gauls

had conquered, the Romans had fled, but in the Romans' tales, they [the Romans] were the

brave ones, they [the Gauls] were the stupid ones because they hadn't liked to swim.

diligenter *adv.* carefully (**Díligens** forms its adverb by adding **-er** to the stem)
história -ae *f.* history, story

Lesson Eighteen — Worksheet 1

I. Word Study and Grammar

1. Give the eight kinds of pronouns. _personal, possessive, reflexive, intensive, relative, interrogative, demonstrative, indefinite_

2. Give the four demonstrative pronouns.
hic haec hoc   is ea id   ille illa illud   iste ista istud

3. In English, reflexive and intensive pronouns are formed by adding what endings to pronouns?
-self or _-selves_

4. Give the 1st person reflexive/intensive pronouns in English. _myself, ourselves_

5. Give the 2nd person reflexive/intensive pronouns in English. _yourself, yourselves_

6. Give the 3rd person reflexive/intensive pronouns in English. _himself, herself, itself, themselves_

7. The forms for _reflexive_ and _intensive_ pronouns are identical in English, but different in Latin.

8. An intensive pronoun _emphasizes_ another word in the sentence.

9. The reflexive pronoun is always in the _predicate_ and reflects back on the _subject_ .

10. Most 3rd-declension nouns ending in **us** are what gender? _neuter_

11. What three declensions have nouns ending in **us** in the nominative? _2nd, 3rd, 4th_

Saying
Say aloud and write 3X.

Latin	Ipsa sciéntia potestas est.
Latin	Ipsa sciéntia potestas est.
Latin	Ipsa sciéntia potestas est.
English	Knowledge itself is power.

Lesson Eighteen — Worksheet 2

II. New Vocabulary
Say aloud and write with dictionary form, meaning, and derivative.

Latin (dictionary form)	Meaning	Derivative
agmen ágminis n.	army on the march, column	
carmen cárminis n.	song	
corpus córporis n.	body	corpse
genus géneris n.	race, kind, class	genus
iter itíneris n.	journey	itinerary
onus óneris n.	burden	onerous
opus óperis n.	work	opera
tempus témporis n.	time	temporary
ver veris n.	spring	vernal
vulnus vúlneris n.	wound	vulnerable

Derivatives

1. The responsibilities of a general are _onerous_ .
2. The job is permanent, but the job-holder is _temporary_ .
3. The _vernal_ equinox is in March.
4. Our _itinerary_ includes visits to five countries.
5. He feels less _vulnerable_ when wearing his lucky shirt.

III. Declensions
3rd-Declension Neuter Nouns

Case	Singular	Plural
nom.	**carmen**	cármina
gen.	cárminis	cárminum
dat.	cármini	carmínibus
acc.	carmen	cármina
abl.	cármine	carmínibus

Singular	Plural
iter	itínera
itíneris	itínerum
itíneri	itinéribus
iter	itínera
itínere	itinéribus

Case	Singular	Plural
nom.	**agmen**	ágmina
gen.	ágminis	ágminum
dat.	ágmini	agmínibus
acc.	agmen	ágmina
abl.	ágmine	agmínibus

Singular	Plural
tempus	témpora
témporis	témporum
témpori	tempóribus
tempus	témpora
témpore	tempóribus

Case	Singular	Plural
nom.	**genus**	génera
gen.	géneris	génerum
dat.	géneri	genéribus
acc.	genus	génera
abl.	génere	genéribus

Singular	Plural
vulnus	vúlnera
vúlneris	vúlnerum
vúlneri	vulnéribus
vulnus	vúlnera
vúlnere	vulnéribus

Case	Singular	Plural
nom.	**ver**	vera
gen.	veris	verum
dat.	veri	véribus
acc.	ver	vera
abl.	vere	véribus

Singular	Plural
opus	ópera
óperis	óperum
óperi	opéribus
opus	ópera
ópere	opéribus

Case	Singular	Plural
nom.	**onus**	ónera
gen.	óneris	ónerum
dat.	óneri	onéribus
acc.	onus	ónera
abl.	ónere	onéribus

Singular	Plural
corpus	córpora
córporis	córporum
córpori	corpóribus
corpus	córpora
córpore	corpóribus

133

Drill A

1. of the songs _____cárminum_____
2. to/for the column _____ágmini_____
3. wounds _____vúlnera_____
4. spring_____ver_____
5. kinds _____génera_____

6. of the burden _____óneris_____
7. journeys_____itínera_____
8. ibwf the bodies_____corpóribus_____
9. works_____ópera_____
10. ibwf the time _____témpore_____

IV. Reflexive and Intensive Pronouns
Identify each *italicized* word as a reflexive, intensive, or personal pronoun.

Five of *us*[1] arrived early for the concert. *Myself*[2], I just wanted to get a good seat. The others wanted to get *themselves*[3] backstage to meet the musicians. Their luck was good, and they got an autograph of the lead singer *herself*[4]. The show *itself*[5] was not the best *we*[6] had ever seen. My seat was in the center, which was good because the stage *itself*[7] was small. This is good for musicians, because on a small stage they can hear *themselves*[8]. After the show, we all went and got *ourselves*[9] some pizza. *We*[10] thought the pizza was better than the show.

1. ___personal pronoun___
2. ___intensive adjective___
3. ___reflexive pronoun___
4. ___intensive adjective___
5. ___intensive adjective___

6. ___personal pronoun___
7. ___intensive adjective___
8. ___reflexive pronoun___
9. ___reflexive pronoun___
10. ___personal pronoun___

ipse ipsa ipsum — Intensive Pronoun

Case	Singular			Plural		
	Masculine	Feminine	Neuter	Masculine	Feminine	Neuter
nom.	ipse	ipsa	ipsum	ipsi	ipsae	ipsa
gen.	ipsíus	ipsíus	ipsíus	ipsorum	ipsarum	ipsorum
dat.	ipsi	ipsi	ipsi	ipsis	ipsis	ipsis
acc.	ipsum	ipsam	ipsum	ipsos	ipsas	ipsa
abl.	ipso	ipsā	ipso	ipsis	ipsis	ipsis

134

Lesson Eighteen — Worksheet 5

V. Translation
Intensive Pronouns

1. Ipso cármine delectabar. _I was delighted by the song itself._

2. Ab ipso rege salutabímini. _You all will be greeted by the king himself._

3. Ipsum onus non est grave. _The burden itself is not heavy._

4. Ipsā in urbe laboro. _I work in the city itself._

5. Ipsa in urbe laborat. _She herself works in the city._

6. Ipsa urbs occupata est. _The city itself has been seized._

7. Ipse epístulam misi. _I myself sent the letter._

8. Ipsi bellum gerunt. _They themselves are waging war._

9. Ipsa me vocat. _She herself is calling me._

10. Ipsum imperatorem non laudo. Exércitum laudo. _I do not praise the general himself. I praise the army._

11. My father himself built this house. _Ipse pater hanc domum struxit._

12. This song is about Rome itself. _Hoc carmen de ipsā Romā est._

13. You yourself have many friends. _Ipse (ipsa) multos amicos habes._

14. The truth itself will free you. _Ipsa véritas te liberabit._

15. We did not see the soldiers themselves. _Ipsos mílites non vídimus._

16. We ourselves have no grain. _Ipsi nullum frumentum habemus._

17. The city itself is powerful. _Ipsa urbs est potens._

18. The dogs themselves are escaping. _Ipsi canes fúgiunt._

VI. Conjugation

> Make copies of Drill/Test Form A in the Appendix. Conjugate **scio** in all 6 tenses, <u>active</u> and <u>passive</u>, and **sum**, <u>active</u> only. Give the meanings for **scio** (1st P. sing. only). Practice until perfect.

Drill/Test Form A

Principal Parts: scio scire scivi scitus
Present System Stem: sci-

Present			
Indicative Active		Indicative Passive	
scio	scimus	scior	scimur
scis	scitis	sciris	scímini
scit	sciunt	scitur	sciuntur
Imperfect			
sciebam	sciebamus	sciebar	sciebamur
sciebas	sciebatis	sciebaris	sciebámini
sciebat	sciebant	sciebatur	sciebantur
Future			
sciam	sciemus	sciar	sciemur
scies	scietis	scieris	sciémini
sciet	scient	scietur	scientur

Perfect System Stem: sciv-

Perfect			
Indicative Active		Indicative Passive	
scivi	scívimus	scitus sum	sciti sumus
scivisti	scivistis	(a, um) es	(ae, a) estis
scivit	sciverunt	est	sunt
Pluperfect			
scíveram	sciveramus	eram	eramus
scíveras	sciveratis	eras	eratis
scíverat	scíverant	erat	erant
Future Perfect			
scívero	scivérimus	ero	érimus
scíveris	scivéritis	eris	éritis
scíverit	scíverint	erit	erunt

Principal Parts: sum esse fui futurus
Present System Stem: —

Present			
Indicative Active		Indicative Passive	
sum	sumus		
es	estis		
est	sunt		
Imperfect			
eram	eramus		
eras	eratis		
erat	erant		
Future			
ero	érimus		
eris	éritis		
erit	erunt		

Perfect System Stem: fu-

Perfect			
Indicative Active		Indicative Passive	
fui	fúimus		
fuisti	fuistis		
fuit	fuerunt		
Pluperfect			
fúeram	fueramus		
fúeras	fueratis		
fúerat	fúerant		
Future Perfect			
fúero	fuérimus		
fúeris	fuéritis		
fúerit	fúerint		

I know
I was knowing
I will know
I knew (have known)
I had known
I will have known

I am (being) known
I was (being) known
I will be known
I have been known
I had been known
I will have been known

VII. Reading

Translate the reading in the space below.

VER

Ver venit, quod *aves* ex Áfricā *supra* Itáliam in Germániam et Británniam volant. Ipse vidi. Parvi flores per *nivem se* premunt. Ipse vidi. Ursae non dórmiunt et cum *cátulis* in silvā ámbulant. Ipse vidi. Naves in portu non manent et in mare návigant. Ipse vidi. Veris stellae sunt in *noctis* caelo. Ipse vidi. Veris signa in ómnibus locis apparent. Ipse ipsa vidi.

SPRING

Spring is coming, because the birds are flying out of Africa over Italy to Germany and Britain.

I have seen (it) myself. Small flowers are pushing themselves through the snow. I have

seen (it) myself. The bears are not asleep and are walking in the forest with their cubs. I

have seen (it) myself. The ships are not staying in port and are sailing out to sea. I have

seen (it) myself. The stars of spring are in the night sky. I have seen (it) myself. The signs of

spring are appearing everywhere (in all places). I myself have seen the very (signs).

avis avis *f.* bird
supra *prep. w/acc.* over
nix nivis *f.* snow
se themselves (**Se** will be explained in Lesson 19.)
cátulus -i *m.* animal offspring, cub
nox noctis *f.* night

I. Word Study and Grammar

1. Give the eight kinds of pronouns. personal, possessive, reflexive, intensive, relative, interrogative, demonstrative, indefinite

2. Give the four demonstrative pronouns.
   hic haec hoc   is ea id   ille illa illud   iste ista istud

3. In English, reflexive and intensive pronouns are formed by adding what endings to pronouns? -self or -selves

4. Give the 1st person reflexive/intensive pronouns in English. myself, ourselves

5. Give the 2nd person reflexive/intensive pronouns in English. yourself, yourselves

6. Give the 3rd person reflexive/intensive pronouns in English. himself, herself, itself, themselves

7. The forms for reflexive and intensive pronouns are identical in English, but different in Latin.

8. An intensive pronoun emphasizes another word in the sentence.

9. The reflexive pronoun is always in the predicate and reflects back on the subject .

10. In Latin the 1st and 2nd person reflexive pronouns forms are identical to the 1st/2nd personal pronouns .

11. Give the forms for the 3rd person reflexive pronouns. sui, sibi, se, se

12. In Latin the 3rd person reflexive possessive pronoun adjective is suus sua suum .

13. Most 3rd-declension nouns ending in **us** are what gender? neuter

14. What three declensions have nouns ending in **us** in the nominative? 2nd, 3rd, 4th

Saying

Say aloud and write 3X.

Latin	per se
Latin	per se
Latin	per se
English	in itself

Lesson Nineteen — Worksheet 2

II. Reflexive Pronouns
Give Reflexive Meanings Only

1st Person
Reflexive Pronouns

Case	S.	Meaning	Pl.	Meaning
gen.	mei	of myself	nostri, nostrum	of ourselves
dat.	mihi	to/for myself	nobis	to/for ourselves
acc.	me	myself	nos	ourselves
abl.	me	ibwf myself	nobis	ibwf ourselves

2nd Person
Reflexive Pronouns

Case	S.	Meaning	Pl.	Meaning
gen.	tui	of yourself	vestri, vestrum	of yourselves
dat.	tibi	to/for yourself	vobis	to/for yourselves
acc.	te	yourself	vos	yourselves
abl.	te	ibwf yourself	vobis	ibwf yourselves

3rd Person
Reflexive Pronouns

Case	Latin	Meaning
gen.	sui	of himself, herself, itself, themselves
dat.	sibi	to/for himself, herself, itself, themselves
acc.	se	himself, herself, itself, themselves
abl.	se	ibwf himself, herself, itself, themselves

3rd Person
Possessive Pronoun Adjective (Reflexive)

Latin	Meaning
suus sua suum	his (own), her (own), their (own)

Lesson Nineteen — Worksheet 3

III. Form Drills
Drill A
3rd Person Reflexives

1. Puellae in lacu se vident. _The girls see themselves in the lake._
2. Magistri non se dúbitant. _Teachers do not doubt themselves._
3. Centúrio donum sibi dedit. _The centurion gave himself a gift._
4. Cena non se facit. _Dinner does not make itself._
5. Urbs propter bellum se munivit. _The city fortified itself on account of the war._
6. The boys hid themselves. _Púeri se celaverunt._
7. They built themselves a house. _Sibi domum struxerunt._
8. The dog hurled himself into the river. _Canis in flumen se jecit._
9. He lifted himself out of the water. _Ex aquã se sústulit._
10. The maiden protected herself with an arrow. _Virgo sagittã se munivit._

Drill B
1st and 2nd Person Reflexives

1. Epístulam mihi scripsi. _I wrote myself a letter._
2. Debetis vos parare. _You should prepare yourselves._
3. Nos in flúmine lávimus. _We washed ourselves in the river._
4. Delecta te. _Please yourself._
5. In perículum te posuisti. _You have put yourself in(to) danger._
6. I wounded myself with a knife. _Cultro me vulneravi._
7. You all ought not to blame yourselves. _Non debetis vos culpare._
8. We will set ourselves free. _Nos liberábimus._
9. Give yourselves up. _Cédite vos._
10. Guard yourself. _Serva te._

IV. Translation

Reflexive and Intensive Pronouns

1. Agmen ipsum ab hóstibus in flumen actum erat._____
   The column itself was driven into the river by the enemy.

2. Ipsa onus sústulit. _____
   She lifted up the burden herself.

3. Puer in lacūs aquā se vidit._____
   The boy saw himself in the water of the lake.

4. Scribe tibi epístulam.___Write yourself a letter._____

5. Post próelium contra hóstium exércitum Romani óppidum ipsum oppugnaverunt. _____
   After the battle against the enemy's army, the Romans attacked the town itself.

6. He put himself in danger._____
   In perículum se pósuit.

7. He put the army itself in danger. _____
   Exércitum ipsum in perículum pósuit.

8. Itíneris ipsíus pars prima erat longa et diffícilis. _____
   The first part of the journey itself was long and difficult.

9. The door closes itself. _____
   Jánua se claudit.

10. We will close the door itself. _____
    Jánuam ipsam claudemus.

V. Conjugation

> Make copies of Drill/Test Form A in the Appendix. Conjugate **vivo** in all 6 tenses, <u>active</u> only.
> Give the meanings (1st P. sing. only). Practice until perfect.

Drill/Test Form A

Principal Parts: vivo vívere vixi victus
Present System Stem: viv-

Present			
Indicative Active		Indicative Passive	
vivo	vívimus		
vivis	vívitis		
vivit	vivunt		

Imperfect			
vivebam	vivebamus		
vivebas	vivebatis		
vivebat	vivebant		

Future			
vivam	vivemus		
vives	vivetis		
vivet	vivent		

I live
I was living
I will live
I (have) lived
I had lived
I will have lived

Perfect System Stem: vix-

Perfect			
Indicative Active		Indicative Passive	
vixi	víximus		
vixisti	vixistis		
vixit	vixerunt		

Pluperfect			
víxeram	vixeramus		
víxeras	vixeratis		
víxerat	víxerant		

Future Perfect			
víxero	vixérimus		
víxeris	vixéritis		
víxerit	víxerint		

VI. Vocabulary Review
Give the dictionary form.

arrow	sagitta -ae f.	column	agmen -inis n.
Europe	Europa -ae f.	Scotland	Caledónia -ae f.
lack	inópia -ae f.	speech	oratio -onis f.
summer	aestas -atis f.	lion	leo -onis m.
temptation	tentátio -onis f.	truth	véritas -atis f.
legion	légio -onis f.	human being	homo -inis m.
wound	vulnus -eris n.	Germany	Germánia -ae f.
speed	celéritas -atis f.	body	corpus -oris n.
Spain	Híspania -ae f.	authority	auctóritas -atis f.
liberty	libertas -atis f.	memory	memória -ae f.
suffering	pássio -onis f.	wisdom	sapiéntia -ae f.
kind	genus -eris n.	will	voluntas -atis f.
centurion	centúrio -onis m.	injury, injustice	injúria -ae f.
journey	iter itíneris n.	Ireland	Hibérnia -ae f.
Switzerland	Helvétia -ae f.	Carthage	Carthago -inis f.
charity, love	cáritas -atis f.	friendship	amicítia -ae f.
Athens	Athenae -arum f.	burden	onus -eris n.
storm	tempestas -atis f.	ditch	fossa -ae f.
lesson	léctio -onis f.	knowledge	sciéntia -ae f.
spring	ver veris n.	flight	fuga -ae f.
spear	hasta -ae f.	Britain	Británnia -ae f.
state	cívitas -atis f.	song	carmen -inis n.
piety, duty	píetas -atis f.	work	opus -eris n.
maiden	virgo -inis f.	order, rank	ordo -inis m.
Greece	Graécia -ae f.	time	tempus -oris n.

VII. Reading
Translate the reading in the space below.

AESTATIS TEMPESTATES

Aestas tempestates suas habet. Hae autem sunt saepe dulces. Étiam sunt saepe breves cum adventu céleri. Ventus súbito venit, tum *imber* cálidus, posteáque súbito sol. Et viae et domūs lavantur. In his aqua in *implúvia cadit*. *Aves* se lavant, canes se celant. Agrícolae sunt laeti. Post tempestatem piscatores *pisces* fácile invéniunt. Totus mundus est novus.

THE STORMS OF SUMMER.

Summer has its storms. These, however, are often pleasant. They are also often short

with a swift arrival. Suddenly a wind comes, then a warm rain, and afterward, suddenly

sun. Both the streets and the houses are washed. In these [the houses], water falls into

impluvia. Birds wash themselves, dogs hide themselves. The farmers are happy. After a

storm, fishermen easily find fish. The whole world is new.

imber imbris *m.* rain
implúvium -i *n.* basin in the atrium of a house to catch rain water
cado cádere cécidi casus to fall
avis avis *f.* bird
piscis piscis *m.* fish

I. Word Study and Grammar

1. Give the eight kinds of pronouns, in pairs. _personal and possessive; reflexive and intensive; relative and interrogative; demonstrative and indefinite_

2. Give the Pronoun Agreement Rule. _A pronoun agrees with its antecedent in gender and number, but its case is determined by its function in its own clause._

3. Give the Adjective Agreement Rule. _An adjective agrees with its noun in gender, number, and case._

4. Name the four Latin demonstrative pronouns. _hic haec hoc   ille illa illus   iste ista istud   is ea id_

5. Name the Latin intensive pronoun. _ipse ipsa ipsum_

6. The genitives of the 1st and 2nd person personal pronouns **do** / (**do not**) show possession.

7. The genitives of the 3rd person personal pronoun (**do**) / **do not** show possession.

8. The Naughty Nine have exceptional forms in the _genitive and dative singular_ .

9. Forms of **is** and **ea** mean _he_ and _she_ when referring to _persons and animals_ .

10. Forms of **is** and **ea** mean _it_ when referring to _non-living things with grammatical gender_ .

11. **Hic, ille, iste,** and **ipse** can be used as both _pronouns and adjectives_ .

12. Third-declension nouns ending in **-o** are usually _feminine_ .

13. Third-declension nouns ending in **-tas -tatis** are always _feminine_ .

14. When used together, **hic** and **ille** mean, respectively, _the latter, the former_ .

15. The reflexive pronoun refers to _the subject_ .

16. Why does the reflexive pronoun have no nominative form? _because it is always in the predicate and can never be a subject_

17. In Latin, the 1st and 2nd person reflexive pronouns forms are identical to _1st and 2nd personal pronouns_ .

18. Give the forms for the 3rd person reflexive pronouns. _sui, sibi, se, se_

19. In Latin, the 3rd person reflexive possessive pronoun adjective is _suus sua suum_ .

II. Latin Sayings

1. Faith, hope, and love, these three _Fides, spes, cáritas, tria haec_

2. A day of wrath, that day _Dies irae, dies illa_

3. Knowledge itself is power. _Ipsa sciéntia potestas est._

4. in itself _per se_

III. Vocabulary

Give the dictionary form.

arrow	sagitta -ae f.	column	agmen -inis n.
Europe	Europa -ae f.	Scotland	Caledónia -ae f.
lack	inópia -ae f.	speech	oratio -onis f.
summer	aestas -atis f.	lion	leo -onis m.
temptation	tentátio -onis f.	truth	véritas -atis f.
legion	légio -onis f.	human being	homo -inis m.
wound	vulnus -eris n.	Germany	Germánia -ae f.
speed	celéritas -atis f.	body	corpus -oris n.
Spain	Híspania -ae f.	authority	auctóritas -atis f.
liberty	libertas -atis f.	memory	memória -ae f.
suffering	pássio -onis f.	wisdom	sapiéntia -ae f.
kind	genus -eris n.	will	voluntas -atis f.
centurion	centúrio -onis m.	injury, injustice	injúria -ae f.
journey	iter itíneris n.	Ireland	Hibérnia -ae f.
Switzerland	Helvétia -ae f.	Carthage	Carthago -inis f.
charity, love	cáritas -atis f.	friendship	amicítia -ae f.
Athens	Athenae -arum f.	burden	onus -eris n.
storm	tempestas -atis f.	ditch	fossa -ae f.
lesson	léctio -onis f.	knowledge	sciéntia -ae f.
spring	ver veris n.	flight	fuga -ae f.
spear	hasta -ae f.	Britain	Británnia -ae f.
state	cívitas -atis f.	song	carmen -inis n.
piety, duty	píetas -atis f.	work	opus -eris n.
maiden	virgo -inis f.	order, rank	ordo -inis m.
Greece	Graécia -ae f.	time	tempus -oris n.

Unit III Review   Worksheet 3

IV. Declensions

1st and 2nd Person
Reflexive Pronouns

Case	Singular	Plural	Singular	Plural
gen.	mei	nostri, nostrum	tui	vestri, vestrum
dat.	mihi	nobis	tibi	vobis
acc.	me	nos	te	vos
abl.	me	nobis	te	vobis

3rd Person
Reflexive Pronouns

Case	Latin	Meaning
gen.	sui	of himself, herself, itself, themselves
dat.	sibi	to/for himself, herself, itself, themselves
acc.	se	himself, herself, itself, themselves
abl.	se	ibwf himself, herself, itself, themselves

3rd Person
Possessive Pronoun Adjective (Reflexive)

Latin	Meaning
suus sua suum	his (own), her (own), their (own)

3rd-Declension Nouns

Case	Singular	Plural	Singular	Plural
nom.	opus	ópera	homo	hómines
gen.	óperis	óperum	hóminis	hóminum
dat.	óperi	opéribus	hómini	homínibus
acc.	opus	ópera	hóminem	hómines
abl.	ópere	opéribus	hómine	homínibus

V. Conjugation

Make copies of Drill/Test Form A in the Appendix. Conjugate **cogo** and **ag**o in all 6 tenses, <u>active</u> and <u>passive</u>. Practice until perfect.

Drill/Test Form A

Principal Parts: cogo cógere coegi coactus
Present System Stem: cog-

Present			
Indicative Active		Indicative Passive	
cogo	cógimus	cogor	cógimur
cogis	cógitis	cógeris	cogímini
cogit	cogunt	cógitur	coguntur
Imperfect			
cogebam	cogebamus	cogebar	cogebamur
cogebas	cogebatis	cogebaris	cogebámini
cogebat	cogebant	cogebatur	cogebantur
Future			
cogam	cogemus	cogar	cogemur
coges	cogetis	cogēris	cogémini
coget	cogent	cogetur	cogentur

Perfect System Stem: coeg-

Perfect			
Indicative Active		Indicative Passive	
coegi	coégimus	coactus sum	coacti sumus
coegisti	coegistis	(a, um) es	(ae, a) estis
coegit	coegerunt	est	sunt
Pluperfect			
coégeram	coegeramus	eram	eramus
coégeras	coegeratis	eras	eratis
coégerat	coégerant	erat	erant
Future Perfect			
coégero	coegérimus	ero	érimus
coégeris	coegéritis	eris	éritis
coégerit	coégerint	erit	erunt

Principal Parts: ago ágere egi actus
Present System Stem: ag-

Present			
Indicative Active		Indicative Passive	
ago	ágimus	agor	ágimur
agis	ágitis	ágeris	agímini
agit	agunt	ágitur	aguntur
Imperfect			
agebam	agebamus	agebar	agebamur
agebas	agebatis	agebaris	agebámini
agebat	agebant	agebatur	agebantur
Future			
agam	agemus	agar	agemur
ages	agetis	agēris	agémini
aget	agent	agetur	agentur

Perfect System Stem: eg-

Perfect			
Indicative Active		Indicative Passive	
egi	égimus	actus sum	acti sumus
egisti	egistis	(a, um) es	(ae, a) estis
egit	egerunt	est	sunt
Pluperfect			
égeram	egeramus	eram	eramus
égeras	egeratis	eras	eratis
égerat	égerant	erat	erant
Future Perfect			
égero	egérimus	ero	érimus
égeris	egéritis	eris	éritis
égerit	egerint	erit	erunt

IV. Declensions (cont.)

Demonstrative Pronouns and Adjectives

Case	Singular			Plural		
	M	F	N	M	F	N
nom.	is	ea	id	ei	eae	ea
gen.	ejus	ejus	ejus	eorum	earum	eorum
dat.	ei	ei	ei	eis	eis	eis
acc.	eum	eam	id	eos	eas	ea
abl.	eo	eā	eo	eis	eis	eis

Case	Singular			Plural		
	M	F	N	M	F	N
nom.	hic	haec	hoc	hi	hae	haec
gen.	hujus	hujus	hujus	horum	harum	horum
dat.	huic	huic	huic	his	his	his
acc.	hunc	hanc	hoc	hos	has	haec
abl.	hoc	hac	hoc	his	his	his

Case	Singular			Plural		
	M	F	N	M	F	N
nom.	ille	illa	illud	illi	illae	illa
gen.	illíus	illíus	illíus	illorum	illarum	illorum
dat.	illi	illi	illi	illis	illis	illis
acc.	illum	illam	illud	illos	illas	illa
abl.	illo	illā	illo	illis	illis	illis

Case	Singular			Plural		
	M	F	N	M	F	N
nom.	ipse	ipsa	ipsum	ipsi	ipsae	ipsa
gen.	ipsíus	ipsíus	ipsíus	ipsorum	ipsarum	ipsorum
dat.	ipsi	ipsi	ipsi	ipsis	ipsis	ipsis
acc.	ipsum	ipsam	ipsum	ipsos	ipsas	ipsa
abl.	ipso	ipsā	ipso	ipsis	ipsis	ipsis

146

Drill A: -us Nouns

Give the declension (2nd, 3rd, or 4th) for each of these nouns ending in **-us**.

1. fructus __4__
2. amicus __2__
3. cibus __2__
4. ludus __2__
5. lacus __4__
6. onus __3__
7. óculus __2__
8. domus __4__
9. deus __2__
10. opus __3__
11. locus __2__
12. metus __4__
13. hortus __2__
14. portus __4__
15. mundus __2__
16. annus __2__
17. senatus __4__
18. tempus __3__
19. lupus __2__
20. ventus __2__
21. manus __4__
22. exércitus __4__
23. vulnus __3__
24. sócius __2__
25. genus __3__
26. spíritus __4__
27. corpus __3__
28. nimbus __2__
29. adventus __4__
30. campus __2__

Drill B: Pronouns

Express the *italicized* pronoun or prepositional phrase in Latin.

1. I will sail *with you*. __tecum__
2. The gold is hidden under *that* rock. __illo__
3. They placed *themselves* in danger. __se__
4. The general will give a prize *to you all*. __vobis__
5. The king *himself* will give a speech. __ipse__
6. We were attacked by *his* soldiers. __ejus__
7. He was warned by *his own* son. __suo__
8. I blame *that* centurion *of yours*. __istum__
9. *These* cities are in danger. __Hae__
10. We will be helped by *that* knowledge. __illā__
11. We doubted *ourselves*. __nos__
12. We must end *our* journey. __nostrum__
13. Here is a horse and a cow. I can ride *the former* but not *the latter*. __illum; hanc__
14. We are fighting the Gauls, but we will not seize *their* lands. __eorum__

Unit III Review   Worksheet 6

VI. Translate

1. Hoc carmen ab eā scriptum est. _This song has been written by her._

2. Illas sagittas milítibus nostris dabit. _____
   He will give those arrows to our soldiers._

3. Hasta non se movet. _The spear does not move itself._

4. Urbem nostram liberábimus. _We will free our (own) city._

5. Ipsa magistra hunc librum scripsit. _The teacher herself wrote this book._

6. Ipsa id scribet. _She will write it herself._

7. Hujus regis amicítiā juvatur. _He is being helped by this king's friendship._

8. Suā auctoritate exercitum mittet. _____
   He will send the army by his own authority._

9. Equum illi agrícolae dabo. _I will give the horse to that farmer._

10. Haec est urbs nostra. Ea oppugnata est. _____
    This is our city. It has been attacked._

11. You, not I, will lead this army. _____
    Tu, non ego, hunc exércitum duces._

12. The king himself has given me the authority. _____
    Ipse rex auctoritatem mihi dedit._

13. Those soldiers are Gauls. We have discovered their weapons. _____
    Illi mílites sunt Galli. Eorum tela invēnimus._

14. Write your own name. _Scribe nomen tuum._

15. Our flight has been prevented by his soldiers. _____
    Fuga nostra ab ejus militibus prohibita est._

16. This is a song of that victory. _Hoc est illíus victóriae carmen._

17. This girl will walk with us. _Haec puella nobiscum ambulabit._

18. I walk to school with her. _Cum eā ad ludum ámbulo._

Unit IV   Introduction

1. Give the three moods of Latin verbs. _____
   indicative, imperative, subjunctive

2. Give some English words that express the subjunctive. _____
   let, may, might, should, could, would

3. Which two tenses are missing from the subjunctive? _____
   future, future perfect

4. The indicative mood is for __actual, real__ action, and the subjunctive
   mood is for __potential__ action.

5. A clause is part of a sentence that has __a subject and verb__

6. An __independent__ clause can stand alone; a __subordinate__
   clause cannot stand alone.

7. The subjunctive is used primarily in __subordinate__ clauses, but it also has
   some uses in __independent__ clauses.

8. Two independent clauses that use the subjunctive are __hortatory and deliberative
   questions__ .

9. A subordinate clause that uses the subjunctive is the __purpose clause__ .

10. What is the difference in a phrase and a clause? __A phrase does not have a subject and
    a verb, and a clause does.__

I. Word Study and Grammar

1. Give the three moods of Latin verbs. _indicative, imperative, subjunctive_

2. Give some English words that express the subjunctive. _let, may, might, should, could, would_

3. Which two tenses are missing from the subjunctive? _future, future perfect_

4. The present subjunctive is formed by _____changing_____ or _____adding_____
   a vowel before the personal ending:
   1st conj. _____change **a** to **e**_____
   2nd conj. _____add **a**_____
   3rd conj. _____change **i, o, u** to **a**_____
   3rd conj. **io** _____add **a**_____
   4th conj. _____add **a**_____

5. What sentence helps you remember the vowel changes in the subjunctive?
   _____We beat a liar._____

6. The subjunctive is used primarily in _____subordinate_____ clauses, but it also has some
   uses in _____independent_____ clauses.

7. The hortatory subjunctive expresses an _____exhortation_____,
   _____indirect command_____, or _____strong wish_____.

8. Hortatory expressions may be translated into English using the verbal helpers_____may_____
   or _____let_____.

9. The meaning of the subjunctive must be determined by the _____context_____, but we will
   use the helping verbs _____*may* and *might*_____ for recitation.

10. All of the vocabulary words in this lesson are _____neuter_____ gender and belong to
    the _____2nd_____ declension.

II. Vocabulary

Say aloud and write with dictionary form, meaning, and derivative.

Latin (dictionary form)	Meaning	Derivative
auxílium -i n.	help, aid	auxiliary
concílium -i n.	council, meeting	council
consílium -i n.	counsel, advice, plan	counsel
Evangélium -i n.	Gospel	evangelical
impérium -i n.	command, power	imperial
ódium -i n.	hate, hatred	odious
ovum -i n.	egg	ovoid
perículum -i n.	danger	peril
princípium -i n.	beginning, origin	principle
vínculum -i n.	chain, bond	

Derivatives

1. The _____odious_____ robber was planning another bank job.

2. Because of all the baconburgers, his body became gradually more_____ovoid_____.

3. The chiefs of the tribes called a _____council_____ of war.

4. Why do you ask my advice if you are not going to heed my _____counsel_____?

5. A hospital must have_____auxiliary_____power in case of emergency.

Saying

Say aloud and write 3X.

Latin	Cáveat emptor.
Latin	Cáveat emptor.
Latin	Cáveat emptor.
English	Let the buyer beware.

Lesson Twenty   Worksheet 3

III. Conjugations
Model Verbs
Present Indicative Active

1st	2nd	3rd	3rd **io**	4th
amo	móneo	rego	cápio	áudio
amas	mónes	regis	cápis	audis
amat	mónet	regit	cápit	audit
amamus	monemus	régimus	cápimus	audimus
amatis	monetis	régitis	cápitis	auditis
amant	mónent	regunt	cápiunt	áudiunt

Present Subjunctive Active

1st	2nd	3rd	3rd **io**	4th
amem	móneam	regam	cápiam	áudiam
ames	móneas	regas	cápias	áudias
amet	móneat	regat	cápiat	áudiat
amemus	moneamus	regamus	capiamus	audiamus
ametis	moneatis	regatis	capiatis	audiatis
ament	móneant	regant	cápiant	áudiant

Present Subjunctive Active Meanings
(Use **amo**.)

Person	Singular	Plural
1st	I may love	we may love
2nd	you may love	you all may love
3rd	he, she, it may love	they may love

IV. Conjugation

Make copies of Drill/Test Form A in the Appendix. Conjugate **celo** in the 6 active and passive tenses of the indicative and the present subjunctive active. Practice until perfect.

154

Drill/Test Form A

Principal Parts: celo celare celavi celatus
Present System Stem: cela-

Present

Indicative Active		Indicative Passive	
celo	celamus	celor	celamur
celas	celatis	celaris	celámini
celat	celant	celatur	celantur

Imperfect

celabam	celabamus	celabar	celabamur
celabas	celabatis	celabaris	celabámini
celabat	celabant	celabatur	celabantur

Future

celabo	celábimus	celabor	celábimur
celabis	celábitis	celáberis	celabímini
celabit	celabunt	celábitur	celabuntur

Perfect System Stem: celav-

Perfect

Indicative Active		Indicative Passive	
celavi	celávimus	celatus sum	celati sumus
celavisti	celavistis	(a, um) es	(ae, a) estis
celavit	celaverunt	est	sunt

Pluperfect

celáveram	celaveramus	eram	eramus
celáveras	celaveratis	eras	eratis
celáverat	celáverant	erat	erant

Future Perfect

celávero	celavérimus	ero	érimus
celáveris	celavéritis	eris	éritis
celáverit	celáverint	erit	erunt

Present

Subjunctive Active		Subjunctive Passive	
celem	celemus		
celes	celetis		
celet	celent		

Imperfect

Perfect

Pluperfect

V. Form Drills
Convert the given indicative form to the corresponding subjunctive form.

Drill A
1st Conjugation

1. rogat _roget_
2. optant _optent_
3. lavamus _lavemus_
4. vocas _voces_
5. nuntiatis _nuntietis_

6. celo _celem_
7. parat _paret_
8. negant _negent_
9. spectas _spectes_
10. damus _demus_

Drill B
2nd Conjugation

1. docemus _doceamus_
2. sedeo _sédeam_
3. movemus _moveamus_
4. manent _máneant_
5. prohibetis _prohibeatis_

6. tenes _téneas_
7. videt _vídeat_
8. monent _móneant_
9. timet _tímeat_
10. respóndeo _respóndeam_

Drill C
3rd Conjugation

1. ponis _ponas_
2. duco _ducam_
3. mittunt _mittant_
4. vívimus _vivamus_
5. dícitis _dicatis_

6. scribit _scribat_
7. cógimus _cogamus_
8. figit _figat_
9. ago _agam_
10. tollunt _tollant_

V. Form Drills (cont.)
Convert the given indicative form to the corresponding subjunctive form.

Drill D
4th Conjugation

1. impedit _impédiat_
2. dormis _dórmias_
3. audio _áudiam_
4. véniunt _véniant_
5. sentimus _sentiamus_

6. finitis _finiatis_
7. scio _sciam_
8. invenimus _inveniamus_
9. nescit _nésciat_
10. munis _múnias_

Drill E
3rd io Conjugation

1. facis _fácias_
2. capit _cápiat_
3. jácimus _jaciamus_
4. fúgiunt _fúgiant_
5. cúpio _cúpiam_

6. cápiunt _cápiant_
7. fácimus _faciamus_
8. jácio _jáciam_
9. cúpitis _cupiatis_
10. fugit _fúgiat_

Drill F
Mixed

1. venit _véniat_
2. laboro _laborem_
3. júngimus _jungamus_
4. sedet _sédeat_
5. cápitis _capiatis_

6. cogis _cogas_
7. movet _móveat_
8. dícimus _dicamus_
9. áudiunt _áudiant_
10. súpero _súperem_

Lesson Twenty — Worksheet 6

VI. Translation
Hortatory Subjunctive
Use *let* or *may*.

1. Urbem nostram liberemus. __Let us free our city.__

2. Let them blame the Gauls. __Gallos culpent.__

3. Let him prepare the chains. __Víncula paret.__

4. Let us give aid to the farmers. __Auxílium agrícolis demus.__

5. Let them find a new house. __Domum novam invéniant.__

6. Let us wage war today. __Bellum hódie geramus.__

7. Let them give him the command. __Impérium ei dent.__

8. Let her remain in the city. __In urbe máneat.__

9. Let us wash the dogs. __Canes lavemus.__

10. May we never yield. __Numquam cedamus.__

11. Nautae in portum tuto návigent. ____
    May the sailors sail into port safely.

12. Centúrio auxílium milítibus det. ____
    May the centurion give aid to the soldiers.

13. Rex impérium et sapiéntiam hábeat. ____
    May the king have power and wisdom.

14. Urbis portas propter perículum claudamus. ____
    Let us close the gates of the city on account of the danger.

15. Let us send the eighth legion into Spain. ____
    Legionem octavam in Hispániam mittamus.

16. Let those men put these chains around the tree. ____
    Illi hómines haec víncula circum árborem ponant.

17. May I have good memories of the journey. ____
    Itíneris memórias bonas hábeam.

18. May he beware the storm. __Tempestatem cáveat.__

19. Let them throw the body into the river. __Corpus in flumen jáciant.__

Lesson Twenty — Worksheet 7

VII. Reading
Translate the reading in the space below.

CONCILIORUM PERÍCULUM

Duces urbis pártium in concílio sedebant. *Praesens* erat dux partis foro finítimae, dux partis flúmini finítimae, dux partis in agro, et dux partis in cóllibus. Dux partis foro finítimae dixit: "Viae partis meae sunt *antiquae*. Saxa in cóllibus sunt viis idónea. Struamus vias novas." Dux partis flumini finítimae dixit: "Portus est antiquus. Saxa in cóllibus sunt pórtui idónea. Struamus portum novum." Dux partis in agro dixit: "Domūs partis meae sunt antiquae. Saxa in cóllibus sunt dómibus idónea. Struamus domūs novas." Dux partis in cóllibus respondit: "Saxa in cóllibus sunt *cara*. Quis ex vobis pecúniam habet?" Nihil factum est.

THE DANGER OF MEETINGS

The leaders of the regions (districts) of the city were sitting in a meeting. Present were the leader of the district near to the forum, the leader of the district near to the river, the leader of the district on the plain (flatland), and the leader of the district in the hills. The leader of the district near to the forum said: "The roads of my district are old. The rocks in the hills are suitable for roads. Let's build some new roads." The leader of the district near to the river said: "The port is old. The rocks in the hills are suitable for a port. Let's build a new port." The leader of the district on the flatland said: "The houses of my district are old. The rocks in the hills are suitable for houses. Let's build some new houses." The leader of the district in the hills responded: "The rocks in the hills are expensive. Who of you has any money?" Nothing was done.

praesens -entis present
antiquus -a -um old
carus -a -um dear, expensive (*dear* can also mean *expensive* in English)

I. Word Study and Grammar

1. Give some English words that express the subjunctive. _____
   let, may, might, should, could, would

2. Which two tenses are missing from the subjunctive? _____
   future, future perfect

3. The present subjunctive is formed by _____ changing _____ or _____ adding _____
   a vowel before the personal ending:
   1st conj. _____ substitute **e** for **a** _____
   2nd conj. _____ add **a** _____
   3rd conj. _____ substitute **a** for **i, o, u** _____
   3rd conj. **io** _____ add **a** _____
   4th conj. _____ add **a** _____

4. The subjunctive is used primarily in _____ subordinate _____ clauses, but it also has some
   uses in _____ independent _____ clauses.

5. The present passive subjunctive is formed by substituting the _____ passive personal endings _____
   for the _____ active personal endings _____ .

6. A subjunctive clause is made negative by using the conjunction _____ **ne** _____ .

7. A deliberative question is asked in _____ doubt _____ or _____ indignation _____
   and is expressed in English by the helping verb _____ should _____ .

8. The hortatory subjunctive expresses an _____ exhortation _____ ,
   _____ indirect command _____ , or _____ strong wish _____ .

9. Hortatory expressions may be translated into English using the verbal helpers _____ may _____
   or _____ let _____ .

10. The meaning of the subjunctive must be determined by the _____ context _____ , but we will
    use the helping verbs _____ *may* and *might* _____ for recitation.

Saying
Say aloud and write 3X.

Latin	Sanctificetur nomen tuum
Latin	Sanctificetur nomen tuum
Latin	Sanctificetur nomen tuum
English	Hallowed be thy name

II. Vocabulary
Say aloud and write with dictionary form, meaning, and derivative.

Latin (dictionary form)	Meaning	Derivative
astrum -i n.	heavenly body, heavens	astral
castellum -i n.	fort	castle
exílium -i n.	exile	exile
fatum -i n.	destiny, fate	fate
inítium -i n.	starting point	initial
pábulum -i n.	fodder, nourishment	
praesídium -i n.	protection, garrison	preside
prétium -i n.	price	precious
spátium -i n.	space, interval	spatial
vestígium -i n.	trace, footprint	vestige

Derivatives

1. The _____ initial _____ phase of the project is the most difficult.

2. Little _____ vestige _____ remains of the Roman presence in Scotland.

3. A black hole is an _____ astral _____ graveyard.

4. Cartesian coordinates define two _____ spatial _____ dimensions.

5. My dog always steals what is most _____ precious _____ to me.

III. Subjunctives
(from music and prayers)

Hallowed be thy Name	Sanctificetur nomen tuum
Thy kingdom come	Advéniat regnum tuum
Thy will be done	Fiat voluntas tua
Let us rejoice therefore	Gaudeamus ígitur
O come let us adore him	Venite adoremus
Let us pray	Oremus

Lesson Twenty-one   Worksheet 3

IV. Conjugations
Model Verbs
Present Indicative Passive

1st	2nd	3rd	3rd **io**	4th
amor	móneor	regor	cápior	áudior
amaris	moneris	régeris	cáperis	audiris
amatur	monetur	régitur	cápitur	auditur
amamur	monemur	régimur	cápimur	audimur
amámini	monémini	regímini	capímini	audímini
amantur	monentur	reguntur	capiuntur	audiuntur

Present Subjunctive Passive

1st	2nd	3rd	3rd **io**	4th
amer	mónear	regar	cápiar	áudiar
ameris	monearis	regaris	capiaris	audiaris
ametur	moneatur	regatur	capiatur	audiatur
amemur	moneamur	regamur	capiamur	audiamur
amémini	moneámini	regámini	capiámini	audiámini
amentur	moneantur	regantur	capiantur	audiantur

Present Subjunctive Passive Meanings
(Use **amo**.)

Person	Singular	Plural
1st	I may be loved	we may be loved
2nd	you may be loved	you all may be loved
3rd	he, she, it may be loved	they may be loved

V. Conjugation

Make copies of Drill/Test Form A in the Appendix. Conjugate **júbeo** in the <u>6 active and passive tenses of the indicative</u> and the <u>present subjunctive active and passive</u>. Practice until perfect.

Drill/Test Form A

Principal Parts: júbeo jubēre jussi jussus
Present System Stem: jube-

Present			
Indicative Active		Indicative Passive	
júbeo	jubemus	júbeor	jubemur
jubes	jubetis	juberis	jubémini
jubet	jubent	jubetur	jubentur
Imperfect			
jubebam	jubebamus	jubebar	jubebamur
jubebas	jubebatis	jubebaris	jubebámini
jubebat	jubebant	jubebatur	jubebantur
Future			
jubebo	jubébimus	jubebor	jubébimur
jubebis	jubébitis	jubéberis	jubebímini
jubebit	jubebunt	jubébitur	jubebuntur

Perfect System Stem: juss-

Perfect			
Indicative Active		Indicative Passive	
jussi	jússimus	jussus sum	jussi sumus
jussisti	jussistis	(a, um) es	(ae, a) estis
jussit	jusserunt	est	sunt
Pluperfect			
jússeram	jusseramus	eram	eramus
jússeras	jusseratis	eras	eratis
jússerat	jusserant	erat	erant
Future Perfect			
jússero	jussérimus	ero	érimus
jússeris	jusséritis	eris	éritis
jússerit	jússerint	erit	erunt

Present			
Subjunctive Active		Subjunctive Passive	
júbeam	jubeamus	júbear	jubeamur
júbeas	jubeatis	jubearis	jubeámini
júbeat	júbeant	jubeatur	jubeantur
Imperfect			
Perfect			
Pluperfect			

VI. Form Drills

Convert the given indicative form to the corresponding subjunctive form.

Drill A
1st Conjugation

1. clamatur _clametur_
2. oppugnantur _oppugnentur_
3. portor _porter_
4. culpámini _culpémini_
5. lavatur _lavetur_

6. liberaris _libereris_
7. optamur _optemur_
8. vulneratur _vulneretur_
9. mutaris _muteris_
10. judicantur _judicentur_

Drill B
2nd Conjugation

1. habentur _habeantur_
2. vídeor _vídear_
3. tenetur _teneatur_
4. terreris _terrearis_
5. dóceor _dócear_

6. cavetur _caveatur_
7. moventur _moveantur_
8. monémini _moneámini_
9. jubemur _jubeamur_
10. debetur _debeatur_

Drill C
3rd Conjugation

1. mítteris _mittaris_
2. pónitur _ponatur_
3. agor _agar_
4. vincuntur _vincantur_
5. strúitur _struatur_

6. dúcimur _ducamur_
7. premímini _premámini_
8. clauduntur _claudantur_
9. tóllitur _tollatur_
10. trahor _trahar_

VI. Form Drills (cont.)

Convert the given indicative form to the corresponding subjunctive form.

Drill D
4th Conjugation

1. sentitur _sentiatur_
2. nesciuntur _nesciantur_
3. impédior _impédiar_
4. audimur _audiamur_
5. invenímini _inveniámini_

6. finitur _finiatur_
7. sentiris _sentiaris_
8. finiuntur _finiantur_
9. scitur _sciatur_
10. múnior _múniar_

Drill E
3rd **io** Conjugation

1. cúpitur _cupiatur_
2. cápior _cápiar_
3. jaciuntur _jaciantur_
4. jácitur _jaciatur_
5. cáperis _capiaris_

6. jacímini _jaciámini_
7. cúpimur _cupiamur_
8. cápitur _capiatur_
9. jaciuntur _jaciantur_
10. munímini _muniámini_

Drill F
Mixed

1. regor _regar_
2. dubitatur _dubitetur_
3. monemur _moneamur_
4. ponuntur _ponantur_
5. audimur _audiamur_

6. jácitur _jaciatur_
7. vincímini _vincámini_
8. véheris _veharis_
9. perturbantur _perturbentur_
10. móveor _móvear_

VII. Translation
Hortatory Subjunctive

1. Inítium faciamus. _____ Let us make a starting point. _____

2. Ne ullum vestígium videatur. _____ Let no trace be seen. _____

3. Illud castellum superetur. _____ Let that fort be conquered. _____

4. Gallorum fatum sciatur. _____ Let the fate of the Gauls be known. _____

5. Post tempestatem astra a nautis videantur. _____
   After the storm let the heavens be seen by the sailors.

6. Let this senator be sent into exile. _____ Hic senator in exílium mittatur. _____

7. Let aid be given to the soldiers. _____ Auxílium mílitibus detur. _____

8. Let those citizens not be blamed on account of hatred. _____
   Ne illi cives propter ódium culpentur.

9. Let fodder be collected for the fort. _____ Pábulum pro castello cogatur. _____

10. Let chains be placed across the road. _____ Víncula trans viam ponantur. _____

VIII. Translation
Deliberative Questions

1. Senatores salutemus? _____ Should we greet the senators? _____

2. Quid cívibus mittam? _____ What should I send to the citizens? _____

3. Ad urbem véniant? _____ Should they come to the city? _____

4. Quid cogatur? _____ What should be collected? _____

5. Quis in foro máneat? _____ Who should remain in the forum? _____

6. Are we to flee? _____ Fugiamus? _____

7. Who should find the fault? _____ Quis culpam invéniat? _____

8. Should we put the rocks in the cave? _____ Saxa in antrum ponamus? _____

9. Is the money to be given to the king? _____ Pecúnia regi detur? _____

10. What should be lifted into the fort? _____ Quid in castellum tollatur? _____

IX. Reading
Translate the reading in the space below.

FATI VESTIGIA

Consílium meum est: ne astra temptemus. Olim erant in urbe nostrā duo cívium génera. Bonos nos vocabamus. Álteros míseros pigrósque vocabamus. Inter nos pugnávimus, et ex urbe in exílium álteros sine cibo, sine pábulo égimus. Sub móntibus castellum struxerunt. Lente, lente urbem novam fecerunt. Tum in móntibus aurum invenerunt. Súbito ómnium *prétium* habebant—prétium *armorum*, equorum, telorum. Póstea in nos bellum gesserunt et ex urbe nostrā nos egerunt. Silvas nunc habitamus, cum feris. Vestígia nostra ex urbe nostrā *rursus* spectamus. Astra temptávimus et haec vita diffícilis est fatum nostrum.

THE FOOTPRINTS OF FATE

My advice is: let us not tempt the stars. Once, in our city, there were two classes of

citizens. We called ourselves "the good ones (nobles)." We called the others the

wretched and lazy ones. We fought between ourselves (each other), and we drove the

others out of the city into exile without food, without fodder. They built a fort at the foot

of the mountains. Slowly, slowly they built a new city. Then they discovered gold in the

mountains. Suddenly they had the money for everything—the money for arms, horses,

spears. Afterward, they waged war on us and drove us out of our own city. Now we live

in the forest, with the wild animals. We look back at our own footprints out of our own city.

We tempted the stars and this difficult life is our fate.

_____

_____

_____

_____

_____

_____

prétium -i *n.* the value of, enough money for (*w/gen.*)
arma armorum *n.* arms (weapons)
rursus *adv.* back

I. Word Study and Grammar

1. Which two tenses are missing from the subjunctive? _____
   future, future perfect

2. The present subjunctive is formed by _____changing_____ or _____adding_____
   a vowel before the personal ending:
   1st conj. _____substitute **e** for **a**_____
   2nd conj. _____add **a**_____
   3rd conj. _____substitute **a** for **i, o, u**_____
   3rd conj. **io** _____add **a**_____
   4th conj. _____add **a**_____

3. What sentence helps you remember the vowel changes in the present subjunctive?
   _____We beat a liar._____

4. The imperfect subjunctive is built on the _____infinitive_____ .

5. The passive subjunctive is formed by substituting _____passive_____ personal endings for
   _____active_____ personal endings.

6. The subjunctive is used primarily in _____subordinate_____ clauses, but it also has some
   uses in _____independent_____ clauses.

7. A subjunctive clause is made negative by using the conjunction _____ne_____ .

8. A deliberative question is asked in _____doubt_____ or _____indignation_____
   and is expressed in English by the helping verb _____should_____ .

9. A deliberative question uses the _____present_____ subjunctive for present time
   and the _____imperfect_____ subjunctive for past time.

10. The hortatory subjunctive expresses an _____exhortation_____ ,
    _____indirect command_____ , or _____strong wish_____ .

11. Hortatory expressions may be translated into English using the verbal helpers _____let_____
    or _____may_____ .

II. New Vocabulary

Say aloud and write with dictionary form, meaning, and derivative.

Latin (dictionary form)	Meaning	Derivative
aedifícium -i n.	building	edifice
antrum -i n.	cave	
letum -i n.	death	
mandatum -i n.	commandment, order	mandatory
ótium -i n.	ease, leisure	
sepulchrum -i n.	tomb	sepulchre
theatrum -i n.	theater	
tríduum -i n.	three days	
vítium -i n.	vice, blemish	vicious
votum -i n.	vow, prayer	votive

Derivatives

1. The corrupt senator's career was an _____edifice_____ of shame.

2. It is _____mandatory_____ to wash your hands before handling food.

3. Hundreds of _____votive_____ figurines were found in the ruins of the temple.

4. _____Vicious_____ birds the size of kangaroos used to roam the earth.

Saying

Say aloud and write 3X.

Latin	Requiescat in pace (RIP)
Latin	Requiescat in pace (RIP)
Latin	Requiescat in pace (RIP)
English	May he rest in peace

III. Conjugations
Model Verbs
Present Subjunctive Active

1st	2nd	3rd	3rd io	4th
amem	móneam	regam	cápiam	áudiam
ames	móneas	regas	cápias	áudias
amet	móneat	regat	cápiat	áudiat
amemus	moneamus	regamus	capiamus	audiamus
ametis	moneatis	regatis	capiatis	audiatis
ament	móneant	regant	cápiant	áudiant

Present Subjunctive Passive

1st	2nd	3rd	3rd io	4th
amer	mónear	regar	cápiar	áudiar
ameris	monearis	regaris	capiaris	audiaris
ametur	moneatur	regatur	capiatur	audiatur
amemur	moneamur	regamur	capiamur	audiamur
amémini	moneámini	regámini	capiámini	audiámini
amentur	moneantur	regantur	capiantur	audiantur

Present Subjunctive Active and Passive Meanings
(Use **amo**.)

Person	Singular Active	Plural Active
1st	I may love	we may love
2nd	you may love	you all may love
3rd	he, she, it may love	they may love
Person	Singular Passive	Plural Passive
1st	I may be loved	we may be loved
2nd	you may be loved	you all may be loved
3rd	he, she, it may be loved	they may be loved

III. Conjugations (cont.)

Imperfect Subjunctive Active

1st	2nd	3rd	3rd io	4th
amarem	monerem	régerem	cáperem	audirem
amares	moneres	régeres	cáperes	audires
amaret	moneret	régeret	cáperet	audiret
amaremus	moneremus	regeremus	caperemus	audiremus
amaretis	moneretis	regeretis	caperetis	audiretis
amarent	monerent	régerent	cáperent	audirent

Imperfect Subjunctive Passive

1st	2nd	3rd	3rd io	4th
amarer	mónerer	régerer	cáperer	audirer
amareris	monereris	regereris	capereris	audireris
amaretur	moneretur	regeretur	caperetur	audiretur
amaremur	moneremur	regeremur	caperemur	audiremur
amarémini	monerémini	regerémini	caperémini	audirémini
amarentur	monerentur	regerentur	caperentur	audirentur

Imperfect Subjunctive Active and Passive Meanings
(Use **amo**.)

Person	Singular Active	Plural Active
1st	I might love	we might love
2nd	you might love	you all might love
3rd	he, she, it might love	they might love
Person	Singular Passive	Plural Passive
1st	I might be loved	we might be loved
2nd	you might be loved	you all might be loved
3rd	he, she, it might be loved	they might be loved

IV. Conjugation

Make copies of Drill/Test Form A in the Appendix. Conjugate **vinco** in the 6 active and passive tenses of the indicative and the present and imperfect subjunctive active and passive. Practice until perfect.

Drill/Test Form A

Principal Parts: vinco vincere vici victus
Present System Stem: vinc-

Present

Indicative Active		Indicative Passive	
vinco	víncimus	vincor	víncimur
vincis	víncitis	vínceris	vincímini
vincit	vincunt	víncitur	vincuntur

Imperfect

vincebam	vincebamus	vincebar	vincebamur
vincebas	vincebatis	vincebaris	vincebámini
vincebat	vincebant	vincebatur	vincebantur

Future

vincam	vincemus	vincar	vincemur
vinces	vincetis	vincēris	vincémini
vincet	vincent	vincetur	vincentur

Perfect System Stem: vic-

Perfect

Indicative Active		Indicative Passive		
vici	vícimus	victus	sum	victi	sumus
vicisti	vicistis	(a, um)	es	(ae, a)	estis
vicit	vicerunt		est		sunt

Pluperfect

víceram	viceramus	eram	eramus
víceras	viceratis	eras	eratis
vícerat	vicerant	erat	erant

Future Perfect

vícero	vicérimus	ero	érimus
víceris	vicéritis	eris	éritis
vícerit	vícerint	erit	erunt

Present

Subjunctive Active		Subjunctive Passive	
vincam	vincamus	vincar	vincamur
vincas	vincatis	vincaris	vincámini
vincat	vincant	vincatur	vincantur

Imperfect

víncerem	vinceremus	víncerer	vinceremur
vínceres	vinceretis	víncereris	vincerémini
vínceret	víncerent	vinceretur	vincerentur

Perfect

Pluperfect

V. Form Drills

Convert the given indicative form to the corresponding subjunctive form (1-5) or translate (6-10).

Drill A
1st Conjugation

1. stabat ___staret___
2. accusabam ___accusarem___
3. natabamus ___nataremus___
4. volabant ___volarent___
5. juvabatis ___juvaretis___

6. she might give ___daret___
7. they might tempt ___temptarent___
8. you might deny ___negares___
9. I might work ___laborarem___
10. we might change ___mutaremus___

Drill B
2nd Conjugation

1. docebam ___docerem___
2. tacebamus ___taceremus___
3. videbant ___viderent___
4. sedebat ___sederet___
5. tenebas ___teneres___

6. he might teach ___dóceret___
7. we might fear ___timeremus___
8. you might beware ___cáveres___
9. they might hold ___ténerent___
10. I might owe ___déberem___

Drill C
3rd Conjugation

1. gerebat ___géreret___
2. scribebam ___scríberem___
3. jungebatis ___jungeretis___
4. figebant ___fígerent___
5. premebas ___prémeres___

6. you might rule ___régeres___
7. he might yield ___céderet___
8. we might lead ___duceremus___
9. they might drag ___tráherent___
10. I might conquer ___víncerem___

V. Form Drills (cont.)

Convert the given indicative form to the corresponding subjunctive form (1-5) or translate (6-10).

Drill D
4th, 3rd **io** Conjugation

1. finiebamus _finiremus_
2. impediebat _impediret_
3. cupiebam _cúperem_
4. audiebant _audirent_
5. dormiebas _dormires_

6. I might throw _jácerem_
7. it might take _cáperet_
8. it might make _fáceret_
9. they might know _scirent_
10. we might flee _fugeremus_

Drill E
Mixed

1. agebas _ágeres_
2. faciebant _fácerent_
3. spectabamus _spectaremus_
4. debebat _déberet_
5. claudebam _cláuderem_

6. it might lift _tólleret_
7. we might walk _ambularemus_
8. you might have _haberes_
9. they might hear _audirent_
10. you all might make _faceretis_

Drill F
Mixed

1. orabatur _oraretur_
2. gerebatur _gereretur_
3. capiebamur _caperemur_
4. gaudebaris _gaudereris_
5. dabantur _darentur_

6. she might be hidden _celaretur_
7. it might be ordered _juberetur_
8. we might be lifted up _tolleremur_
9. they might be forced _cogerentur_
10. it might be finished _finiretur_

VI. Translation

1. Quid faceremus? _What should we have made? (What were we to make?)_
2. Quid strueretur? _What should have been built?_
3. Fugeremus? _Should we have fled? (Were we to flee?)_
4. Quómodo respónderent? _How should they have responded?_
5. A milítibus exploraretur? _Should it have been explored by the soldiers?_
6. Equis traheretur? _Should it have been dragged by horses?_
7. Haec a cívibus viderentur? _Should these things have been seen by the citizens?_
8. Eum finiremus? _Should we have finished it?_
9. Urbs oppugnaretur? _Should the city have been attacked?_
10. Mílites moneres? _Should you have warned the soldiers?_
11. Who should have judged? _Quis judicaret?_
12. Should they have remained? _Manerent?_
13. Should I have responded? _Respónderem?_
14. Should he have been led? _Duceretur?_
15. Should he have led? _Dúceret?_
16. Should we have greeted? _Salutaremus?_
17. Should we have been greeted? _Salutaremur?_
18. Who should have asked? _Quis rogaret?_
19. Who should have been asked? _Quis rogaretur?_
20. How should we have prevented the death? _Quómodo letum prohiberemus?_

VII. Reading

Translate the reading in the space below.

PRO ÓTIO

Quot theatra struamus? Ubi ea struamus? Est res gravis. Cívium ótium est res gravis. Cur cives laborent? *Orbem* regunt. Ótium non est vítium. In princípio erat ótium. Vidistíne umquam servum senem? Labor est letum. Vita cárminum, non laborum, plena est. Mandata contra laborem scribamus. Votorum tríduum pro ótio! Votorum tríduum pro theatro, pro ludis, pro cenis!

FOR LEISURE

How many theaters should we build? Where should we build them? It is a serious matter.

The leisure of the citizens is a serious matter. Why should the citizens work? They rule

the world. Leisure is not vice. In the beginning was leisure. Have you ever seen an old

slave? Work is death. Life is full of songs, not work. Let us write commandments against

work. Three days of prayers for leisure! Three days of prayers for the theater, for games,

for dinners (dinner parties)!

orbis orbis *m.* world

I. Word Study and Grammar

1. The present subjective is formed by _____changing_____ or _____adding_____ a vowel before the personal ending:
   1st conj. _____substitute **e** for **a**_____
   2nd conj. _____add **a**_____
   3rd conj. _____substitute **a** for **i, o, u**_____
   3rd conj. **io** _____add **a**_____
   4th conj. _____add **a**_____

2. The imperfect subjunctive is built on the _____infinitive_____ .

3. The passive subjunctive is formed by substituting _____passive_____ personal endings for _____active_____ personal endings.

4. The subjunctive is used primarily in _____subordinate_____ clauses, but it also has some uses in _____independent_____ clauses.

5. A subjunctive clause is made negative by using the conjunction _____ne_____ .

6. A deliberative question is asked in _____doubt_____ or _____indignation_____ and is expressed in English by the helping verb _____should_____ .

7. A deliberative question uses the _____present_____ subjunctive for present time and the _____imperfect_____ subjunctive for past time.

8. The hortatory subjunctive expresses an _____exhortation_____ , _____indirect command_____ , or _____strong wish_____ .

9. Hortatory expressions may be translated into English using the verbal helpers _____let_____ or _____may_____ .

10. In English the _____infinitive_____ is a way to show purpose. In Latin the _____ut clause_____ is a way to show purpose.

11. In a sentence with a purpose clause, the main verb is in the _____indicative_____ , and the purpose clause is in the _____subjunctive_____ .

12. The verbs in a sentence with a purpose clause must _____correspond_____ in tense.

II. Vocabulary

Say aloud and write with dictionary form, meaning, and derivative.

Latin (dictionary form)	Meaning	Derivative
aer áeris m.	the air	aerial
comes cómitis m.	companion	
flos floris m.	flower	floral
grex gregis m.	herd, flock	egregious
hiems híemis f.	winter	
júvenis júvenis m./f.	young person	juvenile
lapis lápidis m.	stone	lapidary
plebs plebis f.	common people, plebeians	
obses óbsidis m.	hostage	
uxor uxoris f.	wife	uxorious

Saying

Say aloud and write 3X.

Latin	Credo ut intéllegam.
Latin	Credo ut intéllegam.
Latin	Credo ut intéllegam.
English	I believe in order that I may understand.

Derivatives

1. Many ancient Roman forts have been discovered by means of _____aerial_____ photography.

2. This war is an_____egregious_____ waste of money.

3. The queen dominated the_____uxorious_____ king.

4. In Italy there are_____lapidary_____ artists who make pictures out of various colored stones.

III. Conjugations

Model Verbs

Sum - Present Subjunctive

Person	Singular		Plural	
	Latin	Meaning	Latin	Meaning
1st	sim	I may be	simus	we may be
2nd	sis	you may be	sitis	you all may be
3rd	sit	hsi may be	sint	they may be

Sum - Imperfect Subjunctive

Person	Singular		Plural	
	Latin	Meaning	Latin	Meaning
1st	essem	I might be	essemus	we might be
2nd	esses	you might be	essetis	you all might be
3rd	esset	hsi might be	essent	they might be

Present Subjunctive Active

1st	2nd	3rd	3rd io	4th
amem	móneam	regam	cápiam	áudiam
ames	móneas	regas	cápias	áudias
amet	móneat	regat	cápiat	áudiat
amemus	moneamus	regamus	capiamus	audiamus
ametis	moneatis	regatis	capiatis	audiatis
ament	móneant	regant	cápiant	áudiant

Present Subjunctive Passive

1st	2nd	3rd	3rd io	4th
amer	mónear	regar	cápiar	áudiar
ameris	monearis	regaris	capiaris	audiaris
ametur	moneatur	regatur	capiatur	audiatur
amemur	moneamur	regamur	capiamur	audiamur
amémini	moneámini	regámini	capiámini	audiámini
amentur	moneantur	regantur	capiantur	audiantur

III. Conjugations (cont.)

Imperfect Subjunctive Active

1st	2nd	3rd	3rd io	4th
amarem	monerem	régerem	cáperem	audirem
amares	moneres	régeres	cáperes	audires
amaret	moneret	régeret	cáperet	audiret
amaremus	moneremus	regeremus	caperemus	audiremus
amaretis	moneretis	regeretis	caperetis	audiretis
amarent	monerent	régerent	cáperent	audirent

Imperfect Subjunctive Passive

1st	2nd	3rd	3rd io	4th
amarer	monerer	régerer	cáperer	audirer
amareris	monereris	regereris	capereris	audireris
amaretur	moneretur	regeretur	caperetur	audiretur
amaremur	moneremur	regeremur	caperemur	audiremur
amarémini	monerémini	regerémini	caperémini	audirémini
amarentur	monerentur	regerentur	caperentur	audirentur

IV. Conjugation

Make copies of Drill/Test Form A in the Appendix. Conjugate **séntio** in the 6 active and passive tenses of the indicative and the present and imperfect subjunctive active and passive. Practice until perfect.

Drill/Test Form A

Principal Parts: séntio sentire sensi sensus
Present System Stem: senti-

Present			
Indicative Active		Indicative Passive	
séntio	sentimus	séntior	sentimur
sentis	sentitis	sentiris	sentímini
sentit	sentiunt	sentitur	sentiuntur
Imperfect			
sentiebam	sentiebamus	sentiebar	sentiebamur
sentiebas	sentiebatis	sentiebaris	sentiebámini
sentiebat	sentiebant	sentiebatur	sentiebantur
Future			
séntiam	sentiemus	séntiar	sentiemur
sénties	sentietis	sentieris	sentiémini
séntiet	séntient	sentietur	sentientur

Perfect System Stem: sens-

Perfect			
Indicative Active		Indicative Passive	
sensi	sénsimus	sensus sum	sensi sumus
sensisti	sensistis	(a, um) es	(ae, a) estis
sensit	senserunt	est	sunt
Pluperfect			
sénseram	senseramus	eram	eramus
sénseras	senseratis	eras	eratis
sénserat	sénserant	erat	erant
Future Perfect			
sénsero	sensérimus	ero	érimus
sénseris	senséritis	eris	éritis
sénserit	sénserint	erit	erunt

Present			
Subjunctive Active		Subjunctive Passive	
séntiam	sentiamus	séntiar	sentiamur
séntias	sentiatis	sentiaris	sentiámini
séntiat	séntiant	sentiatur	sentiantur
Imperfect			
sentirem	sentiremus	sentirer	sentiremur
sentires	sentiretis	sentireris	sentirémini
sentiret	sentirent	sentiretur	sentirentur
Perfect			
Pluperfect			

V. Form Drills

Drill A

1. simus _we may be_
2. essent _they might be_
3. sim _I may be_
4. esset _hsi might be_
5. essetis _you all might be_

6. sit _hsi may be_
7. sint _they may be_
8. essemus _we might be_
9. essem _I might be_
10. sis _you may be_

Drill B

1. dóceat _hsi may teach_
2. rogaremus _we might ask_
3. véheret _hsi might transport_
4. jungas _you may join_
5. sentirent _they might feel_

6. figat _hsi may fasten_
7. vocaretis _you all might call_
8. terreamus _we may frighten_
9. céderet _hsi might yield_
10. dubitarem _I might doubt_

Drill C

1. you might be _esses_
2. they may be _sint_
3. we may be _simus_
4. I might be _essem_
5. you all may be _sitis_

6. hsi might be _esset_
7. we might be _essemus_
8. I may be _sim_
9. hsi may be _sit_
10. you may be _sis_

VI. Translation

Complete the sentence with the purpose clause.

1. Návigant ut tempestatem (fúgio) _fúgiant_ .
2. Explorabat ut cibum (invénio) _inveniret_ .
3. Óppidum oppugnaverunt ut cives ejus (súpero) _superarent_ .
4. Cédimus ut pacem (hábeo) _habeamus_ .
5. Mílites mánserant ut urbem (servo) _servarent_ .
6. Eis lignum dábimus ut domum (struo) _struant_ .
7. Magister fábulam narrabat ut discípulos (delecto) _delectaret_ .
8. Cives pugnáverint ut civitatem (servo) _servent_ .
9. Imperator oraverat ut mílites (laudo) _laudaret_ .
10. Discípuli tacent ut magistram (áudio) _áudiant_ .

Translate, giving two versions for the subordinate clause.

1. Viam tenébimus ut hóstium exércitum impediamus. _____
   We will hold the road so that we may hinder the enemy's army. _____
   _____ (in order) to hinder the enemy's army.

2. Milites silvam explorant ut cibum invéniant. _____
   The soldiers are exploring the forest so that they may find food. _____
   _____ (in order) to find food.

3. Aurum in templum pósitum erit ut servetur. _____
   The gold will have been placed in the temple so that it may be guarded. _____
   _____ (in order) to guard it.

4. Imperator mílites ad portum mittet ut eum múniant. _____
   The general will send soldiers to the port so that they may fortify it. _____
   _____ (in order) to fortify it.

5. Claudamus portas ut urbem servemus. _____
   Let us close the gates so that we may guard the city. _____
   _____ (in order) to guard the city.

VII. Translation (cont.)

Translate, giving one version for the subordinate clause.

1. Urbis júvenes laborant ut aedifícium ante híemem struant._____
   The young men of the city are working to build the building before winter.

2. Pacem cúpimus ut cives sint felices. _____
   We want peace so that the citizens may be happy.

3. Flores paremus ut dómini uxorem salutemus. _____
   Let us prepare flowers to greet the master's wife.

4. Mílites saxa et lápides cogunt ut viam fáciant. _____
   Soldiers are collecting rocks and stones to make a road.

5. Pastores clamant ut greges agant._____
   The shepherds are shouting in order to drive the flocks.

6. Soldiers are attacking the fort in order to free the hostages._____
   Mílites castellum oppugnant ut óbsides líberent.

7. Who will move the stones so that we may close the gate? _____
   Quis lápides movebit ut portam claudamus?

8. The wife is carrying fodder to give it to the dogs. _____
   Uxor pábulum portat ut id cánibus det.

9. Senatorum uxores pecúniam cívibus dant ut theatrum struant. _____
   The senators' wives are giving the citizens money so that they may build a theater.

10. A young woman is putting flowers onto the altar to praise the god. _____
    Júvenis flores in aram ponit ut deum laudet.

VIII. Reading

Translate the reading in the space below.

HÍEMIS FLOS

Júvenis in antri *ore* stabat. Áerem frígidum sentiebat. *Nivem* albam in terrā *extra* antrum spectabat. Cómites omnes erant apud *famílias* suas. Vaccae omnes in grégibus errabant in agris villae finítimis. Haec júvenis erat sola sed felix. Híemis *solitudo* eam delectabat. Lápidem vidit, tum sústulit. Lapis erat frígidus in manu, sed pulcher et *colorum* plenus. "Florem inveni," putavit, "híemis florem."

FLOWER OF WINTER

The young girl was standing in the mouth of the cave. She was feeling the cold air. She was looking at the white snow on the ground outside of the cave. All (her) companions were with their families. All the cows were wandering in herds in the fields near the farmhouse. This young girl was alone, but happy. The solitude of winter was pleasing her. She saw a stone, then picked it up. The stone was cold in her hand, but beautiful and full of colors. "I have found a flower," she thought, "a flower of winter."

os oris *n.* mouth
nix nivis *f.* snow
extra *prep. w/acc.* outside of

família -ae *f.* family
solitudo solitúdinis *f.* solitude
color -oris *m.* color

Lesson Twenty-four

I. Word Study and Grammar

1. The present subjunctive is formed by ___changing___ or ___adding___ a vowel before the personal ending:

   1st conj. ___substitute **e** for **a**___

   2nd conj. ___add **a**___

   3rd conj. ___substitute **a** for **i, o, u**___

   3rd conj. **io** ___add a___

   4th conj. ___add a___

2. The imperfect subjunctive is built on the ___infinitive___ .

3. The subjunctive is used primarily in ___subordinate___ clauses, but it also has some uses in ___independent___ clauses.

4. A deliberative question is asked in ___doubt___ or ___indignation___ and is expressed in English by the helping verb ___should___ .

5. A deliberative question uses the ___present___ subjunctive for present time and the ___imperfect___ subjunctive for past time.

6. The hortatory subjunctive expresses an ___exhortation___ , ___indirect command___ , or ___strong wish___ .

7. Hortatory expressions may be translated into English using the verbal helpers ___let___ or ___may___ .

8. In English the ___infinitive___ is a way to show purpose. In Latin the ___ut clause___ is a way to show purpose.

9. In a sentence with a purpose clause, the main verb is in the ___indicative___ , and the purpose clause is in the ___subjunctive___ .

10. The verbs in a sentence with a purpose clause must ___correspond___ in tense.

11. What two tenses have identical forms except for the 1st person singular? ___indicative future perfect active and subjunctive perfect active___

Lesson Twenty-four

II. Vocabulary

Say aloud and write with dictionary form, meaning, and derivative.

Latin (dictionary form)	Meaning	Derivative
aequor aéquoris n.	smooth surface, sea	
certamen certáminis n.	struggle, contest	
crus cruris n.	leg	
latus láteris n.	side, flank	lateral
litus lítoris n.	shore, coast	littoral
munus múneris n.	office, duty	immunity
os oris n.	mouth	oral
os ossis n.	bone	ossify
rus ruris n.	countryside	rural
scelus scéleris n.	crime, evil deed	

Saying

Say aloud and write 3X.

Latin	Hábeas corpus.
Latin	Hábeas corpus.
Latin	Hábeas corpus.
English	You may have the body.

Derivatives

1. The Greeks colonized ___littoral___ regions of Sicily.

2. ___Immunity___ from prosecution usually requires full disclosure.

3. When a baby is born, its bones still need to ___ossify___ .

4. Ancient ships had almost no capability for controlled ___lateral___ movement.

5. Pre-Roman Gaul was a ___rural___ society, not an urban society.

III. Conjugations
Model Verbs
Present Subjunctive Active

1st	2nd	3rd	3rd io	4th
amem	móneam	regam	cápiam	áudiam
ames	móneas	regas	cápias	áudias
amet	móneat	regat	cápiat	áudiat
amemus	moneamus	regamus	capiamus	audiamus
ametis	moneatis	regatis	capiatis	audiatis
ament	móneant	regant	cápiant	áudiant

Present Subjunctive Passive

1st	2nd	3rd	3rd io	4th
amer	mónear	regar	cápiar	áudiar
ameris	monearis	regaris	capiaris	audiaris
ametur	moneatur	regatur	capiatur	audiatur
amemur	moneamur	regamur	capiamur	audiamur
amémini	moneámini	regámini	capiámini	audiámini
amentur	moneantur	regantur	capiantur	áudiantur

Imperfect Subjunctive Active

1st	2nd	3rd	3rd io	4th
amarem	monerem	régerem	cáperem	audirem
amares	moneres	régeres	cáperes	audires
amaret	moneret	régeret	cáperet	audiret
amaremus	moneremus	regeremus	caperemus	audiremus
amaretis	moneretis	regeretis	caperetis	audiretis
amarent	monerent	régerent	cáperent	audirent

Imperfect Subjunctive Passive

1st	2nd	3rd	3rd io	4th
amarer	monerer	régerer	cáperer	audirer
amareris	monereris	regereris	capereris	audireris
amaretur	moneretur	regeretur	caperetur	audiretur
amaremur	moneremur	regeremur	caperemur	audiremur
amarémini	monerémini	regerémini	caperémini	audirémini
amarentur	monerentur	regerentur	caperentur	audirentur

III. Conjugations (cont.)

Perfect Subjunctive Active

1st	2nd	3rd	3rd io	4th
amáverim	monúerim	réxerim	céperim	audíverim
amáveris	monúeris	réxeris	céperis	audíveris
amáverit	monúerit	réxerit	céperit	audíverit
amavérimus	monuérimus	rexérimus	cepérimus	audivérimus
amavéritis	monuéritis	rexéritis	cepéritis	audivéritis
amáverint	monúerint	réxerint	céperint	audíverint

Perfect Subjunctive Passive

1st	2nd	3rd	3rd io	4th
amatus -a -um sim	mónitus -a -um sim	rectus -a -um sim	captus -a -um sim	auditus -a -um sim
sis	sis	sis	sis	sis
sit	sit	sit	sit	sit
amati -ae -a simus	móniti -ae -a simus	recti -ae -a simus	capti -ae -a simus	auditi -ae -a simus
sitis	sitis	sitis	sitis	sitis
sint	sint	sint	sint	sint

Perfect Subjunctive Active Meanings
(Use **amo**.)

Person	Singular	Plural
1st	I may have loved	we may have loved
2nd	you may have loved	you all may have loved
3rd	he, she, it may have loved	they may have loved

Perfect Subjunctive Passive Meanings
(Use **amo**.)

Person	Singular	Plural
1st	I may have been loved	we may have been loved
2nd	you may have been loved	you all may have been loved
3rd	he, she, it may have been loved	they may have been loved

Lesson Twenty-four   Worksheet 5

Sum - Present Subjunctive

Person	Singular		Plural	
	Latin	Meaning	Latin	Meaning
1st	sim	I may be	simus	we may be
2nd	sis	you may be	sitis	you all may be
3rd	sit	hsi may be	sint	they may be

Sum - Imperfect Subjunctive

Person	Singular		Plural	
	Latin	Meaning	Latin	Meaning
1st	essem	I might be	essemus	we might be
2nd	esses	you might be	essetis	you all might be
3rd	esset	hsi might be	essent	they might be

IV. Conjugation

Make copies of Drill/Test Form A in the Appendix. Conjugate **jácio** in the 6 active and passive tenses of the indicative, the present and imperfect subjunctive active and passive, and the perfect subjunctive active. Practice until perfect.

Drill/Test Form A

Principal Parts: jácio jácere jeci jactus
Present System Stem: jaci-

Present			
Indicative Active		Indicative Passive	
jácio	jácimus	jácior	jácimur
jacis	jácitis	jáceris	jacímini
jacit	jáciunt	jácitur	jaciuntur
Imperfect			
jaciebam	jaciebamus	jaciebar	jaciebamur
jaciebas	jaciebatis	jaciebaris	jaciebámini
jaciebat	jaciebant	jaciebatur	jaciebantur
Future			
jáciam	jaciemus	jáciar	jaciemur
jácies	jacietis	jacieris	jaciémini
jáciet	jácient	jacietur	jacientur

Perfect System Stem: jec-

Perfect			
Indicative Active		Indicative Passive	
jeci	jécimus	jectus sum	jecti sumus
jecisti	jecistis	(a, um) es	(ae, a) estis
jecit	jecerunt	est	sunt
Pluperfect			
jéceram	jeceramus	eram	eramus
jéceras	jeceratis	eras	eratis
jécerat	jécerant	erat	erant
Future Perfect			
jécero	jecérimus	ero	érimus
jéceris	jecéritis	eris	éritis
jécerit	jécerint	erit	erunt

Present			
Subjunctive Active		Subjunctive Passive	
jáciam	jaciamus	jáciar	jaciamur
jácias	jaciatis	jaciaris	jaciámini
jáciat	jáciant	jaciatur	jaciantur
Imperfect			
jácerem	jaceremus	jácerer	jaceremur
jáceres	jaceretis	jacereris	jacerémini
jáceret	jácerent	jaceretur	jacerentur
Perfect			
jécerim	jecérimus		
jéceris	jecéritis		
jécerit	jécerint		
Pluperfect			

V. Form Drills

Convert the given indicative form to the corresponding subjunctive form (1-5) or translate (6-10).
[mh = may have]

Drill A
1st Conjugation

1. dubitavit _dubitáverit_
2. putavi _putáverim_
3. sperávimus _speravérimus_
4. juverunt _júverint_
5. servavistis _servavéritis_

6. you mh asked _rogáveris_
7. she mh judged _judicáverit_
8. I mh praised _laudáverim_
9. they mh blamed _culpáverint_
10. she mh given _déderit_

Drill B
2nd Conjugation

1. arsit _árserit_
2. hábui _habúerim_
3. móvimus _movérimus_
4. térruit _terrúerit_
5. sederunt _séderint_

6. we mh seen _vidérimus_
7. he mh taught _docúerit_
8. I mh ordered _jússerim_
9. they mh remained _mánserint_
10. you mh warned _monúeris_

Drill C
3rd Conjugation

1. coegistis _coegéritis_
2. clausit _cláuserit_
3. vicerunt _vícerint_
4. fixisti _fíxeris_
5. posúimus _posuérimus_

6. he mh sent _míserit_
7. you mh waged _gésseris_
8. they mh put _posúerint_
9. I mh written _scrípserim_
10. we mh said _dixérimus_

V. Form Drills (cont.)

Convert the given indicative form to the corresponding subjunctive form (1-5) or translate (6-10).
[mh = may have]

Drill D
4th, 3rd **io** Conjugation

1. audívimus _audivérimus_
2. scivit _scíverit_
3. ceperunt _céperint_
4. fecisti _féceris_
5. fugi _fúgerim_

6. we mh found _invenérimus_
7. they mh come _vénerint_
8. he mh known _scíverit_
9. you mh thrown _jéceris_
10. I mh heard _audíverim_

Drill E
Mixed

1. junxit _júnxerit_
2. sustulerunt _sustúlerint_
3. dedi _déderim_
4. vídimus _vidérimus_
5. finivistis _finivéritis_

6. he mh plowed _aráverit_
7. they mh said _díxerint_
8. we mh moved _movérimus_
9. she mh praised _laudáverit_
10. you mh desired _cupíveris_

Drill F
Perfect Passive

1. jussi estis _jussi sitis_
2. recta est _recta sit_
3. sensi sunt _sensi sint_
4. jactus sum _jactus sim_
5. tenti sumus _tenti simus_

6. I mh been loved _amatus sim_
7. you mh been seen _visus sis_
8. it mh been finished _finitum sit_
9. it mh been dragged _tractum sit_
10. they mh been thrown _jacta sint_

VI. Translation

1. Áquilae volant ut perículum fugiant._____
   The eagles are flying in order to flee danger._____

2. Cives aurum celaverunt ut servaretur._____
   The citizens hid the gold in order that it might be kept [safe]._____

3. Dux in colle stabat ut videretur. _____
   The leader was standing on the hill in order to be seen._____

4. In hac fossā maneamus ut celemus. _____
   Let us remain in this ditch in order to hide._____

5. Qúomodo moneremur? _____ How were we to be warned?

6. Epístulam scribam ut magistram móneam._____
   I will write a letter in order to warn the teacher._____

7. Portas claudimus ut urbem muniamus._____
   We are closing the gates in order to protect the city._____

8. Agrum occupavi ut aedifícium strúerem._____
   I seized a field in order to build a building._____

9. Quis viam servet? _____ Who is to (should) guard the road?

10. Cívitas multos mílites coegit ut exércitum fáceret._____
    The state collected many soldiers in order to make an army.___

11. Imperator legionem misit ut óppidum hóstium oppugnarent. ___
    The general sent a legion in order to attack the enemy's town.__

12. Ad litus alienum navigávimus ut urbem strueremus._____
    We sailed to a foreign shore in order to build a city._____

VI. Translation (cont.)

1. Iter longum fecerunt ut in campo pugnarent._____
   They made a long journey in order to fight on a plain._____

2. Ad Ítaliae litus vēnimus ut urbem novam faceremus._____
   We came to the shore of Italy to make a new city._____

3. Óbsidum crura vínculis juncta erant ut fuga impediretur. _____
   The legs of the hostages had been joined by chains so that escape was hindered.___

4. Dóminus fenestram in domūs látere fecit ut montes videret.____
   The lord made a window in the side of the house to see the mountains.___

5. Munus sústuli ut civitatem juvarem. _____
   I have lifted up the duty in order to help the state._____

6. He did many crimes in order to have money._____
   Multa scélera fecit ut pecúniam haberet._____

7. We gave up the countryside in order to hold the city._____
   Rus céssimus ut urbem teneremus._____

8. They sent the senator into exile in order to prevent a struggle.___
   Senatorem in exílium miserunt ut certamen prohiberent._____

9. Two new ships had been built to transport grain. _____
   Naves novae duae structae erant ut frumentum véherent._____

10. He wrote a letter to report the fate of the army. _____
    Epístulam scripsit ut exércitūs fatum nuntiaret._____

VII. Reading

Translate the reading in the space below.

CERTAMEN

Glóriae famaéque cúpidus Lúcius certamen pro múnere gerit. *Ruri* et in urbe contra scelus *orat*. Nóbiles et plebes, agrícolas et dóminos laudat. Pátria est semper in Lúcii ore. Pecúniam autem non habet. Lúcii uxor pecúniam omnem tenet. Uxor ei pecúniam líberē laetēque dat ut eum juvet. Lúcius *vincit*. Munus et glóriam et famam habet Lúcius. Sed *potestatem* habet uxor.

THE CONTEST

Desirous of glory and fame, Lucius wages a contest for office. In the country and in the city,

he speaks against crime. He praises the nobles and the plebeians, the farmers and the lords.

The fatherland is always in Lucius' mouth. However, he does not have any money. Lucius'

wife has all the money. His wife freely and happily gives him money to help him. Lucius wins.

Lucius has the office and the glory and the fame. But his wife has the power.

_____

_____

_____

_____

_____

_____

_____

_____

glória -ae *f.* glory
fama -ae *f.* fame
Glóriae famaéque cúpidus - modifies **Lúcius**
Lúcius -i *m.* a Roman name
ruri in the country (**Ruri** is the *locative* form of **rus ruris** *n.* You will learn about the locative in *Fourth Form*.)
oro here means *to speak, give a speech*
vinco here means *to win*
potestas potestatis *f.* power

I. Word Study and Grammar

1. The imperfect subjunctive active is built on the _____infinitive_____ .

2. The perfect subjunctive active is the same as _____future perfect active_____ tense except for the 1st person singular.

3. The perfect and pluperfect subjunctives are built on the _____perfect_____ stem by adding _____-eri-_____ and _____-isse-_____ , respectively.

4. The subjunctive is used primarily in _____subordinate_____ clauses, but it also has some uses in _____independent_____ clauses.

5. A deliberative question is asked in _____doubt_____ or _____indignation_____ and is expressed in English by the helping verb _____should_____ .

6. A deliberative question uses the _____present_____ subjunctive for present time and the _____imperfect_____ subjunctive for past time.

7. The hortatory subjunctive expresses an _____exhortation_____ , _____indirect command_____ , or _____strong wish_____ .

8. Hortatory expressions may be translated into English using the verbal helpers _____let_____ or _____may_____ .

9. In English the _____infinitive_____ is a way to show purpose. In Latin the _____ut clause_____ is a way to show purpose.

10. In a sentence with a purpose clause, the main verb is in the _____indicative_____ and the purpose clause is in the _____subjunctive_____ .

11. The verbs in a sentence with a purpose clause must _____correspond_____ in tense.

12. A negative clause of purpose replaces **ut** with _____ne_____ .

13. The two indications that a noun is an **i-stem** are:
    1) the same number of syllables in the nominative and genitive singular: **collis, collis**
    2) a stem ending in two consonants: **pons, pontis**

14. Which vocabulary word is an exception? _____nix, nivis_____

II. Vocabulary

Say aloud and write with dictionary form, meaning, and derivative.

Latin (dictionary form)	Meaning	Derivative
avis avis f.	bird	aviation
fames famis f.	hunger, starvation	famine
fons fontis m.	fountain, spring, source	font
ignis ignis m.	fire	ignite
imber imbris m.	rain	
nix nivis f.	snow	Nevada
nox noctis f.	night	nocturnal
nubes nubis f.	cloud	
ovis ovis f.	sheep	ovine
vestis vestis f.	clothes	vest

Saying

Say aloud and write 3X.

Latin	Dum vívimus, vivamus.
Latin	Dum vívimus, vivamus.
Latin	Dum vívimus, vivamus.
English	While we live, let us live.

Derivatives

1. Thanks to artificial lighting, humans have become a ___nocturnal___ species.

2. Mad cow disease is also an ___ovine___ disorder.

3. Ancient agriculture was never able to eliminate ___famine___.

4. To the ancient general, the *Iliad* was a major ___font___ of military tactics.

5. Repression eventually ___ignites___ revolution.

III. Conjugations

Model Verbs

Present Subjunctive Active

1st	2nd	3rd	3rd io	4th
amem	móneam	regam	cápiam	áudiam
ames	móneas	regas	cápias	áudias
amet	móneat	regat	cápiat	áudiat
amemus	moneamus	regamus	capiamus	audiamus
ametis	moneatis	regatis	capiatis	audiatis
ament	móneant	regant	cápiant	áudiant

Present Subjunctive Passive

1st	2nd	3rd	3rd io	4th
amer	mónear	regar	cápiar	áudiar
ameris	monearis	regaris	capiaris	audiaris
ametur	moneatur	regatur	capiatur	audiatur
amemur	moneamur	regamur	capiamur	audiamur
amémini	moneámini	regámini	capiámini	audiámini
amentur	moneantur	regantur	capiantur	audiantur

Imperfect Subjunctive Active

1st	2nd	3rd	3rd io	4th
amarem	monerem	régerem	cáperem	audirem
amares	moneres	régeres	cáperes	audires
amaret	moneret	régeret	cáperet	audiret
amaremus	moneremus	regeremus	caperemus	audiremus
amaretis	moneretis	regeretis	caperetis	audiretis
amarent	monerent	régerent	cáperent	audirent

Imperfect Subjunctive Passive

1st	2nd	3rd	3rd io	4th
amarer	monerer	régerer	cáperer	audirer
amareris	monereris	regereris	capereris	audireris
amaretur	moneretur	regeretur	caperetur	audiretur
amaremur	moneremur	regeremur	caperemur	audiremur
amarémini	monerémini	regerémini	caperémini	audirémini
amarentur	monerentur	regerentur	caperentur	audirentur

III. Conjugations (cont.)

Perfect Subjunctive Active

1st	2nd	3rd	3rd io	4th
amáverim	monúerim	réxerim	céperim	audíverim
amáveris	monúeris	réxeris	céperis	audíveris
amáverit	monúerit	réxerit	céperit	audíverit
amavérimus	monuérimus	rexérimus	cepérimus	audivérimus
amavéritis	monuéritis	rexéritis	cepéritis	audivéritis
amáverint	monúerint	réxerint	céperint	audíverint

Perfect Subjunctive Passive

1st	2nd	3rd	3rd io	4th
amatus -a -um sim	mónitus -a -um sim	rectus -a -um sim	captus -a -um sim	auditus -a -um sim
sis	sis	sis	sis	sis
sit	sit	sit	sit	sit
amati -ae -a simus	móniti -ae -a simus	recti -ae -a simus	capti -ae -a simus	auditi -ae -a simus
sitis	sitis	sitis	sitis	sitis
sint	sint	sint	sint	sint

Pluperfect Subjunctive Active

1st	2nd	3rd	3rd io	4th
amavissem	monuissem	rexissem	cepissem	audivissem
amavisses	monuisses	rexisses	cepisses	audivisses
amavisset	monuisset	rexisset	cepisset	audivisset
amavissemus	monuissemus	rexissemus	cepissemus	audivissemus
amavissetis	monuissetis	rexissetis	cepissetis	audivissetis
amavissent	monuissent	rexissent	cepissent	audivissent

Pluperfect Subjunctive Passive

1st		2nd		3rd		3rd io		4th	
amatus	essem	mónitus	essem	rectus	essem	captus	essem	auditus	essem
-a -um	esses	-a -um	esses	-a -um	esses	-a -um	esses	-a -um	esses
	esset		esset		esset		esset		esset
amati	essemus	móniti	essemus	recti	essemus	capti	essemus	auditi	essemus
-ae -a	essetis	-ae -a	essetis	-ae -a	essetis	-ae -a	essetis	-ae -a	essetis
	essent		essent		essent		essent		essent

Pluperfect Subjunctive Active Meanings
(Use **amo**.)

Person	Singular	Plural
1st	I might have loved	we might have loved
2nd	you might have loved	you all might have loved
3rd	he, she, it might have loved	they might have loved

Pluperfect Subjunctive Passive Meanings
(Use **amo**.)

Person	Singular	Plural
1st	I might have been loved	we might have been loved
2nd	you might have been loved	you all might have been loved
3rd	he, she, it might have been loved	they might have been loved

IV. Conjugation

Make copies of Drill/Test Form A in the Appendix. Conjugate **aro** in the 6 active and passive tenses of the indicative and the 4 active and passive tenses of the subjunctive. Practice until perfect.

Drill/Test Form A

Principal Parts: aro arare aravi aratus
Present System Stem: ara-

Present			
Indicative Active		Indicative Passive	
aro	aramus	aror	aramur
aras	aratis	araris	arámini
arat	arant	aratur	arantur
Imperfect			
arabam	arabamus	arabar	arabamur
arabas	arabatis	arabaris	arabámini
arabat	arabant	arabatur	arabantur
Future			
arabo	arábimus	arabor	arábimur
arabis	arábitis	aráberis	arabímini
arabit	arabunt	arábitur	arabuntur

Perfect System Stem: arav-

Perfect			
Indicative Active		Indicative Passive	
aravi	arávimus	aratus sum	arati sumus
aravisti	aravistis	(a, um) es	(ae, a) estis
aravit	araverunt	est	sunt
Pluperfect			
aráveram	araveramus	eram	eramus
aráveras	araveratis	eras	eratis
aráverat	áraverant	erat	erant
Future Perfect			
arávero	aravérimus	ero	érimus
aráveris	avéritis	eris	éritis
aráverit	aráverint	erit	erunt

Present			
Subjunctive Active		Subjunctive Passive	
arem	aremus	arer	aremur
ares	aretis	areris	arémini
aret	arent	aretur	arentur
Imperfect			
ararem	araremus	ararer	araremur
arares	araretis	arareris	ararémini
araret	ararent	araretur	ararentur
Perfect			
aráverim	aravérimus	aratus sim	arati simus
aráveris	aravéritis	(a, um) sis	(ae, a) sitis
aráverit	aráverint	sit	sint
Pluperfect			
aravissem	aravissemus	essem	essemus
aravisses	aravissetis	esses	essetis
aravisset	aravissent	esset	essent

V. Form Drills

Convert the given indicative form to the corresponding subjunctive form (1-5) or translate (6-10).
[mth = might have]

Drill A
1st Conjugation

1. rogáverat ___rogavisset___   6. we mth judged ___judicavissemus___
2. creáverant ___creavissent___   7. they mth worked ___laboravissent___
3. nuntiáveram ___nuntiavissem___   8. you mth hoped ___speravisses___
4. narraveramus ___narravissemus___   9. it mth changed ___mutavisset___
5. déderas ___dedisses___   10. he mth called ___vocavisset___

Drill B
2nd Conjugation

1. terrúeras ___terruisses___   6. he mth owed ___debuisset___
2. moveratis ___movissetis___   7. you mth remained ___mansisses___
3. prohibúerant ___prohibuissent___   8. they mth held ___tenuissent___
4. tenúerat ___tenuisset___   9. I mth taught ___docuissem___
5. habueramus ___habuissemus___   10. we mth frightened ___terruissemus___

Drill C
3rd Conjugation

1. véxerant ___vexissent___   6. she mth ruled ___rexisset___
2. égerat ___egisset___   7. they mth written ___scripsissent___
3. sustúleram ___sustulissem___   8. we mth placed ___posuissemus___
4. dixeramus ___dixissemus___   9. she mth closed ___clausisset___
5. strúxeras ___struxisses___   10. you mth joined ___junxisses___

V. Form Drills (cont.)

Convert the given indicative form to the corresponding subjunctive form (1-5) or translate (6-10).
[mth = might have] [mthb = might have been]

Drill D

4th, 3rd **io** Conjugation

1. inveneras _invenisses_
2. audíveram _audivissem_
3. finíverant _finivissent_
4. céperat _cepisset_
5. jeceramus _jecissemus_

6. I mth captured _cepissem_
7. he mth thrown _jecisset_
8. they mth known _scivissent_
9. we mth heard _audivissemus_
10. you mth finished _finivisses_

Drill E

Mixed

1. portáverat _portavisset_
2. coegeramus _coegissemus_
3. tráxeras _traxisses_
4. stéterant _stetissent_
5. feceratis _fecissetis_

6. they mth seen _vidissent_
7. we mth built _struxissemus_
8. she mth given _dedisset_
9. I mth slept _dormivissem_
10. you mth desired _cupivisses_

Drill F

Pluperfect Passive

Convert the given passive form to the corresponding active form (1-5) or translate (6-10).

1. sessus esset _sedisset_
2. exspectati essemus _exspectavissemus_
3. missa esset _misisset_
4. impediti essetis _impedivissetis_
5. pósitus esses _posuisses_

6. we mthb blamed _culpati essemus_
7. it mthb made _factum esset_
8. they mthb lifted up _sublata essent_
9. you mthb heard _auditus esses_
10. I mthb ordered _jussus essem_

VI. Declensions

Case	Singular	Plural
nom.	**avis**	aves
gen.	avis	ávium
dat.	avi	ávibus
acc.	avem	aves
abl.	ave	ávibus

	Singular	Plural
nom.	**nox**	noctes
	noctis	nóctium
	nocti	nóctibus
	noctem	noctes
	nocte	nóctibus

Case	Singular	Plural
nom.	**ignis**	ignes
gen.	ignis	ígnium
dat.	igni	ígnibus
acc.	ignem	ignes
abl.	igne (igni)	ígnibus

	Singular	Plural
nom.	**nubes**	nubes
	nubis	núbium
	nubi	núbibus
	nubem	nubes
	nube	núbibus

Case	Singular	Plural
nom.	**lapis**	lápides
gen.	lápidis	lápidum
dat.	lápidi	lapídibus
acc.	lápidem	lápides
abl.	lápide	lapídibus

	Singular	Plural
nom.	**flos**	flores
	floris	florum
	flori	flóribus
	florem	flores
	flore	flóribus

VII. Translation

1. In antro manserunt ne ab ávibus oppugnarentur. _____
   They remained in the cave lest they be attacked by birds.

2. Pastor clamat ut oves ex agro agat. _____
   The shepherd is shouting in order to drive the sheep from the field.

3. Sine imbre fontem debemus invenire ut aquam habeamus. _____
   Without rain, we ought to find a spring in order to have water.

4. Ignis de perículo líberos moneamus ne vulnerentur. _____
   Let us warn the children about the danger of fire lest they be injured.

5. Laboremus celériter ne nive impediamur. _____
   Let's work quickly lest we be obstructed by the snow.

6. The king sent grain so that the plebeians would not be forced from the city by hunger. _____
   Rex frumentum misit ne plebes ex urbe fame cogerentur.

7. She closed the door in order not to look at the crime. _____
   Jánuam clausit ne scelus spectaret.

8. We ought to find good clothes in order not to feel the wind. _____
   Bonas vestes invenire debemus ne ventum sentiamus.

9. The bird flew into a cloud in order not to be attacked. _____
   Avis in nubem volavit ne oppugaretur.

10. The soldiers built a rampart lest they be forced to yield the town. _____
    Mílites vallum struxerunt ne óppidum cédere cogerentur.

VIII. Reading

Translate the reading in the space below.

IGNIS FONS

Ignis fontem meum vobis demonstrem. In eum aquam pono, aqua est súbito cálida. Vestem lavo, celériter autem ne árdeat. *Véniat* imber, nubes facit. *Véniat* ovis aut avis, cenam facit. *Noctu* lucem dat. *Quam* útilis ignis fons meus!

FOUNTAIN OF FIRE

Let me show you all my fountain of fire. I put water onto it, the water is hot suddenly (right

away). I wash my (suit of) clothes, quickly, however, so it doesn't burn. If rain comes, it

makes clouds. If a sheep or a bird comes, it makes dinner. At night, it gives light. How

useful is my fountain of fire!

véniat - here, the subjunctive can be translated *if*
noctu at night
quam! how!

I. Word Study and Grammar

1. The imperfect subjunctive active is built on the _____ infinitive _____ .

2. The perfect subjunctive active is the same as _____ future perfect active _____ tense except for the 1st person singular.

3. The perfect and pluperfect subjunctives are built on the _____ perfect _____ stem by adding _____ -eri- _____ and _____ -isse- _____ , respectively.

4. The subjunctive is used primarily in _____ subordinate _____ clauses, but it also has some uses in _____ independent _____ clauses.

5. A deliberative question is asked in _____ doubt _____ or _____ indignation _____ and is expressed in English by the helping verb _____ should _____ .

6. A deliberative question uses the _____ present _____ subjunctive for present time and the _____ imperfect _____ subjunctive for past time.

7. The hortatory subjunctive expresses an _____ exhortation _____ _____ indirect command _____ , or _____ strong wish _____ .

8. Hortatory expressions may be translated into English using the verbal helpers _____ let _____ or _____ may _____ .

9. In English the _____ infinitive _____ is a way to show purpose. In Latin the _____ ut clause _____ is a way to show purpose.

10. In a sentence with a purpose clause, the main verb is in the _____ indicative _____ , and the purpose clause is in the _____ subjunctive _____ .

11. The verbs in a sentence with a purpose clause must _____ correspond _____ in tense.

12. The two indications that a noun is an **i-stem** are:
    1) _the same number of syllables in the nominative and genitive singular: **collis, collis**_
    2) _a stem ending in two consonants: **pons, pontis**_

13. Give the two neuter and two feminine nouns of the 4th declension. **Domus** and _**manus** are feminine, and **cornu** and **genu** are neuter._

II. Vocabulary
Say aloud and write with dictionary form, meaning, and derivative.

Latin (dictionary form)	Meaning	Derivative
occasus -ūs m.	falling, misfortune	occasion, case
usus -ūs m.	use, experience	usual
éxitus -ūs m.	end, outcome, exit	exit
currus -ūs m.	chariot, cart, wagon	car
vultus -ūs m.	countenance, expression	
cursus -ūs m.	course, running	
equitatus -ūs m.	cavalry	
arcus -ūs m.	bow	arc
ímpetus -ūs m.	attack	impetuous
passus -ūs m.	step, pace	pace

Saying
Say aloud and write 3X.

Latin	Cedant arma togae.
Latin	Cedant arma togae.
Latin	Cedant arma togae.
English	Let arms yield to the toga.

Derivatives

1. In _____ case _____ of fire, find the nearest _____ exit _____ .

2. A Roman mile is a thousand _____ paces _____ .

3. A Roman _____ arch _____ has the shape of an _____ arc _____ .

4. Never be _____ impetuous _____ behind the wheel of a _____ car _____ .

III. Conjugations

Sum - Present Subjunctive

Person	Singular		Plural	
	Latin	Meaning	Latin	Meaning
1st	sim	I may be	simus	we may be
2nd	sis	you may be	sitis	you all may be
3rd	sit	hsi may be	sint	they may be

Sum - Imperfect Subjunctive

Person	Singular		Plural	
	Latin	Meaning	Latin	Meaning
1st	essem	I might be	essemus	we might be
2nd	esses	you might be	essetis	you all might be
3rd	esset	hsi might be	essent	they might be

Sum - Perfect Subjunctive

Person	Singular		Plural	
	Latin	Meaning	Latin	Meaning
1st	fúerim	I may have been	fuérimus	we mh been
2nd	fúeris	you mh been	fuéritis	you all mh been
3rd	fúerit	hsi mh been	fúerint	they mh been

Sum - Pluperfect Subjunctive

Person	Singular		Plural	
	Latin	Meaning	Latin	Meaning
1st	fuissem	I might have been	fuissemus	we mth been
2nd	fuisses	you mth been	fuissetis	you all mth been
3rd	fuisset	hsi mth been	fuissent	they mth been

III. Conjugations (cont.)
Model Verbs
Present Subjunctive Active

1st	2nd	3rd	3rd io	4th
amem	móneam	regam	cápiam	áudiam
ames	móneas	regas	cápias	áudias
amet	móneat	regat	cápiat	áudiat
amemus	moneamus	regamus	capiamus	audiamus
ametis	moneatis	regatis	capiatis	audiatis
ament	móneant	regant	cápiant	áudiant

Present Subjunctive Passive

1st	2nd	3rd	3rd io	4th
amer	mónear	regar	cápiar	áudiar
ameris	monearis	regaris	capiaris	audiaris
ametur	moneatur	regatur	capiatur	audiatur
amemur	moneamur	regamur	capiamur	audiamur
amémini	moneámini	regámini	capiámini	audiámini
amentur	moneantur	regantur	capiantur	audiantur

Imperfect Subjunctive Active

1st	2nd	3rd	3rd io	4th
amarem	monerem	régerem	cáperem	audirem
amares	moneres	régeres	cáperes	audires
amaret	moneret	régeret	cáperet	audiret
amaremus	moneremus	regeremus	caperemus	audiremus
amaretis	moneretis	regeretis	caperetis	audiretis
amarent	monerent	régerent	cáperent	audirent

III. Conjugations (cont.)

Imperfect Subjunctive Passive

1st	2nd	3rd	3rd **io**	4th
amarer	monerer	régerer	cáperer	audirer
amareris	monereris	regereris	capereris	audireris
amaretur	moneretur	regeretur	caperetur	audiretur
amaremur	moneremur	regeremur	caperemur	audiremur
amarémini	monerémini	regerémini	caperémini	audirémini
amarentur	monerentur	regerentur	caperentur	audirentur

Perfect Subjunctive Active

1st	2nd	3rd	3rd **io**	4th
amáverim	monúerim	réxerim	céperim	audíverim
amáveris	monúeris	réxeris	céperis	audíveris
amáverit	monúerit	réxerit	céperit	audíverit
amavérimus	monuérimus	rexérimus	cepérimus	audivérimus
amavéritis	monuéritis	rexéritis	cepéritis	audivéritis
amáverint	monúerint	réxerint	céperint	audíverint

Perfect Subjunctive Passive

1st	2nd	3rd	3rd **io**	4th
amatus -a -um sim	mónitus -a -um sim	rectus -a -um sim	captus -a -um sim	auditus -a -um sim
sis	sis	sis	sis	sis
sit	sit	sit	sit	sit
amati -ae -a simus	móniti -ae -a simus	recti -ae -a simus	capti -ae -a simus	auditi -ae -a simus
sitis	sitis	sitis	sitis	sitis
sint	sint	sint	sint	sint

Pluperfect Subjunctive Active

1st	2nd	3rd	3rd **io**	4th
amavissem	monuissem	rexissem	cepissem	audivissem
amavisses	monuisses	rexisses	cepisses	audivisses
amavisset	monuisset	rexisset	cepisset	audivisset
amavissemus	monuissemus	rexissemus	cepissemus	audivissemus
amavissetis	monuissetis	rexissetis	cepissetis	audivissetis
amavissent	monuissent	rexissent	cepissent	audivissent

Pluperfect Subjunctive Passive

1st	2nd	3rd	3rd **io**	4th
amatus essem	mónitus essem	rectus essem	captus essem	audítus essem
-a -um esses	-a -um esses	-a -um esses	-a -um esses	-a -um esses
esset	esset	esset	esset	esset
amati essemus	móniti essemus	recti essemus	capti essemus	auditi essemus
-ae -a essetis	-ae -a essetis	-ae -a essetis	-ae -a essetis	-ae -a essetis
essent	essent	essent	essent	essent

Meanings
(1st person only)

present active	I may love
present passive	I may be loved
imperfect active	I might love
imperfect passive	I might be love
perfect active	I may have loved
present passive	I may have been loved
pluperfect active	I might have loved
pluperfect passive	I might have been loved

IV. Conjugation

Make copies of Drill/Test Form A in the Appendix. Conjugate **móveo** in the 6 active and passive tenses of the indicative and the 4 active and passive tenses of the subjunctive. Practice until perfect.

Drill/Test Form A

Principal Parts: móveo movēre movi motus
Present System Stem: move-

Present			
Indicative Active		**Indicative Passive**	
móveo	movemus	móveor	movemur
moves	movetis	moveris	movémini
movet	movent	movetur	moventur
Imperfect			
movebam	movebamus	movebar	movebamur
movebas	movebatis	movebaris	movebámini
movebat	movebant	movebatur	movebantur
Future			
movebo	movébimus	movebor	movébimur
movebis	movébitis	movéberis	movebímini
movebit	movebunt	movébitur	movebuntur

Perfect System Stem: mov-

Perfect			
Indicative Active		**Indicative Passive**	
movi	móvimus	motus sum	moti sumus
movisti	movistis	(a, um) es	(ae, a) estis
movit	moverunt	est	sunt
Pluperfect			
móveram	moveramus	eram	eramus
móveras	moveratis	eras	eratis
móverat	móverant	erat	erant
Future Perfect			
móvero	movérimus	ero	érimus
móveris	movéritis	eris	éritis
móverit	móverint	erit	erunt

Present			
Subjunctive Active		**Subjunctive Passive**	
móveam	moveamus	móvear	moveamur
móveas	moveatis	movearis	moveámini
móveat	móveant	moveatur	moveantur
Imperfect			
moverem	moveremus	moverer	moveremur
moveres	moveretis	movereris	moverémini
moveret	moverent	moveretur	moverentur
Perfect			
móverim	movérimus	motus sim	moti simus
móveris	movéritis	(a, um) sis	(ae, a) sitis
móverit	móverint	sit	sint
Pluperfect			
movissem	movissemus	essem	essemus
movisses	movissetis	esses	essetis
movisset	movissent	esset	essent

V. Form Drills
Drill A

1. fuissemus ___we might have been___
2. fúerit ___hsi may have been___
3. fuéritis ___you all may have been___
4. fuissem ___I might have been___
5. fuissent ___they might have been___

6. fúeris ___you may have been___
7. fuérimus ___we may have been___
8. fuisset ___hsi might have been___
9. fúerim ___I may have been___
10. fuissetis ___you all might have been___

Drill B

1. you might have been ___fuisses___
2. I may have been ___fúerim___
3. they may have been ___fúerint___
4. we might have been ___fuissemus___
5. hsi may have been ___fúerit___

6. you all might have been ___fuissetis___
7. you may have been ___fúeris___
8. I might have been ___fuissem___
9. they might have been ___fuissent___
10. we may have been ___fuérimus___

VI. Declensions

Case	Singular	Plural
nom.	**arcus**	arcūs
gen.	arcūs	árcuum
dat.	árcui	árcibus
acc.	arcum	arcūs
abl.	arcu	árcibus

	Singular	Plural
nom.	**cornu**	córnua
gen.	cornūs	córnuum
dat.	cornu	córnibus
acc.	cornu	córnua
abl.	cornu	córnibus

Case	Singular	Plural
nom.	**passus**	passūs
gen.	passūs	pássuum
dat.	pássui	pássibus
acc.	passum	passūs
abl.	passu	pássibus

	Singular	Plural
nom.	**lectio**	lectiones
gen.	lectionis	lectionum
dat.	lectioni	lectiónibus
acc.	lectionem	lectiones
abl.	lectione	lectiónibus

Case	Singular	Plural
nom.	**comes**	cómites
gen.	cómitis	cómitum
dat.	cómiti	comítibus
acc.	cómitem	cómites
abl.	cómite	comítibus

	Singular	Plural
nom.	**impetus**	ímpetūs
gen.	ímpetūs	impétuum
dat.	impétui	impétibus
acc.	ímpetum	ímpetūs
abl.	ímpetu	impétibus

VII. Translation

1. Galli bellum gesserunt ut se liberarent. _____
   The Gauls waged war to free themselves.

2. Lava vultum et manūs ut cenam pares. _____
   Wash your face and hands in order to prepare the dinner.

3. Equitatus currūs habet ut tela vehant. _____
   The cavalry has carts to carry weapons.

4. Puer vultum mánibus celavit ne véritas inveniretur. The boy hid his face in his hands
   (literally, "with") so that the truth would not be discovered (lest the truth be discovered).

5. Ímpetus in equitatum erit difficilis. _____
   An attack against the cavalry will be difficult.

6. The fort was attacked by the cavalry with bows and arrows. _____
   Castellum ab equitatu árcibus sagittísque oppugnatum est.

7. I will send a big wagon to carry many stones. _____
   Magnum currum mittam ut multos lápides vehat.

8. The general wrote a letter to report the outcome of the battle to the senate. _____
   Imperator epístulam scripsit ut proélii éxitum senátui nuntiaret.
   _____

9. We are carrying a heavy load by cart and a small load by horse. _____
   Onus grave curru et onus parvum equo véhimus.

10. The cavalry made an attack against (on) the flank of the army in order to wound many soldiers.
    Equitatus ímpetum in exércitūs latus fecit ut multos mílites vulneraret.

11. We sailed toward the shore in order to be safe. _____
    Ad litus navigávimus ut essemus tuti.

12. They have leisure in order to be happy. _____
    Ótium habent ut sint laeti.

Lesson Twenty-six   Worksheet 10

VIII. Reading
Translate. Use additional sheets of paper if necessary.

TRÍDUUM

Dies primus. Álii fugerunt. In castello *vulneratus* mansi. *Neque* pábulum *neque* aquam hábeo. Auxílium numquam véniet. Hóstium *cohors* portam nunc *óbsidet*. Nox frígida venit. Timeo. Qúomodo dormire, sed débeo dormire. Sola spes mihi est quod *adhuc* vivo. Fatum meum cras mutetur!

Dies secundus. *Semper* vivo. Hóstium clamorem *extra* portam áudio. Famem *sitímque* séntio. Lente me móveo. *Umbram* súbito vídeo. Quid est? Vir? Álias tum vídeo. Cómites mei? Auxílium? Fuga? Aut *phantásmata*? Me spectant, sed nihil fáciunt. Tímeo.

Dies tértius. Per noctem, *intra* castellum víncula et voces audiebam. Me terrebant. Non dormiebam. *Primā luce*, una sola umbra manet. *Supra* me stat. Locum sub *muro* manu demonstrat. Ad locum lente et difficíliter ámbulo. Sub saxis, os *cunículi antiqui* invénio. Bonam Fortunam! Sit letum aut fuga, ero liber!

THREE DAYS

First day. The others have fled. I have stayed behind (remained), wounded, in the fort.

I have neither food nor water. Help will never come. A cohort of the enemy is now blocking

the gate. The cold night is coming. I am afraid. How to sleep? But I must (should) sleep. My

only hope is that so far I am alive. May my fate be changed tomorrow!

Second day. I am still alive. I hear the shout(ing) of the enemy outside the gate. I am

feeling hunger and thirst. Slowly I move myself. Suddenly I see a shade. What is it? A man?

Then I see others. My companions? Help? Escape? Or ghosts? They are looking at me, but

do nothing. I am afraid.

Third day. During (through) the night, I heard chains and voices inside the fort. They

frightened me. I did not sleep. At dawn, only one shade remains. It is standing above me.

With its hand, it points out a spot (place) at the base of the wall. Slowly and with difficulty,

I walk to the spot. Under some rocks, I discover the mouth of an old tunnel. Good fortune

(luck)! [**Bonam fortunam** is a special use of the acc.] Be it death or escape, I shall be free!

vulneratus -a -um wounded
Neque ... neque neither ... nor
cohors cohortis *f.* cohort, tenth part of a legion
obsideo -ēre -sedi -sessus to block
adhuc *so far, until now*
semper *here means* still

extra *prep. w/acc.* outside of
sitis sitis *f.* thirst (**i-stem**, accusative is **sitim**)
umbra *here means* shade (ghost)
phantasma -matis *n.* ghost
intra *prep. w/acc.* inside of
primā luce at dawn, at first light

supra *prep. w/acc.* above
murus -i *m.* wall
cunículus -i *m.* tunnel
antiquus -a -um ancient, old

Unit IV Review   Worksheet 1

I. Word Study and Grammar

1. Give the three moods of the Latin verb. _____indicative, imperative, subjunctive_____

2. The indicative mood describes activity that is _____actual_____.

3. The subjunctive mood describes activity that is _____potential_____.

4. The subjunctive is used mainly in _____subordinate clauses_____

5. Give two ways to use the subjunctive in an independent clause. _____
hortatory subjunctive, deliberative subjunctive_____

6. The present subjunctive is formed by _____changing_____ or _____adding_____ a vowel before the personal ending:
   1st conj. _____change **a** to **e**_____
   2nd conj. _____add **a**_____
   3rd conj. _____change **i, o, u** to **a**_____
   3rd conj. **io** _____add **a**_____
   4th conj. _____add **a**_____

7. The hortatory subjunctive is used to express _____an indirect command or strong wish_____ and is usually translated with _____let or may_____.

8. The deliberative subjunctive is used to express _____doubt or indignation_____.

9. A subjunctive clause is made negative with the conjunction _____ne_____.

10. One way to express purpose is with the conjunction _____ut_____ and the _____subjunctive mood_____.

11. Purpose in Latin is never expressed with _____the infinitive_____.

12. If the verb of the main clause is in the present, future, or future perfect tense, the verb of the subjunctive clause is in the _____present subjunctive_____.

13. If the verb of the main clause is in the imperfect, perfect, or pluperfect tense, the verb of the subjunctive clause is in the _____imperfect subjunctive_____.

Unit IV Review — Worksheet 2

II. Latin Sayings

1. Let the buyer beware. _____ Cáveat emptor.

2. Hallowed be thy name. _____ Sanctificetur nomen tuum.

3. May he rest in peace. _____ Requiescat in pace.

4. I believe in order that I may understand. _____ Credo ut intéllegam.

5. You may have the body. _____ Hábeas corpus.

6. While we live, let us live. _____ Dum vívimus, vivamus.

7. Let arms yield to the toga. _____ Cedant arma togae.

III. Conjugations
Model Verbs
Present Subjunctive Active

1st	2nd	3rd	3rd io	4th
amem	móneam	regam	cápiam	áudiam
ames	móneas	regas	cápias	áudias
amet	móneat	regat	cápiat	áudiat
amemus	moneamus	regamus	capiamus	audiamus
ametis	moneatis	regatis	capiatis	audiatis
ament	móneant	regant	cápiant	áudiant

Present Subjunctive Passive

1st	2nd	3rd	3rd io	4th
amer	mónear	regar	cápiar	áudiar
ameris	monearis	regaris	capiaris	audiaris
ametur	moneatur	regatur	capiatur	audiatur
amemur	moneamur	regamur	capiamur	audiamur
amémini	moneámini	regámini	capiámini	audiámini
amentur	moneantur	regantur	capiantur	audiantur

IV. Conjugation

> Make copies of Drill/Test Form A in the Appendix. Conjugate **tollo** in the <u>6 active and passive tenses of the indicative</u> and <u>the 4 active and passive tenses of the subjunctive</u>. Practice until perfect.

Drill/Test Form A

Principal Parts: tollo tóllere sústuli sublatus
Present System Stem: toll-

Present			
Indicative Active		Indicative Passive	
tollo	tóllimus	tollor	tóllimur
tollis	tóllitis	tólleris	tollímini
tollit	tollunt	tóllitur	tolluntur
Imperfect			
tollebam	tollebamus	tollebar	tollebamur
tollebas	tollebatis	tollebaris	tollebámini
tollebat	tollebant	tollebatur	tollebantur
Future			
tollam	tollemus	tollar	tollemur
tolles	tolletis	tóllēris	tollémini
tollet	tollent	tolletur	tollentur

Perfect System Stem: sustul-

Perfect			
Indicative Active		Indicative Passive	
sústuli	sustúlimus	sublatus sum	-lati sumus
sustulisti	sustulistis	(a, um) es	(ae, a) estis
sústulit	sustulerunt	est	sunt
Pluperfect			
sustúleram	sustuleramus	eram	eramus
sustúleras	sustuleratis	eras	eratis
sustúlerat	sustúlerant	erat	erant
Future Perfect			
sustúlero	sustulérimus	ero	érimus
sustúleris	sustuléritis	eris	éritis
sustúlerit	sustúlerint	erit	erunt

Present			
Subjunctive Active		Subjunctive Passive	
tollam	tollamus	tollar	tollamur
tollas	tollatis	tollaris	tollámini
tollat	tollant	tollatur	tollantur
Imperfect			
tóllerem	tolleremus	tóllerer	tolleremur
tólleres	tolleretis	tollereris	tollerémini
tólleret	tóllerent	tolleretur	tollerentur
Perfect			
sustúlerim	sustulérimus	sublatus sim	-lati simus
sustúleris	sustuléritis	(a, um) sis	(ae, a) sitis
sustúlerit	sustúlerint	sit	sint
Pluperfect			
sustulissem	sustulissemus	essem	essemus
sustulisses	sustulissetis	esses	essetis
sustulisset	sustulissent	esset	essent

Unit IV Review   Worksheet 3

Imperfect Subjunctive Active

1st	2nd	3rd	3rd io	4th
amarem	monerem	régerem	cáperem	audirem
amares	moneres	régeres	cáperes	audires
amaret	moneret	régeret	cáperet	audiret
amaremus	moneremus	regeremus	caperemus	audiremus
amaretis	moneretis	regeretis	caperetis	audiretis
amarent	monerent	régerent	cáperent	audirent

Imperfect Subjunctive Passive

1st	2nd	3rd	3rd io	4th
amarer	monerer	régerer	cáperer	audirer
amareris	monereris	regereris	capereris	audireris
amaretur	moneretur	regeretur	caperetur	audiretur
amaremur	moneremur	regeremur	caperemur	audiremur
amarémini	monerémini	regerémini	caperémini	audirémini
amarentur	monerentur	regerentur	caperentur	audirentur

Perfect Subjunctive Active

1st	2nd	3rd	3rd io	4th
amáverim	monúerim	réxerim	céperim	audíverim
amáveris	monúeris	réxeris	céperis	audíveris
amáverit	monúerit	réxerit	céperit	audíverit
amavérimus	monuérimus	rexérimus	cepérimus	audivérimus
amavéritis	monuéritis	rexéritis	cepéritis	audivéritis
amáverint	monúerint	réxerint	céperint	audíverint

Perfect Subjunctive Passive

1st	2nd	3rd	3rd io	4th
amatus -a -um sim	mónitus -a -um sim	rectus -a -um sim	captus -a -um sim	auditus -a -um sim
sis	sis	sis	sis	sis
sit	sit	sit	sit	sit
amati -ae -a simus	móniti -ae -a simus	recti -ae -a simus	capti -ae -a simus	auditi -ae -a simus
sitis	sitis	sitis	sitis	sitis
sint	sint	sint	sint	sint

Unit IV Review   Worksheet 4

Pluperfect Subjunctive Active

1st	2nd	3rd	3rd io	4th
amavissem	monuissem	rexissem	cepissem	audivissem
amavisses	monuisses	rexisses	cepisses	audivisses
amavisset	monuisset	rexisset	cepisset	audivisset
amavissemus	monuissemus	rexissemus	cepissemus	audivissemus
amavissetis	monuissetis	rexissetis	cepissetis	audivissetis
amavissent	monuissent	rexissent	cepissent	audivissent

Pluperfect Subjunctive Passive

1st	2nd	3rd	3rd io	4th
amatus essem	mónitus essem	rectus essem	captus essem	auditus essem
-a -um esses	-a -um esses	-a -um esses	-a -um esses	-a -um esses
esset	esset	esset	esset	esset
amati essemus	móniti essemus	recti essemus	capti essemus	auditi essemus
-ae -a essetis	-ae -a essetis	-ae -a essetis	-ae -a essetis	-ae -a essetis
essent	essent	essent	essent	essent

Subjunctive of Sum

Present	Imperfect	Perfect	Pluperfect
sim	essem	fúerim	fuissem
sis	esses	fúeris	fuisses
sit	esset	fúerit	fuisset
simus	essemus	fuérimus	fuissemus
sitis	essetis	fuéritis	fuissetis
sint	essent	fúerint	fuissent

Meanings
(1st person only)

Present Active	I may love
Present Passive	I may be loved
Imperfect Active	I might love
Imperfect Passive	I might be love
Perfect Active	I may have loved
Present Passive	I may have been loved
Pluperfect Active	I might have loved
Pluperfect Passive	I might have been loved

V. Vocabulary

Study until you can do this page perfectly from memory. Give the dictionary form.

cavalry	equitatus -ūs m.	falling	occasus -ūs m.
snow	nix nivis f.	fountain	fons fontis m.
common people	plebs plebis f.	danger	perículum -i n.
bow	arcus -ūs m.	advice	consílium -i n.
attack	ímpetus -ūs m.	egg	ovum -i n.
theater	theatrum -i n.	chain	vínculum -i n.
bird	avis avis f.	smooth surface	aequor -oris n.
fire	ignis ignis f.	young person	júvenis júvenis m. or f.
vow	votum -i n.	countryside	rus ruris n.
building	aedifícium -i n.	cart	carrus -ūs m.
leisure	ótium -i n.	mouth	os oris n.
beginning	princípium -i n.	in order that	ut
leg	crus cruris n.	fort	castellum -i n.
death	letum -i n.	winter	hiems híemis f.
clothes	vestis vestis f.	price	prétium -i n.
meeting	concílium -i n.	Gospel	Evangélium -i n.
flower	flos floris m.	sheep	ovis ovis f.
countenance	vultus -ūs m.	trace	vestígium -i n.
contest	certamen -inis n.	aid	auxílium -i n.
hostage	obses -idis m.	rain	imber imbris m.
fodder	pábulum -i n.	tomb	sepulchrum -i n.
heavenly body	astrum -i n.	cave	antrum -i n.
stone	lapis -idis m.	cloud	nubes nubis f.
use	usus -ūs m.	wife	uxor -oris f.
hunger	fames famis f.	companion	comes -itis m.
commandment	mandatum -i n.	starting point	inítium -i n.
crime	scelus -eris n.	space	spátium -i n.
air	aer -is m.	course, running	cursus -ūs m.
flock	grex gregis m.	side	latus -eris n.
three days	triduum -i n.	vice	vítium -i n.
exile	exílium -i n.	exit	éxitus -ūs m.
power	impérium -i n.	shore	litus -oris n.
step	passus -ūs m.	office	munus -eris n.
fate	fatum -i n.	night	nox noctis f.
hatred	ódium -i n.	bone	os ossis n.
garrison	praesídium -i n.		

VI. Form Drills

Convert the given indicative form to the corresponding subjunctive form (1-5) or translate (6-10).
[mh = may have] [mth = might have]

Drill A
1st Conjugation

1. dubitávimus dubitavérimus
2. optat optet
3. negabant negarent
4. appelláveras appellávisses
5. salutatis salutetis

6. they mth called vocávissent
7. I might wander errarem
8. you mh loved amáveris
9. she may stand stet
10. we mh changed mutavérimus

Drill B
2nd Conjugation

1. tacebat taceret
2. docuisti docúeris
3. cavent cáveant
4. tenueramus tenuissemus
5. jussi jússerim

6. they may have hábeant
7. we mh remained mansérimus
8. he mth moved movisset
9. I might sit sederem
10. you mh frightened terrúeris

Drill C
3rd Conjugation

1. egistis egéritis
2. mittit mittat
3. ducebamus duceremus
4. posuerant posuissent
5. premo premam

6. you mh waged gésseris
7. they might yield cederent
8. we mth closed clausissemus
9. I might write scríberem
10. she may lift up tollat

VI. Form Drills (cont.)

Convert the given indicative form to the corresponding subjunctive form (1-5) or translate (6-10).
[mh = may have] [mth = might have]

Drill D
4th Conjugation

1. dormiebamus __dormiremus__
2. fíniunt __finiant__
3. veni __vénerim__
4. sénseram __sensissem__
5. scis __scias__

6. they may hear __áudiant__
7. we mh fortified __munivérimus__
8. he might hinder __impediret__
9. you mth finished __finivisses__
10. I may find __invéniam__

Drill E
3rd **io** Conjugation, **sum**

1. cepistis __cepéritis__
2. erat __esset__
3. jaciebamus __jaceremus__
4. fúerant __fuissent__
5. cupis __cúpias__

6. we mh been __fuérimus__
7. you might make __fáceres__
8. they mth seized __cepissent__
9. she may be __sit__
10. I mth thrown __jecissem__

Drill F
Passive

1. liberatus est __liberatus sit__
2. videtur __videatur__
3. scribebantur __scriberentur__
4. finitum erat __finitum esset__
5. cápimur __capiamur__

6. we may be led __ducamur__
7. it mh been given __datum sit__
8. you might be warned __monereris__
9. I mth been sent __missus (a) essem__
10. they may be lifted up __tollantur__

VII. Translate

1. Laboremus. __Let us work.__
2. Ne cedant. __Let them not yield.__
3. Quid tímeam? __What am I to fear? What should I fear?__
4. Manūs lavat ut cenam paret. __He is washing (his) hands in order to prepare dinner.__
5. Se celavit ne inveniretur. __He has hidden himself lest he be discovered.__
6. Agamus gratias. __Let us give thanks.__
7. Imperator epístulam misit ut victóriam nuntiaret. __The general sent a letter in order to report the victory.__
8. Bellum gérerent? __Should they have waged war?__
9. Mílites vallum struxerunt ut urbem munirent. __The soldiers have built a rampart in order to protect the city.__
10. Fúgio ne vulnerer. __I am fleeing lest I be wounded.__
11. Let us build a new temple. __Struamus templum novum.__
12. Who should explore the cave? __Quis antrum exploret?__
13. Let them ask in order to know. __Rogent ut sciant.__
14. I will push the door in order to close it. __Jánuam premam ut eam claudam.__
15. I am swimming in order to wash my clothes. __Nato ut vestem meam lavem.__
16. Let us close the gates in order to be safe. __Portas claudamus ut simus tuti.__
17. May they sleep well. __Dórmiant bene.__
18. Let us teach the children so that they may be wise. __Doceamus líberos ut sint sapientes.__

1. The three degrees of comparison of adverbs and adjectives are _____
   _____ positive, comparative, and superlative _____ .

2. In English, many positive adjectives can be changed into comparatives by adding _____ -er _____
   and into superlatives by adding _____ -est _____ .

3. Give an example of the above in English using the adjective *great*. _____
   _____ great, greater, greatest _____

4. In English, other adjectives and adverbs are compared by means of the words _____ more _____
   and _____ most _____ .

5. The _____ positive _____ degree is descriptive only.

6. The _____ comparative _____ implies a comparison between two persons or things.

7. The _____ superlative _____ implies a comparison among more than two persons or things.

8. In English, many adjectives can be changed into adverbs by adding _____ -ly _____ .

9. Many of the most common adjectives and adverbs have _____ irregular comparisons _____ .

I. Word Study and Grammar

1. In adjectives and adverbs, there are three _____ degrees of comparison _____ .

2. These are: _____ positive, comparative, superlative _____

3. Give an example of these in English using the adjective *great*. _____
   _____ great, greater, greatest _____

4. The _____ positive _____ is descriptive only.

5. The _____ comparative _____ implies a comparison between two persons or things.

6. The _____ superlative _____ implies a comparison among more than two persons or things.

7. Many of the most common adjectives and adverbs have _____ irregular comparisons _____ .

8. In Latin, the comparative adjective is formed from the positive by adding _____ -ior _____
   and _____ -ius _____ to the stem.

9. In Latin, the superlative adjective is formed by adding _____ -issimus -a -um _____ to the stem.

10. The comparative adjective is declined like the regular _____ 3rd-declension _____ noun.

11. The comparative adjective _____ does not _____ follow the **i-stem** pattern of the regular
    adjective, **brevis -e**.

12. The superlative adjective is declined like the regular _____ 1st/2nd-declension _____ adjective.

II. New Vocabulary
Say aloud and write with dictionary form, meaning, and derivative.

Latin (dictionary form)	Meaning	Derivative
alienus -a -um	foreign, strange, unfavorable	alien
angustus -a -um	narrow, confined	anguish
beatus -a -um	blessed	beatitude
dúbius -a -um	doubtful	dubious
durus -a -um	hard	durable
pius -a -um	dutiful, pious	pious
verus -a -um	true	verily
citus -a -um	rapid, quick	
clarus -a -um	clear, famous	clarity
rústicus -a -um	of the country, rural	rustic

Lesson Twenty-seven   Worksheet 2

Derivatives

1. _____Alien_____ abduction is a _____dubious_____ excuse for your absence.

2. Diamond is the most _____durable_____ natural material.

3. The slick lawyer always wore _____rustic_____ clothes to confuse his opponent.

4. Although the rest of the city goes mad, I am not a basketball fan and feel no_____anguish_____ when our team loses.

Saying

Say aloud and write 3X.

Latin	Cítius, Áltius, Fórtius
Latin	Cítius, Áltius, Fórtius
Latin	Cítius, Áltius, Fórtius
English	Faster, Higher, Stronger

III. Declensions

Comparative Adjective - **fortis -e**

Case	M/F		N	
nom.	fórtior	fortiores	fórtius	fortiora
gen.	fortioris	fortiorum	fortioris	fortiorum
dat.	fortiori	fortióribus	fortiori	fortióribus
acc.	fortiorem	fortiores	fórtius	fortiora
abl.	fortiore	fortióribus	fortiore	fortióribus

IV. Conjugation

Make copies of Drill/Test Form A in the Appendix. Conjugate **servo** in the 6 active and passive tenses of the indicative and the 4 active and passive tenses of the subjunctive. Practice until perfect.

Drill/Test Form A

Principal Parts: servo servare servavi servatus
Present System Stem: serva-

Present			
Indicative Active		Indicative Passive	
servo	servamus	servor	servamur
servas	servatis	servaris	servámini
servat	servant	servatur	servantur
Imperfect			
servabam	servabamus	servabar	servabamur
servabas	servabatis	servabaris	servabámini
servabat	servabant	servabatur	servabantur
Future			
servabo	servábimus	servabor	servábimur
servabis	servábitis	serváberis	servabímini
servabit	servabunt	servábitur	servabuntur

Perfect System Stem: servav-

Perfect			
Indicative Active		Indicative Passive	
servavi	servávimus	servatus sum	-ati sumus
servavisti	servavistis	(a, um) es	(ae, a) estis
servavit	servaverunt	est	sunt
Pluperfect			
serváveram	servaveramus	eram	eramus
serváveras	servaveratis	eras	eratis
serváverat	serváverant	erat	erant
Future Perfect			
servávero	servavérimus	ero	érimus
serváveris	servavéritis	eris	éritis
serváverit	serváverint	erit	erunt

Present			
Subjunctive Active		Subjunctive Passive	
servem	servemus	server	servemur
serves	servetis	serveris	servémini
servet	servent	servetur	serventur
Imperfect			
servarem	servaremus	servarer	servaremur
servares	servaretis	servareris	servarémini
servaret	servarent	servaretur	servarentur
Perfect			
serváverim	servavérimus	servatus sim	-ati simus
serváveris	servavéritis	(a, um) sis	(ae, a) sitis
serváverit	serváverint	sit	sint
Pluperfect			
servavissem	servavissemus	essem	essemus
servavisses	servavissetis	esses	essetis
servavisset	servavissent	esset	essent

V. Comparison of adjectives
1st/2nd Declension

Positive	Comparative	Superlative
aeternus -a -um	aetérnior -ius	aeterníssimus -a -um
albus -a -um	álbior -ius	albíssimus -a -um
alienus -a -um	aliénior -ius	alieníssimus -a -um
altus -a -um	áltior -ius	altíssimus -a -um
angustus -a -um	angústior-ius	angustíssimus -a -um
beatus -a -um	beátior -ius	beatíssimus -a -um
cálidus -a -um	calídior -ius	calidíssimus -a -um
carus -a -um	cárior -ius	caríssimus -a -um
certus -a -um	cértior -ius	certíssimus -a -um
citus -a -um	cítior -ius	citíssimus -a -um
clarus -a -um	clárior -ius	claríssimus -a -um
cúpidus -a -um	cupídior -ius	cupidíssimus -a -um
durus -a -um	dúrior -ius	duríssimus -a -um
excelsus -a -um	excélsior -ius	excelsíssimus -a -um
foedus -a -um	foédior -ius	foedíssimus -a -um
frígidus -a -um	frigídior -ius	frigidíssimus -a -um
laetus -a -um	laétior -ius	laetíssimus -a -um
latus -a -um	látior -ius	latíssimus -a -um
lentus -a -um	léntior -ius	lentíssimus -a -um
longus -a -um	lóngior -ius	longíssimus -a -um
novus -a -um	nóvior -ius	novíssimus -a -um
paratus -a -um	parátior -ius	paratíssimus -a -um
plenus -a -um	plénior -ius	pleníssimus -a -um
sanctus -a -um	sánctior -ius	sanctíssimus -a -um
tutus -a -um	tútior -ius	tutíssimus -a -um
verus -a -um	vérior -ius	veríssimus -a -um

VI. Form Drills
Drill A

1. dúrior __harder__
2. cítius __more rapid__
3. plénius __fuller__
4. pígrior __lazier__
5. facílior __easier__

6. audácius __bolder__
7. alácrior __livelier__
8. cértius __more certain__
9. misérior __more wretched__
10. dúlcius __sweeter__

Drill B

1. asperíssimus __roughest__
2. fidelíssima __most faithful__
3. latíssimum __widest__
4. beatíssima __most blessed__
5. felicíssimus __luckiest__

6. lentíssimum __slowest__
7. laetíssimus __happiest__
8. novíssima __newest__
9. caríssimum __dearest__
10. fortíssima __bravest__

Drill C
Nom. Sing. M, F, N

1. most serious __grávior, grávius__
2. freer __libérior, libérius__
3. safer __tútior, tútius__
4. shorter __brévior, brévius__
5. truest __veríssimus -a -um__

6. longest __longíssimus -a -um__
7. wisest __sapientíssimus -a -um__
8. more huge __ingéntior, ingentius__
9. narrower __angústior, angustius__
10. most certain __certíssimus -a -um__

VII. Translation

1. Caesar est imperatorum sapientíssimus.
   Caesar is the wisest of the generals.

2. Exércitus fórtior vincat.
   Let the stronger army conquer.

3. Pone saxum grávius in fossam.
   Put the heavier rock in the ditch.

4. Scribe nómina senatorum clarissimorum.
   Write the names of the brightest senators.

5. Gládios ferro fortíssimo faciemus.
   We will make swords with the strongest iron.

6. Marcus is the taller of the two brothers.
   Marcus est duorum fratrum áltior.

7. I want the faster of the two horses and Mark wants the stronger.
   Celeriorem duorum equorum cúpio et Marcus fortiorem cupit.

8. This is the widest of the three gates.
   Haec est trium portarum latíssima.

9. Let the most noble citizen guard the gold.
   Civis nobilíssimus aurum servet.

10. The house on the right is the newer.
    Domus dextra est nóvior.

VIII. Reading
Translate the reading in the space below.

VESTIS RÚSTICA

Consul in veste rústicā per urbis vias ámbulat. "Nulli cónsulem sub hac veste vident," sibi dicit. "*Ita fácio* ut civitátium veram vitam vídeam, ut eorum veras *senténtias* áudiam."

Féminam videt. "Es laeta, cara?" rogat. "Láetior, láetior," respondet.

Mílitem videt. "Duces vostros amas, miles?" rogat. "Duces nostri sunt excelsiores," respondet.

Virum cum ferro in manu videt. "Bene laboras, civis?" rogat. "Labor meus non est difficílior," respondet.

Consul *excedit*. Tum puer féminam, mílitem, et virum rogat, "Quis erat?"

Respondent omnes, "O, erat consul stultus noster in veste rústicā."

COUNTRY OUTFIT

The consul in rustic clothes is walking through the streets of the city. "None see the consul beneath this suit," he says to himself. "I am doing like this in order to see the true life of the citizens, to hear their true opinions."

He sees a woman. "Are you happy, dear?" he asks. "Rather (Quite) happy, quite happy," she replies.

He sees a soldier. "Do you like your leaders, soldier?" he asks. "Our leaders are rather (really) excellent," he replies.

He sees a man with a tool in hand. "Is your work going well, citizen?" he asks. "My work is not so difficult," he replies.

The consul leaves. Then a boy asks the woman, the soldier, and the man, "Who was that?"

They all answer, "Oh, that was our silly consul in a country outfit."

consul cónsulis *m.* consul
ita *adv.* thus, in this way, like this; **ita fácio** I am doing like this
senténtia -ae *f.* opinion
excedo -cédere -cedi -cessus to go away, leave

I. Word Study and Grammar

1. In adjectives and adverbs, there are three __degrees of comparison__ .

2. These are: __positive, comparative, superlative__

3. The __positive__ is descriptive only.

4. The __comparative__ implies a comparison between two persons or things.

5. The __superlative__ implies a comparison among more than two persons or things.

6. The comparative adjective is formed by adding __-ior__ and __-ius__ to the stem.

7. The superlative adjective is formed by adding __-issimus -a -um__ to the stem.

8. The comparative adjective is declined like the regular __3rd declension__ noun.

9. The superlative adjective is declined like the regular __1st/2nd-declension__ adjective.

10. The superlative of adjectives ending in **er** is formed by adding __-rimus -a -um to the masculine nominative singular__ .

11. The superlatives of **facilis**, **difficilis**, **similis**, and **humilis** are formed by adding __-limus -a -um to the stem__ .

12. Two nouns or pronouns compared using the adverb **quam** must be __in the same case__ .

13. A comparative adjective used to indicate degree rather than comparison means __too, rather, greater than average__ .

II. Vocabulary

Say aloud and write with dictionary form, meaning, and derivative.

Latin (dictionary form)	Meaning	Derivative
agrestis -e	boorish, crude	
civilis -e	civil, of a citizen	civility
communis -e	common	
crudelis -e	cruel	cruelty
húmilis -e	humble	humility
inanis -e	vain, inane	inane
lenis -e	mild, gentle	lenient
mollis -e	soft, yielding, easy	mollify
sublimis -e	sublime, elevated	sublime
tristis -e	sad	

Derivatives

1. Only catnip could __mollify__ the agitated feline.

2. The punishment was __lenient__ , given the severity of the crime.

3. His __civility__ always disappeared when he was losing.

4. He was reelected even though his policies were more __inane__ than ever.

5. It is occasionally possible to be __sublime__ and ridiculous at the same time.

Saying

Say aloud and write 3X.

Latin	Novus ordo seclorum
Latin	Novus ordo seclorum
Latin	Novus ordo seclorum
English	New order of the ages

III. Declensions

Comparative Adjective - **acer -cris -cre**

Case	M/F		N	
nom.	ácrior	acriores	ácrius	acriora
gen.	acrioris	acriorum	acrioris	acriorum
dat.	acriori	acrióribus	acriori	acrióribus
acc.	acriorem	acriores	ácrius	acriora
abl.	acriore	acrióribus	acriore	acrióribus

IV. Conjugation

Make copies of Drill/Test Form A in the Appendix. Conjugate **térreo** in the 6 active and passive tenses of the indicative and the 4 active and passive tenses of the subjunctive. Practice until perfect.

Drill/Test Form A

Principal Parts: térreo terrēre térrui térritus
Present System Stem: terre-

Present			
Indicative Active		Indicative Passive	
térreo	terremus	térreor	terremur
terres	terretis	terreris	terrémini
terret	terrent	terretur	terrentur
Imperfect			
terrebam	terrebamus	terrebar	terrebamur
terrebas	terrebatis	terrebaris	terrebámini
terrebat	terrebant	terrebatur	terrebantur
Future			
terrebo	terrébimus	terrebor	terrébimur
terrebis	terrébitis	terréberis	terrebímini
terrebit	terrebunt	terrébitur	terrebuntur

Perfect System Stem: terru-

Perfect			
Indicative Active		Indicative Passive	
térrui	terrúimus	térritus sum	-iti sumus
terruisti	terruistis	(a, um) es	(ae, a) estis
térruit	terruerunt	est	sunt
Pluperfect			
terrúeram	terrueramus	eram	eramus
terrúeras	terrueratis	eras	eratis
terrúerat	terrúerant	erat	erant
Future Perfect			
terrúero	terrúerimus	ero	érimus
terrúeris	terrúéritis	eris	éritis
terrúerit	terrúerint	erit	erunt

Present			
Subjunctive Active		Subjunctive Passive	
térream	terreamus	térrear	terreamur
térreas	terreatis	terrearis	terreámini
térreat	térreant	terreatur	terreantur
Imperfect			
terrerem	terreremus	terrerer	terreremur
terreres	terreretis	terrereris	terrerémini
terreret	terrerent	terreretur	terrerentur
Perfect			
terúerim	teruérimus	térritus sim	-iti simus
terúeris	teruéritis	(a, um) sis	(ae, a) sitis
terúerit	terúerint	sit	sint
Pluperfect			
teruissem	teruissemus	essem	essemus
teruisses	teruissetis	esses	essetis
teruisset	teruissent	esset	essent

V. Comparison of Adjectives

3rd Declension

Positive	Comparative	Superlative
audax, audacis	audácior -ius	audacíssimus -a -um
brevis -e	brévior -ius	brevíssimus -a -um
díligens -entis	diligéntior -ius	diligentíssimus -a -um
dulcis -e	dúlcior -ius	dulcíssimus -a -um
felix, felicis	felícior -ius	felicíssimus -a -um
fidelis -e	fidélior -ius	fidelíssimus -a -um
fortis -e	fórtior -ius	fortíssimus -a -um
gravis -e	grávior -ius	gravíssimus -a -um
ingens -entis	ingéntior -ius	ingentíssimus -a -um
nóbilis -e	nobílior -ius	nobilíssimus -a -um
potens -entis	poténtior -ius	potentíssimus -a -um
sápiens -entis	sapiéntior -ius	sapientíssimus -a -um
senex, senis*	sénior -ius	-----
turpis -e	túrpior -ius	turpíssimus -a -um

*Comparative only

VI. Form Drills
Drill A

1. lénior _____milder_____
2. crudélius _____more cruel_____
3. inánius _____vainer_____
4. trístior _____sadder_____
5. púlchrius _____more beautiful_____

6. humílior _____more humble_____
7. misérior _____more wretched_____
8. ácrius _____sharper_____
9. agréstior _____more boorish_____
10. móllius _____softer_____

Drill B

1. humíllima _____most humble_____
2. sublimíssimus _____most lofty_____
3. leníssimus _____mildest_____
4. acérrimum _____sharpest_____
5. facíllimum _____easiest_____

6. misérrima _____most wretched_____
7. fidelíssima _____most faithful_____
8. utilíssimum _____most useful_____
9. difficíllimum _____most difficult_____
10. pulchérrima _____most beautiful_____

Drill C
Nom. Sing. M, F, N

1. most similar _____simíllimus -a -um_____
2. softest _____mollíssimus -a -um_____
3. freest _____libérrimus -a -um_____
4. fastest _____celérrimus -a -um_____
5. most difficult _____difficíllimus -a -um_____

6. saddest _____tristíssimus -a -um_____
7. sharpest _____acérrimus -a -um_____
8. most noble _____nobilíssimus -a -um_____
9. cruelest _____crudelíssimus -a -um_____
10. most humble _____humíllimus -a -um_____

VII. Translation

1. Pater humílior est quam fílius. _____
   The father is more humble than the son.

2. Poeta próelii fábulam verbis lenióribus narravit. _____
   The poet told the story of the battle with rather gentle words.

3. Equus tuus celerior quam meus est. _____
   Your horse is faster than mine.

4. Flúmine angustiore quam nave impédimur. _____
   We are being hindered by a river narrower than the ship.

5. Nostros crudeliores quam hostes tímeo. _____
   I fear our own men (who are) more cruel than the enemy.

6. Viam latiorem quam currūs duos fécimus. _____
   We have made a road wider than two wagons.

7. Naves in portu propter tempestatem potentiorem manserunt. _____
   The ships remained in the harbor on account of a rather powerful storm.

8. Discípulam diligentiorem quam Lúciam non invénies. _____
   You will not find a student more diligent than Lucy.

9. The town had been captured by soldiers bolder than Romans. _____
   Óppidum a mílitibus audacióribus quam Romanis captum erat.

10. The poet told a rather sad story. _____
    Poeta fábulam tristiorem narrávit.

Lesson Twenty-eight — Worksheet 6

VIII. Reading
Translate the reading in the space below.

NEX IN *TÍBERI* (Pars Prima)

Ambulabam, *quo* non sciebam. Ego, alienus ex Hispániā, ambulabam ut urbem célebrem explorarem. Sol in foro erat cálidus. Aer in aedifícibus erat gravis. *Ígitur* flumen *petivi*. Locum in *ripā* inveni, locum pulchrum sine turbā. In saxum *consedi* ut flumen spectarem. "O flumen nóbile," putavi, "*tot* sáecula vidisti, tot cives aquis tuis lavisti!" *Dum* antiquorum fábulas mihi narrabam, vidi … vidi … corpus hóminis! Corpus in *Tíberi*! Et in ejus manu, áquilam tenebat, áquilam legionis Romanae. (*finis* partis primae)

MURDER ON THE TIBER (Part I)

I was walking, where to I did not know. I, a foreigner from Spain, was walking to explore

the famous city. The sun in the forum was hot. The air in the buildings was heavy.

Therefore, I headed for the river. I found a spot (place) on the bank, a pretty spot without

a crowd. I sat down on a rock to look at the river. "Oh noble river," I thought, "so many

ages you have seen, so many citizens you have washed with your waters!" As I was telling

myself stories of the ancients, I saw … saw … the body of a man! A body in the Tiber.

And in its hand, it was holding an eagle, an eagle of a Roman legion. (end of Part I)

nex necis *f.* murder
Tíberis Tíberis *m.* the Tiber (**i-stem** with two irregular forms: acc. sing. **Tíberim** and abl. sing. **Tíberi**)
quo *adv.* where to
Ígitur therefore
peto pétere petivi, petitus to seek, head for
ripa -ae *f.* bank (of a river)
consido -sídere -sedi -sessus to sit down, take one's seat
tot so many
dum *conj.* as
finis finis *m.* end

234

Lesson Twenty-nine — Worksheet 1

I. Word Study and Grammar

1. In adjectives and adverbs, there are three ___degrees of comparison___ .

2. These are: ___positive, comparative, superlative___

3. The ___comparative___ implies a comparison between two persons or things.

4. The ___positive___ implies a comparison among more than two persons or things.

5. The comparative adjective is formed by adding ___-ior___ and ___-ius___ to the stem.

6. The superlative adjective is formed by adding ___-issimus -a -um___ to the stem.

7. The comparative adjective is declined like the regular ___3rd-declension___ noun.

8. The superlative adjective is declined like the regular ___1st/2nd-declension___ adjective.

9. The superlative of adjectives ending in **er** is formed by adding _____ ___-rimus -a -um___ to the masculine nominative singular .

10. The superlatives of **fácilis**, **difficilis**, **símilis**, and **húmilis** are formed by adding _____ ___-limus -a -um___ to the stem .

11. Two nouns or pronouns compared using the adverb **quam** must be _____ ___in the same case___ .

12. A comparative adjective used to indicate degree rather than comparison means _____ ___too, rather, greater than average___

13. A superlative adjective used to indicate degree rather than comparison means _____ ___very___

14. Adjectives with stems ending in a vowel are usually compared using the adverbs _____ ___magis, máximē___ .

235

Give the comparative and superlative forms of the following adjectives.

		Comparative	Superlative
		Latin	Latin
bonus -a -um	good	mélior -ius	óptimus -a -um
malus -a -um	bad	pejor -ius	péssimus -a -um
magnus -a -um	great	major majus	máximus -a -um
parvus -a -um	small	minor minus	mínimus -a -um
multus -a -um	much	plus pluris n.	plúrimus -a -um
multi -ae -a	many	plures plura	plúrimi -ae -a
senex senis	old	sénior sénius	máximus natu
juvenis -is	young	júnior június	mínimus natu

Saying

Say aloud and write 3X.

Latin	E plúribus unum
Latin	E plúribus unum
Latin	E plúribus unum
English	One out of many

II. Declensions

Comparative Adjective - **melior, melius**

Case	M/F		N	
nom.	mélior	meliores	mélius	meliora
gen.	melioris	meliorum	melioris	meliorum
dat.	meliori	melióribus	meliori	melióribus
acc.	meliorem	meliores	melius	meliora
abl.	meliore	melióribus	meliore	melióribus

III. Conjugation

Make copies of Drill/Test Form A in the Appendix. Conjugate **dico** in the 6 active and passive tenses of the indicative and the 4 active and passive tenses of the subjunctive. Practice until perfect.

Drill/Test Form A

Principal Parts: dico dícere dixi dictus
Present System Stem: dic-

Present			
Indicative Active		Indicative Passive	
dico	dícimus	dicor	dícimur
dicis	dícitis	díceris	dicímini
dicit	dicunt	dícitur	dicuntur
Imperfect			
dicebam	dicebamus	dicebar	dicebamur
dicebas	dicebatis	dicebaris	dicebámini
dicebat	dicebant	dicebatur	dicebantur
Future			
dicam	dicemus	dicar	dicemur
dices	dicetis	dicēris	dicémini
dicet	dicent	dicetur	dicentur

Perfect System Stem: dix-

Perfect			
Indicative Active		Indicative Passive	
dixi	díximus	dictus sum	dicti sumus
dixisti	dixistis	(a, um) es	(ae, a) estis
dixit	dixerunt	est	sunt
Pluperfect			
díxeram	dixeramus	eram	eramus
díxeras	dixeratis	eras	eratis
díxerat	díxerant	erat	erant
Future Perfect			
díxero	díxerimus	ero	érimus
díxeris	díxéritis	eris	éritis
díxerit	díxerint	erit	erunt

Present			
Subjunctive Active		Subjunctive Passive	
dicam	dicamus	dicar	dicamur
dicas	dicatis	dicaris	dicámini
dicat	dicant	dicatur	dicantur
Imperfect			
dícerem	diceremus	dícerer	diceremur
díceres	diceretis	dícereris	dicerémini
díceret	dícerent	diceretur	dicerentur
Perfect			
dixerim	dixérimus	dictus sim	dicti simus
díxeris	dixéritis	(a, um) sis	(ae, a) sitis
díxerit	díxerint	sit	sint
Pluperfect			
dixissem	dixissemus	essem	essemus
dixisses	dixissetis	esses	essetis
dixisset	dixissent	esset	essent

IV. Form Drills
Drill A

1. pejor _worse_
2. júnior _younger_
3. mélius _better_
4. minor _smaller_
5. plura _more_

6. péssimus _worst_
7. majus _greater_
8. plus _more_
9. sénior _older_
10. óptimus _best_

Drill B

1. mínimum _smallest_
2. máximē _most_
3. plúrimi _very many_
4. mínimus natu _youngest_
5. óptima _best_

6. máximus _greatest_
7. plúrimum _most_
8. máximus natu _oldest_
9. magis _more_
10. péssima _worst_

Drill C

1. smallest _mínimus -a -um_
2. younger _júnior_
3. most _plúrimus -a -um_
4. smaller _minor, minus_
5. more (adj.) _plures, plura_

6. very many _plúrimi -ae -a_
7. oldest _máximus natu_
8. worse _pejor, pejus_
9. more (noun) _plus pluris n._
10. better _mélior, mélius_

V. Translation

1. Domus mea minor est quam finitima. _____
   My house is smaller than the neighboring one.

2. Hi mílites cum máximo stúdio laborant. _____
   These soldiers are working with the greatest enthusiasm.

3. Pater juniori fílio domum dedit et seniori fílio villam. _____
   The father gave the younger (son) a house and the older a farmhouse.

4. Ómnium Romae domuum óptimam habemus. _____
   Out of all the houses of Rome, we have the best.

5. Cur exércitus melior ab imperatore pejore dúcitur? _____
   Why is the better army being led by the worse general?

6. The younger of the lieutenants will be sent to the larger province. _____
   Legatorum junior ad provínciam majorem mittetur.

7. We will build more ships after the winter. _____
   Post híemem plures naves struemus.

8. My right hand is smaller than my left. _____
   Manus mea dextra minor est quam sinistra.

9. He wrote very many books about the best generals. _____
   Plúrimos libros de imperatóribus óptimis scripsit.

10. The smallest dog has the biggest voice. _____
    Canis mínimus (-a) vocem máximam habet.

VI. Reading

Translate the reading in the space below.

NEX IN TÍBERI (Pars Secunda)

"*Ferte* auxílium!" clamavi.

Par vigílium advenerunt. "Quid est?" dixit unus.

Hic erit dux, putavi, quod gládium gerit. Alter *solum* tabellam habet. "Quid est? Es *caecus*?" dixi, "Specta illud in flúmine! Corpus est, corpus cum áquilā."

"Non *íterum*!" clamavit, "Hoc est *mensis* corpus secundum."

"Plus *scribendi*," dixit alter cum voce defessā. (*finis* partis secundae)

MURDER ON THE TIBER (Part II)

"Bring help!" I shouted.

A pair of cops arrived. "What is it?" one said. This one will be the leader, I thought,

because he's got (is wearing) a sword. The other one only has a writing pad. "What is it?

Are you blind?" I said, "Look at that thing in the river! It's a body, a body with an eagle."

"Not again!" he shouted. "This is the second body this month."

"More paperwork (writing)," said the other one with a weary voice. (end of Part II)

---

ferte! bring! (imperative pl. of **fero: fer, ferte**)
par paris *n.* pair
vigil vígilis *m.* policeman, cop (**i-stem**)
advénio -ire -vēni -ventus to arrive
solum *adv.* only
caecus -a -um blind

íterum *adv.* again (for a second time)
mensis mensis *m.* month
scribendi* (*gen. sing.*) writing (here means *paperwork*)
    *Scribendi is the *gerund* of **scribo**. Gerunds will be taught in *Fourth Form*.
finis finis *m.* end

239

I. Word Study and Grammar

1. In adjectives and adverbs, there are three ____degrees of comparison____ .

2. These are: ____positive, comparative, superlative____

3. The ____comparative____ implies a comparison between two persons or things.

4. The ____positive____ implies a comparison among more than two persons or things.

5. Adverbs stand ____before____ the verbs they modify.

6. 1st/2nd declension adjectives are changed into adverbs by ____
   adding **-ē** to to adjective stem

7. Some adjectives, especially of quantity and number, form adverbs with the ____
   neuter accusative singular .

8. 3rd declension adjectives of two and three terminations are changed into adverbs by
   adding **-iter** to the stem

9. The comparative of regular adverbs is the ____
   neuter accusative singular of the comparative adjective

10. The superlative of regular adverbs is formed by ____
    changing **-us** of the superlative adjective to **-ē**

II. Saying

Say aloud and write 3X.

Latin	Ánnuit coeptis.
Latin	Ánnuit coeptis.
Latin	Ánnuit coeptis.
English	He has favored our undertaking.

III. Conjugation

Make copies of Drill/Test Form A in the Appendix. Conjugate **áudio** in the 6 active and passive tenses of the indicative and the 4 active and passive tenses of the subjunctive. Practice until perfect.

240

Drill/Test Form A

Principal Parts: áudio audire audivi auditus
Present System Stem: audi-

Present			
Indicative Active		Indicative Passive	
áudio	audimus	áudior	audimur
audis	auditis	audiris	audímini
audit	áudiunt	auditur	audiuntur
Imperfect			
audiebam	audiebamus	audiebar	audiebamur
audiebas	audiebatis	audiebaris	audiebámini
audiebat	audiebant	audiebatur	audiebantur
Future			
áudiam	audiemus	áudiar	audiemur
áudies	audietis	audieris	audiémini
áudiet	áudient	audietur	audientur

Perfect System Stem: audiv-

Perfect			
Indicative Active		Indicative Passive	
audivi	audívimus	auditus sum	-iti sumus
audivisti	audivistis	(a, um) es	(ae, a) estis
audivit	audiverunt	est	sunt
Pluperfect			
audíveram	audiveramus	eram	eramus
audíveras	audiveratis	eras	eratis
audíverat	audíverant	erat	erant
Future Perfect			
audívero	audivérimus	ero	érimus
audíveris	audivéritis	eris	éritis
audíverit	audíverint	erit	erunt

Present			
Subjunctive Active		Subjunctive Passive	
áudiam	audiamus	áudiar	audiamur
áudias	audiatis	audiaris	audiámini
áudiat	áudiant	audiatur	audiantur
Imperfect			
audirem	audiremus	audirer	audiremur
audires	audiretis	audireris	audirémini
audiret	audirent	audiretur	audirentur
Perfect			
audíverim	audivérimus	auditus sim	-iti simus
audíveris	audivéritis	(a, um) sis	(ae, a) sitis
audíverit	audíverint	sit	sint
Pluperfect			
audivissem	audivissemus	essem	essemus
audivisses	audivissetis	esses	essetis
audivisset	audivissent	esset	essent

IV. New Vocabulary

Say aloud and write with dictionary form, meaning, and derivative.

Latin (dictionary form)	Meaning	Derivative
aequus -a -um	equal to, even, level	equal
árduus -a -um	steep, arduous	arduous
ávidus -a -um	avid, keen	avid
caecus -a -um	blind	
cunctus -a -um	all	
dignus -a -um	worthy, dignified	dignity
mirus -a -um	wonderful, strange	miracle
periculosus -a -um	dangerous	perilous
superbus -a -um	proud	superb
tardus -a -um	late, delayed	tardy

V. Derivatives

1. The British ton and the American ton are not _____equal_____ .

2. The climb will be more _____arduous_____ because of the _____perilous_____ terrain.

3. Catherine the Great, empress of Russia, was an _____avid_____ collector of _____superb_____ cameos.

4. The job is behind schedule because the delivery of materials is _____tardy_____ .

VI. Comparison of Adjectives and Adverbs

Decl.		Positive	Comparative	Superlative
1st/2nd	adj.	**latus -a -um**	látior -ius	latíssimus -a -um
	adv.	latē	látius	latíssimē
3rd	adj.	**gravis -e**	grávior -ius	gravíssimus -a -um
	adv.	graviter	grávius	gravíssimē
3rd	adj.	**fácilis -e**	facílior -ius	facíllimus -a -um
	adv.	fácile	facílius	facíllimē
3rd	adj.	**sapiens -entis**	sapiéntior -ius	sapientíssimus -a -um
	adv.	sapienter	sapiéntius	sapientíssimē
3rd	adj.	**acer -cris -cre**	ácrior -ius	acérrimus -a -um
	adv.	ácriter	ácrius	acérrimē

VII. Form Drills

Adverbs

Drill A

1. crudélius ___more cruelly___
2. ávidē ___keenly, avidly___
3. leníssimē ___most slowly___
4. inániter ___vainly___
5. utílius ___more usefully___

6. difficíllimē ___with greatest difficulty___
7. alácrius ___more lively___
8. potenter ___powerfully___
9. claríssimē ___most clearly___
10. móllius ___more softly___

Drill B

1. fidelíssimē ___most faithfully___
2. sublímius ___more elevated___
3. trístius ___more sadly___
4. fortíssimē ___most strongly___
5. certē ___certainly___

6. celérius ___more swiftly___
7. diligentíssimē ___most carefully___
8. felícius ___more happily___
9. audáciter ___boldly___
10. acérrimē ___most bitterly___

Drill C

1. most powerfully ___potentíssimē___
2. more swiftly ___celérius___
3. most humbly ___humíllimē___
4. cruelly ___crudéliter___
5. more wretchedly ___misérius___

6. more boldly ___audácius___
7. most easily ___facíllimē___
8. more wisely ___sapiéntius___
9. most softly ___molíssimē___
10. gently ___léniter___

VIII. Translation

1. Mílites post fossam fórtius quam mílites in vallo pugnabant. ___The soldiers behind the ditch were fighting more bravely than the soldiers on the rampart.___

2. Post iter longíssimum nautae in portum defessē navigaverunt. ___After a very long journey, the sailors wearily sailed into the port.___

3. Senator pecúniam pro frumento uxori stultē et túrpiter dedit. ___The senator stupidly and shamefully gave the money instead of* grain to his wife.___

4. Poeta caecus rurum* fábulas dúlcius quam poetae íntegri narrat. ___The blind poet tells stories about nature more sweetly than uninjured (i.e. unimpaired) poets.___

*Rus in the plural is a metaphor for *nature.*

5. Discipulorum cunctorum Marcus diligentíssimē et cum máximo stúdio laborat. ___Of all the students Mark works the most carefully and with the greatest enthusiasm.___

6. Let us live more happily. ___Vivamus laétius.___

7. This ship will make the journey most quickly and most safely. ___Haec navis iter celérrimē et tutíssimē fáciet.___

8. Our men overcame the province slowly and with the most difficulty. ___Nostri próvinciam lentē et difficíllimē superaverunt.___

9. Sheep are driven more easily by dogs than by a shepherd. ___Oves facílius a cánibus quam a pastore aguntur.___

10. The citizens of the city felt the danger of hunger more seriously than the farmers. ___Urbis cives famis perículum grávius quam agrícolae sentiebant.___

*In this sentence, *instead of* is a more accurate translation of **pro** than the usual *for.*

Lesson Thirty — Worksheet 5

IX. Reading
Translate the reading in the space below.

NEX IN TÍBERI (Pars Tértia)

"Aquilámne corpus primum tenebat?" rogavi.

Vigil minor tabellam spectavit. "Ita, is étiam áquilam hábuit, sed non in manu, in tergo."

"Haec est vero res *occulta*," dixit dux. "Quis centuriones nostros *necat*? Sunt alieni in urbe?"

"Ita," respondit minor. "Júvenem alienum in foro vidi, júvenem vultu nefário, *capíllis* longis, et veste foedā*."

"Stulte! Ille erat *cónsulis* fílius. Ex *Ásiā nuper* advenit. Mores *orientales* ei nunc *placent*."

"Ego vidi," dixi, "Ego alienum vidi." (*finis* partis tértiae)

*ablative describing physical appearance

MURDER ON THE TIBER (Part III)

"Was the first body holding an eagle?" I asked.

The smaller (lesser) cop looked at his tablet. "Yes, he had an eagle too, but not in his hand, in his back."

"This is truly a mysterious affair," said the leader. "Who is murdering our centurions? Are there any strangers in the city?"

"Yes," the lesser answered. "I have seen a strange young man in the forum, a young man with a wicked face, long hair, and an ugly outfit."

"Foolish (man)! (Idiot!) That was the consul's son. He just got back from Asia. He likes (are pleasing to him) the eastern fashions now."

"I have," I said, "I have seen a stranger." (end of Part III)

occultus -a -um mysterious, secret
neco (1) to kill, murder
capillus -i *m.* hair
consul consulis *m.* consul
Ásia -ae *f.* Asia

nuper *adv.* recently
orientalis -e eastern
pláceo placēre plácui plácitus *w/dat.* to please
finis finis *m.* end

Lesson Thirty-one — Worksheet 1

I. Word Study and Grammar

1. In adjectives and adverbs, there are three __degrees of comparison__.
2. These are: __positive, comparative, superlative__
3. The __comparative__ implies a comparison between two persons or things.
4. The __positive__ implies a comparison among more than two persons or things.
5. Adverbs stand __before__ the verbs they modify.
6. 1st/2nd declension adjectives are changed into adverbs by __adding -ē to to adjective stem__.
7. Some adjectives, especially of quantity and number, form adverbs with the __neuter accusative singular__.
8. 3rd declension adjectives of two and three terminations are changed into adverbs by __adding -iter to the stem__
9. The comparative of regular adverbs is the __neuter accusative singular of the comparative adjective__.
10. The superlative of regular adverbs is formed by __changing -us of the superlative adjective to -ē__

II. Saying
Say aloud and write 3X.

Latin	multum in parvo
Latin	multum in parvo
Latin	multum in parvo
English	much in little

III. Conjugation

Make copies of Drill/Test Form A in the Appendix. Conjugate **cápio** in the 6 active and passive tenses of the indicative and the 4 active and passive tenses of the subjunctive. Practice until perfect.

Drill/Test Form A

Principal Parts: cápio cápere cepi captus
Present System Stem: capi-

Present			
Indicative Active		Indicative Passive	
cápio	cápimus	cápior	cápimur
capis	cápitis	cáperis	capímini
capit	cápiunt	cápitur	capiuntur
Imperfect			
capiebam	capiebamus	capiebar	capiebamur
capiebas	capiebatis	capiebaris	capiebámini
capiebat	capiebant	capiebatur	capiebantur
Future			
cápiam	capiemus	cápiar	capiemur
cápies	capietis	capieris	capiémini
cápiet	cápient	capietur	capientur

Perfect System Stem: cep-

Perfect			
Indicative Active		Indicative Passive	
cepi	cépimus	captus sum	capti sumus
cepisti	cepistis	(a, um) es	(ae, a) estis
cepit	ceperunt	est	sunt
Pluperfect			
céperam	ceperamus	eram	eramus
céperas	ceperatis	eras	eratis
céperat	céperant	erat	erant
Future Perfect			
cépero	cepérimus	ero	érimus
céperis	cepéritis	eris	éritis
céperit	céperint	erit	erunt

Present			
Subjunctive Active		Subjunctive Passive	
cápiam	capiamus	cápiar	capiamur
cápias	capiatis	capiaris	capiámini
cápiat	cápiant	capiatur	capiantur
Imperfect			
cáperem	caperemus	cáperer	caperemur
cáperes	caperetis	capereris	caperémini
cáperet	cáperent	caperetur	caperentur
Perfect			
céperim	cepérimus	captus sim	capti simus
céperis	cepéritis	(a, um) sis	(ae, a) sitis
céperit	céperint	sit	sint
Pluperfect			
cepissem	cepissemus	essem	essemus
cepisses	cepissetis	esses	essetis
cepisset	cepissent	esset	essent

IV. Irregular Comparisons of Adjectives and Adverbs

	Positive	Comparative	Superlative
adj.	**bonus -a -um**	mélior -ius	óptimus -a -um
adv.	bene	mélius	óptimē

adj.	**malus -a -um**	pejor -ius	péssimus -a -um
adv.	male	pejus	péssimē

adj.	**magnus -a -um**	major -ius	máximus -a -um
adv.	magnópere	magis	máximē

adj.	**parvus -a -um**	minor, minus	mínimus -a -um
adv.	parum	minus	mínimē

adj.	**multus -a -um**	plus, pluris	plúrimus -a -um
adv.	multum	plus	plúrimum

adv.	**diu**	diútius	diutíssimē
adv.	**prope**	própius	próximē
adv.	**saepe**	saépius	saepíssimē

Lesson Thirty-one

V. Form Drills

Adverbs

Drill A

1. próxime _next_
2. parum _little_
3. magis _more_
4. bene _well_
5. óptimē _best_
6. diu _long time_
7. magnópere _greatly_
8. própius _nearer_
9. máximē _most_
10. sáepius _more often_

Drill B

1. diutíssimē _for the longest time_
2. male _badly_
3. minus _less_
4. prope _near_
5. mínimē _least_
6. mélius _better_
7. péssimē _worst_
8. multum _much_
9. pejus _worse_
10. saepe _often_

Drill C

1. better _mélius_
2. nearer _própius_
3. much _multum_
4. worst _péssimē_
5. little _parum_
6. most often _saepíssimē_
7. more _magis_
8. longest time _diutíssimē_
9. most _máximē_
10. greatly _magnópere_

Lesson Thirty-one

VI. Translation

1. Oves curru rústico male vehebantur. _____
   The sheep were being badly transported by the rustic wagon.

2. Mílites in ácie primā ságittis sáepius quam gládiis vulnerati sunt. _____
   Soldiers in the first line were wounded more often by arrows than by swords.

3. Defessi onera gravíssima diutíssimē portáverant. _____
   The exhausted men had carried very heavy loads for a very long time.

4. Caesar castellum struxit ut viam mélius defénderet. _____
   Caesar built a fort in order to better defend the road.

5. Maneamus díutius ut magis dormiamus. _____
   Let's stay longer in order to sleep more.

6. The young are working less than the old. _____
   Júvenes minus quam senes laborant.

7. Write more in order to be more famous. _____
   Scribe magis ut celébrior sis.

8. The legion fought for a longer time but the cavalry fought better. _____
   Légio diútius pugnavit sed equitatus mélius pugnavit.

9. Out of all the legions, the tenth fights the best. _____
   Ómnium legionum décima óptimē pugnat.

10. Who will rule the state next? _____
    Quis civitatem próximē reget?

VII. Reading

Translate the reading in the space below.

NEX IN TÍBERI (Pars Quarta)

"Ego nunc alienum specto," súbito dixit minor. "Tu, tu es alienus!"

Dux me servat: "Hic corpus invēnit et nos vocavit. Quando *necator* vígiles vocat?" Tum mihi, "*Quem* vidisti, *Hispane*?"

"*Mane*, virum in templo vidi. Urbis non erat. Erat in génibus prae arā. 'Feci, feci, feci,' *repetebat*, tum, 'pro patriā et pro fratre.' Non *intellexi*."

"*Intéllego*," dixit dux. "Hoc *nonnumquam* est belli prétium." (*finis*)

MURDER ON THE TIBER (Part IV)

"I am looking at a stranger now," the lesser suddenly said. "You, you are a stranger."

The leader guards me: "This (man) found the body and called us. When does the murderer

call the cops?" Then to me, "Whom did you see, Spaniard?"

"This morning I saw a man in the temple. He was not of the city. He was on his knees in

front of the altar. 'I did it, I did it, I did it,' he kept repeating, then, 'for my country and my

brother.' I didn't get it (understand)."

"I understand," said the leader. "Sometimes this is the price of war." (end)

necator -oris *m.* murderer
quem = *whom* (direct object of **vidisti**)
Hispanus -i *m.* Spaniard
mane *adv.* this morning, in the morning
répeto repétere repetivi repetitus to repeat
intellego -légere -lexi -lectus to understand
nonnumquam *adv.* sometimes
finis finis *m.* end

I. Word Study and Grammar

1. In adjectives and adverbs, there are three ___degrees of comparison___ .

2. These are: ___positive, comparative, superlative___

3. The ___comparative___ implies a comparison between two persons or things.

4. The ___superlative___ implies a comparison among more than two persons or things.

5. The comparative adjective is formed by adding ___-ior___ and ___-ius___ to the stem.

6. The superlative adjective is formed by adding ___-issimus -a -um___ to the stem.

7. The comparative adjective is declined like the regular ___3rd declension___ noun.

8. The superlative adjective is declined like the regular ___1st/2nd-declension___ adjective.

9. Two nouns or pronouns compared using the adverb **quam** must be ___in the same case___ .

10. Adjectives with stems ending in a vowel are usually compared using the adverbs ___**magis, máximē**___ .

11. 1st/2nd-declension adjectives are changed into adverbs by ___adding **-ē** to the stem___ .

12. Some adjectives, especially of quantity and number, form adverbs with the ___neuter accusative singular___ .

13. Third-declension adjectives of two and three terminations are changed into adverbs by ___adding **-iter** to the stem___ .

14. The comparative of regular adverbs is the ___neuter accusative singular of the comparative adjective___ .

15. The superlative of regular adverbs is formed by ___changing **-us** of the superlative adjective to **-ē**___ .

II. Latin Sayings

1. One out of many _____ E plúribus unum

2. Faster, Higher, Stronger _____ Cítius, Áltius, Fórtius

3. New order of the ages _____ Novus ordo seclorum

4. He has favored our undertaking. _____ Ánnuit coeptis.

5. much in little _____ multum in parvo

III. Declensions

	M/F		N	
nom.	**mélior**	meliores	mélius	meliora
gen.	melioris	meliorum	melioris	meliorum
dat.	meliori	melióribus	meliori	melióribus
acc.	meliorem	meliores	mélius	meliora
abl.	meliore	melióribus	meliore	melióribus

IV. Comparison

Positive	Comparative	Superlative
clarus -a -um	clárior -ius	claríssimus -a -um
brevis -e	brévior -ius	brevíssimus -a -um
ingens	ingéntior -ius	ingentíssimus -a -um

Positive	Comparative	Superlative
liber -bera -berum	libérior -ius	libérrimus -a -um
celeber -bris -bre	celébrior -ius	celeberrimus -a -um
celer céleris célere	celérior -ius	celérrimus -a -um
aeger -gra -grum	aégrior -ius	aegérrimus -a -um
humilis -e	humílior -ius	humíllimus -a -um
nobilis -e	nobílior -ius	nobilíssimus -a -um

IV. Comparison (cont.)

Positive	Comparative	Superlative
bonus -a -um	mélior -ius	óptimus -a -um
malus -a -um	pejor -ius	péssimus -a -um
magnus -a -um	major, majus	máximus -a -um
parvus -a -um	minor, minus	mínimus -a -um
multus -a -um	plus, pluris	plúrimus -a -um
multi -ae -a	plures, plura	plúrimi -ae -a
senex, senis	sénior	máximus natu
júvenis -e	júnior	mínimus natu
dúbius -a -um	magis dúbius -a -um	máximē dúbius -a -um

Positive	Comparative	Superlative
lentē	léntius	lentíssimē
bréviter	brévius	brevíssimē
bene	mélius	óptimē
male	pejus	péssimē
magnópere	magis	máximē
parum	minus	mínimē
multum	plus	plúrimum
diu	diútius	diutíssimē
prope	própius	próximē
saepe	saépius	saepíssimē

V. Conjugation

Make copies of Drill/Test Form A in the Appendix. Conjugate **claudo** in the 6 active and passive tenses of the indicative and the 4 active and passive tenses of the subjunctive. Practice until perfect.

Drill/Test Form A

Principal Parts: claudo cláudere clausi clausus
Present System Stem: claud-

Present			
Indicative Active		Indicative Passive	
claudo	cláudimus	claudor	cláudimur
claudis	cláuditis	cláuderis	claudímini
claudit	claudunt	cláuditur	clauduntur
Imperfect			
claudebam	claudebamus	claudebar	claudebamur
claudebas	claudebatis	claudebaris	claudebámini
claudebat	claudebant	claudebatur	claudebantur
Future			
claudam	claudemus	claudar	claudemur
claudes	claudetis	claudēris	claudémini
claudet	claudent	claudetur	claudentur

Perfect System Stem: claus-

Perfect			
Indicative Active		Indicative Passive	
clausi	cláusimus	clausus sum	clausi sumus
clausisti	clausistis	(a, um) es	(ae, a) estis
clausit	clauserunt	est	sunt
Pluperfect			
cláuseram	clauseramus	eram	eramus
cláuseras	clauseratis	eras	eratis
cláuserat	cláuserant	erat	erant
Future Perfect			
cláusero	clausérimus	ero	érimus
cláuseris	clauséritis	eris	éritis
cláuserit	cláuserint	erit	erunt

Present			
Subjunctive Active		Subjunctive Passive	
claudam	claudamus	claudar	claudamur
claudas	claudatis	claudaris	claudámini
claudat	claudant	claudatur	claudantur
Imperfect			
cláuderem	clauderemus	cláuderer	clauderemur
cláuderes	clauderetis	claudereris	clauderémini
cláuderet	cláuderent	clauderetur	clauderentur
Perfect			
cláuserim	clausérimus	clausus sim	clausi simus
cláuseris	clauséritis	(a, um) sis	(ae, a) sitis
cláuserit	cláuserint	sit	sint
Pluperfect			
clausissem	clausissemus	essem	essemus
clausisses	clausissetis	esses	essetis
clausisset	clausissent	esset	essent

VI. Vocabulary

Give the dictionary form.

equal to, even, level	aequus -a -um
boorish, crude	agrestis -e
foreign, alien, strange	alienus -a -um
steep, arduous	árduus -a -um
avid, keen	ávidus -a -um
blessed	beatus -a -um
blind	caecus -a -um
rapid, quick	citus -a -um
civil, of a citizen	civilis -e
clear, bright	clarus -a -um
common	communis -e
cruel	crudelis -e
all (of a group)	cunctus-a -um
worthy, dignified	dignus -a -um
doubtful	dúbius -a -um
hard (not soft)	durus -a -um
humble	húmilis -e
vain, inane	inanis -e
mild, gentle	lenis -e
wondrous	mirus -a -um
soft, yielding	mollis -e
dangerous	periculosus -a -um
pious, dutiful	pius -a -um
than	quam
of the country, rural	rústicus -a -um
sublime, elevated	sublimis -e
proud	superbus -a -um
late, delayed	tardus -a -um
sad	tristis -e
true	verus -a -um

VII. Form Drills
Drill A

1. crudélior crueler
2. móllius softer
3. cértius more certain
4. aliénior stranger
5. vérius truer

6. poténtior more powerful
7. alácrius more lively
8. lénior milder
9. misérius more wretched
10. dúlcior sweeter

Drill B

1. lentíssimus slowest
2. duríssima hardest
3. ingentíssimum hugest
4. humíllimi most humble
5. felicíssimi luckiest

6. digníssimum most worthy
7. laetíssimae happiest
8. celérrima fastest
9. crudelíssimum cruelest
10. claríssima clearest

Drill C
Nom. Sing. M, F, N

1. hardest duríssimus -a -um
2. easiest facíllimus -a -um
3. sharper ácrior -ius
4. boldest audacíssimus -a -um
5. easier facílior -ius

6. milder lénior -ius
7. most dangerous periculosíssimus -a -um
8. softest mollíssimus -a -um
9. more worthy dígnior -ius
10. steepest arduíssimus -a -um

VIII. Translation

1. Lupus est poténtior quam canis. The wolf is more powerful than the dog.
2. Marcus est fratrum sénior. Marcus is the older of the brothers.
3. Haec léctio est difficíllima. This lesson is the most difficult (very difficult).
4. Légio décima ávidius quam nona pugnat. The tenth legion fights more eagerly than the ninth.
5. Própius cóllibus ambulemus. Let us walk closer to the hills.
6. Plura práemia mílitibus sáepius demus. Let us give more prizes more often to the soldiers.
7. Saxa mea sunt dúriora quam tua. My rocks are harder than yours.
8. Hoc lignum est dómibus máximē idóneum. This wood is the most suited to houses.
9. The older citizens are rather lucky. Cives seniores sunt feliciores.
10. The best soldiers are the most eager. Miles óptimi sunt avidiores.
11. Let us walk more slowly. Léntius ambulemus.
12. Our city will be the most famous. Urbs nostra erit celebérrima.
13. I will rule the province more wisely. Provínciam sapiéntius regam.
14. The outcome is more doubtful today than yesterday. Éxitus hódie est magis dúbius quam heri.
15. We will sail more carefully because of the storm. Propter tempestatem diligéntius navigábimus.
16. That building is very huge. Illud aedifícium est ingentíssimum.
17. Marcus is the best speaker out of all the senators. Ómnium senatorum Marcus est orator óptimus.
18. Lucy is a better speaker than Mary. Lúcia est orator mélior quam María.

How to Use Grammar Questions for Rapid-Fire Review

These questions and answers are similar to a catechism. Students should study them and be prepared to answer questions during review time at the beginning of every class. Immediately after the Recitation, ask a selection of these questions in a rapid-fire manner and expect immediate answers. Like all drills, this should be done energetically and quickly. No time for dawdling or fishing for answers. Books are closed, of course. This oral review tests what students really know and know well.

Select grammar questions in an organized way. Always review the previous week's lesson for two or three weeks and then begin to drop questions and add new ones. Always include some really old questions that all students know for fun.

If a student misses a question, quickly go to the next student, but then return to the first student for the correct answer. Continue asking that student the same question all week and thereafter. It adds some humor to the question time. All students miss a question sooner or later, and they know they will be grilled on it for weeks to come.

Third Form Grammar Questions

1. Give the three moods of Latin verbs. __indicative, imperative, subjunctive__

2. The indicative mood is used for __statements and questions__ .

3. The imperative mood is used for __commands__ .

4. The subjunctive mood is used for __potential action, such as opinions, purpose, and wishes__

5. To form the singular imperative of all four conjugations, drop __-re__ from the infinitive.

6. To form the plural imperative of all but the 3rd conjugation, add __-te__ to the singular imperative.

7. Remember __surge, súrgite__ for the 3rd conjugation imperative forms.

8. Give three irregular singular imperatives. __dic, duc, fac__

9. Give the singular and plural imperatives of **sum**. __es, este__

10. The tenses of the perfect passive system are __compound__ verbs.

11. The 4th principal part is a __participle__ .

12. A participle is a __verbal adjective__ .

13. Verbs that can take a direct object are called __transitive__ verbs, and verbs that do not take a direct object are called __intransitive__ .

14. The vocative case is the case of __direct address__

15. Give the **Vocative Rule.** __The vocative is the same as nom. except in 2nd decl. M sing. where **-us** changes to **-e** and **-ius** to **-i**.__

16. Give three vocative expressions that illustrate the vocative rule. _____
    Et tu, Brute?   **Benedíc Dómine nos**   **Christe eleison**   **fili mi**

17. Give the **three** exceptions to the **Vocative Rule**.
    1) __meus = mi__   2) __deus = deus__   3) __Jesus = Jesu__

18. A vocative noun is often used with an __imperative__ verb and usually is not the __first__ word in the sentence.

19. Give the dative and ablative plural of **fília** and **dea**. __filiabus, deabus__

20. Give two common indeclinable nouns. __satis, nihil__

21. What is an appositive? __a word that follows a noun and renames it__

22. An appositive agrees with its noun or pronoun in __case__ , and usually but not necessarily in __gender and number__ .

Third Form Grammar Questions

23. Give two examples of adjectives used as nouns in English. _____
    the poor, the good, the bad, the ugly, the tired, the weary

24. Latin often uses the ___masc. or neuter nom. plural adjective___
    as a noun to describe a group of people or things.

25. Give two examples of the above. _____
    multa = many things; **nostri** = our men; **multi** = many people

26. Give the three kinds of 1st/2nd-declension adjectives. ___regular (**bonus -a -um**),___
    -er adjectives (drop or retain the **e**), the Naughty Nine

27. The Naughty Nine have irregular forms in what cases? ___genitive and dative___

28. Give three kinds of 3rd-declension adjectives. ___1,2,3 terminations___

29. In English, some adjectives require a ___prepositional phrase___ to complete their thought.

30. The three ways in Latin to express this prepositional phrase is by _____
    case, preposition, and infinitive.

31. Which cardinal numbers are declined? ___**unus, duo, tres**___

32. Give three reasons for using a personal pronoun in the nominative case (as a subject). _____
    clarity, contrast, emphasis

33. The preposition **cum** takes the ___ablative___ case, and when combined with 1st/2nd
    personal pronouns results in what forms? ___**mecum, tecum, nobiscum vobiscum**___

34. The genitive of 1st/2nd declension pronouns is used for ___of___ expressions
    that do not show ___possession___.

35. **Nostri** and **vestri** are used for the ___objective___ genitive.

36. **Nostrum** and **vestrum** are used for the ___partitive___ genitive.

37. The 3rd person personal pronoun is ___**is ea id**___.

38. The genitive of **is ea id** is used to show ___possession___ but
    functions as a ___pronoun___.

39. The 3rd person reflexive pronoun adjective in Latin is ___**suus sua suum**___.

40. Forms of **is** and **ea** mean *he* and *she* when referring to ___persons___, and *it*
    when referring to ___things with grammatical gender___.

41. What kind of pronouns point out persons or things? ___demonstrative___

42. Demonstrative pronouns can be used as both ___pronouns and adjectives___.

43. In what three respects does **hic** refer to something close to the speaker? _____
    time, space, thought

44. Third-declension nouns ending in ___-o___ are usually feminine, and those ending in
    ___-tas -tatis___ are always feminine.

45. When used together, **ille** and **hic** mean, respectively, ___the former, the latter___

46. Give two uses of the demonstrative **iste**. _____
    1) point out something close to the person spoken to, 2) in contempt

47. Which demonstrative means *the famous* when it follows a noun? ___**ille illa illud**___

48. Give the four demonstrative pronouns. ___**is ea id; hic haec hoc**___
    ___**ille illa illlud; iste ista istud**___

49. Which demonstrative is also used as the 3rd person personal pronoun? ___**is ea id**___

50. The forms for ___reflexive___ and ___intensive___ pronouns are
    identical in English, but different in Latin.

51. In English, reflexive and intensive pronouns end in ___self, selves___.

52. Give the 1st person reflexive/intensive pronouns in English. ___myself, ourselves___

53. Give the 2nd person reflexive/intensive pronouns in English. ___yourself, yourselves___

54. Give the 3rd person reflexive/intensive pronouns in English. ___himself, herself,___
    ___themselves___

55. An intensive pronoun ___emphasizes___ another word in the sentence.

56. The intensive pronoun in Latin is ___**ipse**___.

57. The reflexive pronoun reflects back on the ___subject___, is
    always in the ___predicate___, and never in the ___nominative___ case.

58. 1st/2nd person personal and reflexive pronouns are ___identical___ in Latin.

59. The 3rd person reflexive pronouns in Latin are ___**sui, sibi, se, se**___

60. What three declensions have nouns ending in **-us** in the nominative? ___2nd, 3rd, 4th___

61. Most 3rd declension nouns ending in **-us** are what gender? ___neuter___

62. Give some English words that express the subjunctive. _____
    may, might, let, should, could, would

63. Which two tenses are missing from the subjunctive? _future, future perfect_

64. The indicative mood describes activity that is _real, actual_.

65. The subjunctive mood describes activity that is _potential_.

66. The subjunctive is used mainly in _subordinate clauses_.

67. Give two ways to use the subjunctive in an independent clause. _hortatory subjunctive and deliberative questions_

68. A clause is part of a sentence that has _a subject and a verb_.

69. What is the difference between a phrase and a clause? _A phrase does not have a subject and a verb, and a clause does._

70. A clause that can stand alone is an _independent_ clause.

71. A clause that cannot stand alone is a _subordinate_ clause.

72. A subordinate clause that uses the subjunctive is the _purpose clause_.

73. The present subjunctive is formed by _adding_ or _changing_ these vowels before the personal ending:
    1st conj. _substitute **e** for **a**_
    2nd conj. _add **a**_
    3rd conj. _substitute **a** for **i, o, u**_
    3rd conj. **io** _add **a**_
    4th conj. _add **a**_

74. What sentence helps you remember the vowel changes in the subjunctive? _We beat a liar._

75. The hortatory subjunctive is used to express _exhortation, indirect command, strong wish_ and is usually translated with _let or may_.

76. The meaning of the subjunctive must be determined by the _context_, but we will use the helping verbs _may and might_ for recitation.

77. A subjunctive clause is made negative by using the conjunction _ne_.

78. A deliberative question is asked in _doubt_ or _indignation_ and is expressed in English by the helping verb _should_.

79. A deliberative question uses the _present_ subjunctive for present time and the _imperfect_ subjunctive for past time.

80. The _infinitive_ can be used to show purpose in English, but not in Latin.

263

81. In a sentence with a purpose clause, the main verb is in the _indicative_, and the purpose clause is in the _subjunctive_.

82. The verbs in a sentence with a purpose clause must _correspond_ in tense.

83. If the verb of the main clause is in the present or future, the verb of the purpose clause is in the _present subjunctive_.

84. If the verb of the main clause is in the past, the verb of the purpose clause is in the _imperfect subjunctive_.

85. The perfect subjunctive is identical to the _future perfect_ tense except for _the first person singular_.

86. A negative clause of purpose replaces **ut** with _ne_.

87. The active perfect and pluperfect subjunctives are built on the _perfect_ stem by adding _-eri-_ and _-isse-_, respectively.

88. Give the two neuter and two feminine nouns of the 4th declension. _**Cornu** and **genu** are neuter, and **domus** and **manus** are feminine._

89. In adjectives and adverbs there are three _degrees of comparison_.

90. These are: _positive, comparative, superlative_

91. The _positive_ is descriptive.

92. The _comparative_ implies a comparison between two persons or things.

93. The _superlative_ implies a comparison among more than two persons or things.

94. In English, many positive adjectives can be changed into comparatives by adding _-er_ and changed into superlatives by adding _-est_.

95. Give an example of these in English using the adjective _great_. _great, greater, greatest_

96. In English, other adjectives and adverbs are compared by means of the words _more_ and _most_.

97. The Latin comparative is formed by adding _-ior_ and _-ius_ to the stem.

98. The Latin comparative is declined like the regular _3rd-declension_ noun.

99. The superlative adjective is formed by adding _-issimus, -rimus, or -limus_ to the stem.

100. The superlative adjective is declined like _**bonus -a -um**_.

101. Two nouns or pronouns compared using the adverb **quam** must be _in the same case_

264

Third Form Grammar Questions

102. A comparative adjective used to indicate degree rather than comparison means _____ rather, too, more than the average .

103. A superlative adjective used to indicate degree rather than comparison means _____ very .

104. Adjectives with stems ending in a vowel are usually compared using the adverbs _____ **magis, máximē** .

105. Adverbs stand _____ before _____ the verbs they modify.

106. 1st/2nd-declension adjectives are changed into adverbs by _____ adding -**ē** to the stem .

107. Some adjectives, especially of quantity and number, form adverbs with the _____ accusative singular .

108. Third-declension adjectives of two and three terminations are changed into adverbs by _____ adding -**iter** or -**er** to the stem .

109. The comparative of regular adverbs is the _____ neuter singular nominative form .

110. The superlative of regular adverbs is formed by _____ adding -**ē** to the superlative stem .

Second Form Grammar Questions

1. Give the three nominative singular endings for 2nd decl. masculine nouns. **-us, -er, -ir**

2. 2nd-decl. -**er** nouns either _____ drop _____ or _____ retain _____ the **e** in the stem.

3. Some nouns have only plural forms. An example is _____ **líberi liberorum** .

4. Four confusing words with the root of **liber** are _____ **líberi liberorum** *children,* **liber libri** *book,* **liber líbera líberum** *free,* **líbero (1)** *to set free* .

5. What kind of verbs have indirect objects? _____ giving and telling
Give Latin examples. _____ **do, demonstro, núntio, narro**

6. What are the two ways to show an indirect object in English? _____ the preposition to; word order - the indirect object precedes the direct object

7. In Latin the indirect object is in the _____ dative _____ case.

8. What is Sentence Pattern #5? _____ subject + verb + I.O. + D.O.

9. Give an example of Sentence Pattern #5 in Latin. _____ **María Marco rosam dedit.**

10. Name the four verb complements you have learned. _____ predicate nominative predicate adjective direct object indirect object

11. What are the two ways to show possession in English? _____ preposition *of* and *'s*

12. In Latin the possessive noun is in the _____ genitive _____ case.

13. Third declension nouns that have a genitive plural in **ium** are called _____ **i-stems** .

14. Give two indications a noun may be an **i-stem** and an example of each.
(1) same number of syllables in nominative and genitive - **collis collis** or
(2) stem ends in two consonants - **pons pontis**

15. What are the two types of adjectives in Latin? _____ 1st/2nd declension and 3rd decl.

16. Third declension adjectives are related to _____ **i-stem** nouns .

17. Define pronoun. _____ A pronoun takes the place of a noun.

18. How many kinds of pronouns are there? Name them in pairs. _____ 8: personal, possessive; reflexive, intensive; interrogative, relative; demonstrative, indefinite

19. What is an antecedent? _____ An antecedent is the noun the pronoun takes the place of.

20. Give the Latin word for *we*: _____ **nos** _____ for *us*: _____ **nos**

21. How do you write **cum** with the 1st/2nd person pronouns? _____ **mecum   tecum   nobiscum   vobiscum**

22. The genitive of 1st and 2nd person pronouns is used for _____ of _____ expressions that do not show _____ possession _____ .

23. To show possession in the 1st and 2nd person, use the possessive pronoun adjectives: _____ **meus   tuus   noster   vester** _____ .

24. The possessive pronoun adjectives function like adjectives or pronouns? __adjectives__

25. Give the Adjective Agreement Rule. _____ An adjective agrees with its noun in gender, number, and case, but not declension.

26. Give the Pronoun Agreement Rule. The pronoun agrees with its antecedent in gender and number, but its case is determined by its function in its own clause.

27. Define preposition. A preposition shows the relationship between its object and another word in the sentence.

28. A prepositional phrase consists of the preposition and its _____ object (and modifiers) .

29. What English word adds an additional letter before words that begin with vowels? __a__

30. What two Latin prepositions are similar to this word? _____ a/ab   e/ex

31. Latin prepositions *govern* either the_____ ablative or _____ accusative case.

32. Prepositions that express motion forward generally take what case? _____ accusative

33. Prepositions that express location, no motion, or motion from, take what case?_____ abl.

34. Give two prepositions that can take either the ablative or the accusative case. _____ **in, sub**

35. The infinitive ending for 2nd-conjugation verbs is _____ **-ēre** _____ ; and for 3rd-conjugation verbs is_____ **-ere** _____ .

36. The 3rd conjugation does not have a stem with a consistent_____ stem vowel .

37. In the 3rd conjugation you must chop to the _____ root to find the present stem.

38. How can you remember the variable vowels in the 3rd conjugation present system? _____ AE in future IOU in present

39. Why is the 3rd conjugation an old maid? _____ it has no bo's in its future

40. The infinitive of the 4th conjugation is _____ **-ire** _____ .

41. Give the stem vowels for all four conjugations. _____ 1st **a**, 2nd **ē**, 3rd (none), 4th **i**

42. The present system of the 4th conjugation is essentially the same as the 3rd conjugation with the addition of _____ the stem vowel **i** _____ .

43. 3rd **io** verbs belong to the 3rd conjugation because their infinitive ends in _____ **-ere**

44. The present system of 3rd **io** verbs looks exactly like _____ the present system of the 4th conj. .

45. Define adverb. _____ An adverb modifies a verb, adjective, or another adverb. _____

46. An adverb most commonly modifies a verb by answering the questions_____ how, when, where, to what extent _____ .

47. Many 1st/2nd declension adjectives can be changed into adverbs by adding _____ **-ē** to the adjective stem.

48. Many 3rd declension adjectives can be changed into adverbs by adding _____ **-iter** to the adjective stem.

49. Some adjectives use their _____ neuter singular accusative _____ forms as adverbs. These forms end in either _____ **-um** or _____ **-e** Two examples are _____ **multum** and _____ **fácile**

50. The perfect system is _____ perfectly regular in all four conjugations.

51. How do you find the perfect stem for all four conjugations? _____ Drop the **-i** from the 3rd principal part.

52. Although 3rd conjugation verbs do not have regular principal parts, they do have _____ patterns that will help you remember them. What is the pattern for verbs like **rego**? _____ **-o -ere -xi -ctus**

53. What are the two types of direct questions? 1) questions introduced by question words 2) questions answered with a *yes* or *no*

54. How do you form yes or no questions in English? _____ by placing the helping verb first

55. How do you form yes or no questions in Latin? _____ Add the enclitic **-ne** to the end of the first word, usually the verb.

56. Give the six common question words in English. _____ who, what, when, where, why, how

57. Give the two voices of Latin verbs. _____ active and passive

58. In the active voice, the subject _____ performs the action of the verb _____ .

59. In the passive voice, the subject _____ receives the action of the verb

60. To form the passive forms of the present system, substitute _____ passive personal endings for _____ active _____ personal endings.

61. When the action of the passive verb is performed by a LIVING AGENT, the construction is called _____ the ablative of agent _____ and requires the preposition _____ **a/ab**

Second Form Grammar Questions

62. Give an example. **Galli a Caésare superantur.** The Gauls are overcome by Caesar.

63. When the action of the verb is performed by a NON-LIVING THING, the construction is called _____ablative of means_____ and the preposition is _____omitted_____ .

64. Give an example. _____**Galli gládio superantur.** The Gauls are overcome by the sword.

65. What is the one irregularity in the present passive system of
    1st conjugation? _____2nd person singular of future tense **-beris**_____
    2nd conjugation? _____2nd person singular of future tense **-beris**_____
    3rd conjugation? _____2nd person singular of present tense **-eris**_____
    3rd **io** conjugation? _____2nd person singular of present tense **-eris**_____
    4th conjugation? _____NONE_____

First Form Grammar Questions

1. Give the five vowel letters and their long sounds in Latin. _____a e i o u_____
   /ah/   /ay/   /ee/   /oh/   /ōō/ (food)

2. Give two Latin words that have the long sound of the five vowels. **glória Jesus**

3. Always in Latin and usually in English, **c, g,** and **sc** are **soft** before _____e, i, ae, oe_____ .

4. Always in Latin and usually in English, **c, g,** and **sc** are **hard** before _____**a, o, u,** consonants_____ .

5. In Latin and English **hard c** has the sound of _____/k/_____ .

6. Soft **c** has the sound of _____/s/_____ in English and _____/ch/_____ in Latin.

7. In Latin, **gn** is pronounced like _____/ny/_____ . Give two examples. _____**pugno** (*I fight*), **magnus** (*large*)_____

8. Give the names, from left to right, of the last three syllables of a Latin word. _____antepenult   penult   ultima_____

9. The accent is on _____penult_____ unless the _____antepenult_____ is marked.

10. Verb families are called _____conjugations_____ .

11. How many conjugations are there? _____four_____ Name them. _____first, second, third, fourth_____

12. Give the six attributes of a Latin verb. conjugation, person, number, tense, voice, and mood

13. Give the three grammar persons. _____first person, second person, third person_____

14. The first person is the person _____speaking_____ .
    The second person is the person _____spoken to_____ .
    The third person is the person _____spoken about_____ .

15. Give the two grammar numbers. _____singular, plural_____

16. How many Latin tenses are there? _____six_____
    Name them. _____present, imperfect, future, perfect, pluperfect, future perfect_____

17. The stem vowel of the 1st Conjugation is _____a_____ .

18. Give the names for the three forms of the English present tense. _____simple present_____
    progressive present   emphatic present

19. In English *I praise* is the _____simple_____ present, *I am praising* is the _____progressive_____ present, and *I do praise* is the _____emphatic_____ present.

20. In Latin *imperfect* means _____not finished_____ .

21. The imperfect tense sign is _____-ba-_____ .

269   270

22. The imperfect tense is used to describe an ___ongoing, repeated, habitual___ or ___interrupted___ action.

23. What English helping verbs translate the imperfect tense? ___were, was___

24. The two basic parts of a sentence are ___the subject and the predicate___.

25. The subject is ___**who** or **what** the sentence is about___.

26. The predicate tells ___what the subject **is** or **does**___.

27. What is Sentence Pattern #1? ___subject + verb___

28. What English helping verb translates the Latin future tense? ___will___

29. The three tenses that make up the Present System are ___present, imperfect, future___.

30. The Present System is built on the ___present stem___.

31. What are principal parts? How many are there? ___The forms that provide the stems needed to conjugate a verb in all its tenses. There are usually four p.p.___

32. What is the name of the 2nd principal part? ___infinitive___

33. The infinitive ending for all 1st conjugation verbs is ___-are___.

34. How do you find the present stem? ___Drop -re from the infinitive.___

35. The English infinitive is written with the particle ___to___ before the verb.

36. The to be verb shows ___existence___ not ___action___.

37. Give the English forms of the **to be** verb. ___am, is, are, was, were, be, being, been___

38. Give the regular endings for the principal parts of 1st conjugation verbs. ___-o -are -avi -atus___

39. What is Sentence Pattern #2? ___subject + verb + direct object___

40. Something that completes the action of the verb is a ___complement___.

41. What is the first complement in this text? ___the complementary infinitive___

42. In Latin grammar *perfect* means ___finished___.

43. The perfect tense describes what kind of action? ___a one-time action completed in the past___

44. The perfect tense is built on the ___perfect___ stem.

45. How do you find the perfect stem? ___Drop -i from the 3rd principal part.___

46. Give three translations for **vocavi**. ___I called, I have called, I did call___

47. What English helping verbs translate the perfect tense? ___have, has, did___

48. The pluperfect tense is built on the ___perfect___ stem.

49. The pluperfect tense describes what kind of action? ___a past action completed prior to another past action___

50. What English helping verb translates the pluperfect tense? ___had___

51. The pluperfect tense endings are identical to ___the imperfect tense of **sum**___

52. The future perfect tense is built on the ___perfect___ stem.

53. The future perfect tense describes ___an action in the future completed prior to another action in the future___

54. What English helping verbs translate the future perfect tense? ___will have___

55. The future perfect tense endings are identical to ___the future tense of **sum**___ except for the ___3rd person plural___

56. The tenses of the Perfect System are ___perfect, pluperfect, future perfect___ and they are built on the ___perfect stem___

57. Verb families are called ___conjugations___, and noun families are called ___declensions___

58. How many declensions are there? Name them. ___five: 1st, 2nd, 3rd, 4th, 5th___

59. Give the four attributes of nouns. ___declension, gender, number, and case___

60. The three genders are ___masculine, feminine, neuter___.

61. Nouns that name male or female persons or animals have ___natural___ gender. Give three English examples. ___sister, brother, father, queen, king, uncle, etc.___

62. Nouns that name non-living things have ___grammatical___ gender.

63. To what does the **case** of a noun refer? ___the job of a noun in a sentence___

64. Name the cases in order. ___nominative, genitive, dative, accusative, ablative___

65. What is the **subject** case? ___nominative___

66. What is the **direct object** case? ___accusative___

67. What is the **indirect object** case? ___dative___

68. What is the **possessive** case? ___genitive___

First Form Grammar Questions

69. What is the **in/by/with/from** case? _____ablative_____

70. What is the **to/for** case? _____dative_____

71. What is the **of** case? _____genitive_____

72. The genitive singular of a 1st declension noun always ends in _____-ae_____ .

73. 1st declension nouns are usually what gender? _____feminine_____

74. Three important exceptions to the 1st declension feminine rule are _**poeta, nauta, agrícola**_ .

75. Latin does not have the English articles _____a, an, the_____ .

76. Give three translations for the Latin noun **mensa**. _____table, a table, the table_____

77. The genitive singular of a 2nd declension noun always ends in _____-i_____ .

78. Second declension **-us** nouns are usually _____masculine_____ in gender.

79. Name the two subgroups of the 2nd declension, and give their gender.
    1) _____**-us** nouns with masculine gender_____
    2) _____**-um** nouns with neuter gender_____

80. Verbs have _____tense, personal_____ endings and nouns have _____case_____ endings.

81. Second declension **-um** nouns are always _____neuter_____ in gender.

82. The declension a noun belongs to is determined by the _____genitive singular_____

83. The natural gender rule _____trumps_____ all other gender rules.

84. What is the neuter rule? _____nominative and accusative endings are the same_____
    _____nominative and accusative plural ending is **-a**_____

85. The subject and verb must agree in _____person and number_____ .

86. What is an adjective? _____An adjective modifies or describes a noun or pronoun._____

87. In Latin an adjective must agree with its noun in _____gender, number, case_____ ,
    but not _____declension_____ .

88. Usually an adjective of _____quantity_____ precedes a noun,
    and an adjective of _____quality_____ follows the noun.

89. Counting numbers are called _____cardinal_____ .

90. Numbers which indicate the order of things in a series are called _____ordinal_____ .

91. What is Sentence Pattern #3? _____subject + linking verb + predicate adjective_____

First Form Grammar Questions

92. What is Sentence Pattern #4? _____subject + linking verb + predicate nominative_____

93. The genitive singular of a 3rd declension noun always ends in _____-is_____ .

94. How can you know the gender of a 3rd declension noun? _____You have to memorize it._____

95. Masculine and feminine nouns of the 3rd declension have _____the same_____ case endings.

96. How do you find the stem of a Latin noun? _____Drop the genitive singular ending._____

97. The usual word order for an English sentence is _____subject - verb - direct object_____ .

98. How many of the seven basic sentence patterns have complements? _____six_____

99. What are the three complements covered in this text? _____direct object, predicate adjective
    predicate nominative_____

100. What are the two kinds of direct objects covered in this text? _____1) complementary infinitive
     2) direct object in the accusative case_____

101. The usual word order for a Latin sentence is _____subject - direct object - verb_____ .

102. What kind of verb is never followed by a direct object? _____the verb **sum**, the **to be** verb_____

103. The genitive singular of the 4th declension always ends in _____-ūs_____ .

104. Fourth declension nouns are usually _____masculine_____ gender,
     and two common exceptions are _____**domus** and **manus**_____

105. The genitive singular of the 5th declension is _____-ei_____ .

106. Most 5th declension nouns are _____feminine_____ gender, and one common exception is _____**dies**_____ .

107. The stem vowel of the 2nd conjugation is _____ē_____ .

108. The infinitive ending for all 2nd conjugation verbs is _____-ēre_____ .

109. The regular endings for the principal parts of a 2nd conjugation verb are _**-eo -ēre -ui -itus**_

110. Draw the gender triangle.

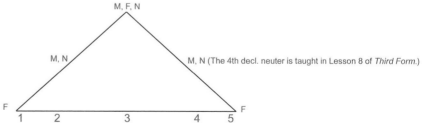

273   274

Drill Form A

Name _____ Date _____

Principal parts _____

Present System Stem _____

	Present		Indicative Active		Indicative Passive	

	Imperfect					

	Future					

Perfect System Stem _____

	Perfect		Indicative Active		Indicative Passive	

	Pluperfect					

	Future Perfect					

Drill Form A

Worksheet 2

Drill Form A

277

Present

	Subjunctive Active			Subjunctive Passive		

Imperfect

Perfect

Pluperfect

Imperatives

Number	Active	Passive
S. and Pl.		

Participles

Tense	Active	Passive
Present		
Perfect		
Future		

Infinitives

Present		
Perfect		
Future		

Gerund

gen.	
dat.	
acc.	
abl.	

Gerundive

Name _____ Date _____

Synopsis of _____ Principal parts _____

Indicative

Tense	Active	Passive
Present		
Imperfect		
Future		
Perfect		
Pluperfect		
Future Perfect		

Subjunctive

	Active	Passive
Present		
Imperfect		
Perfect		
Pluperfect		

Imperative

Present	Active	Passive
Singular		
Plural		

Participles

Tense	Active	Passive
Present		
Perfect		
Future		

Infinitives

	Active	Passive
Present		
Perfect		
Future		

Case	Gerund	Gerundive
gen.		
dat.		
acc.		
abl.		

How to Use
Vocabulary Drill Sheets

Vocabulary mastery is one of the more difficult and unpleasant aspects of learning a new language. Even though students have flashcards, we have found that classroom drills are also necessary. When you see that students are starting to confuse words and lose old vocabulary, begin classroom drills with these drill sheets.

At the beginning of each class, students recite *in choro* the vocabulary on the drill sheets up to and including the lessons you have completed. Recite the vocabulary exactly as it is written on the drill sheets (**amo, amare**, *to love*, **nato, natare**, *to swim*, **do, dare, dedi, datus**, *to give*, etc.).

There are many ways to vary the recitation. Have a student come to the front and give the English, and let the class respond with the Latin, and vice versa; or have the girls give the English and the boys the Latin, or have the teacher say the Latin with the students responding, etc.

Make it lively; do it with rhythm. Make sure students are speaking up loudly, clearly, and *with energy*. They should be looking at the words and listening as they recite *with energy*. Work on only two columns at a time. When you start the next column, drop the first one.

To make this review effective, it is necessary to give a weekly quiz over the vocabulary columns you are working on. Make this your weekend assignment—to study for a cumulative vocab quiz for the next Monday. (The cumulative vocab quiz will be in addition to the weekly Friday vocab quiz over the new lesson, of course.)

Each Monday give a cumulative vocabulary quiz of 5-10 words from the columns you are working on. Vary the quizzes, sometimes giving the Latin and sometimes the English. You can also give an oral **Power Quiz**. Each student is given one word orally for his/her quiz—ten points or a zero. We have found students study harder for this "do or die" quiz than any other.

Third Form Vocab Drill

2	**cedo -ere cessi cessus**	to yield, give way
2	**claudo -ere clausi clausus**	to close
2	**gero -ere gessi gestus**	to wage, carry on
2	**mitto -ere misi missus**	to send
2	**pono -ere pósui pósitus**	to put, place
2	**premo -ere pressi pressus**	to press, push
2	**scribo -ere scripsi scriptus**	to write
3	**ago -ere egi actus**	to do, drive, act, treat; give (*with* **grátias**)
3	**cogo -ere coegi coactus**	to collect, force
3	**tollo -ere sústuli sublatus**	to lift (up), raise
5	**aut** (*conj.*)	or
5	**aut ... aut** (*conj.*)	either ... or
5	**autem** (*conj.*)	however, moreover (*postpositive*)
5	**enim** (*conj.*)	for, in fact, truly (*postpositive*)
5	**et** (*conj.*)	and
5	**et ... et** (*conj.*)	both ... and
5	**ítaque** (*conj.*)	therefore, and so
5	**olim** (*adv.*)	once (upon a time), of old, one day
5	**-que** (*enclitic conj.*)	and
5	**quod** (*conj.*)	because
5	**sed** (*conj.*)	but
5	**sicut** (*conj.*)	as
6	**étiam** (*adv.*)	also
6	**fere** (*adv.*)	almost
6	**ibi** (*adv.*)	there, in that place
6	**ínterim** (*adv.*)	meanwhile
6	**ita** (*adv.*)	yes, so, thus
6	**jam** (*adv.*)	already, now
6	**póstea** (*adv.*)	afterwards
6	**súbito** (*adv.*)	suddenly
6	**tamen** (*adv.*)	nevertheless
8	**Jesus -u**	Jesus
8	**cornu -ūs** *n.*	horn
8	**genu -ūs** *n.*	knee

8	**satis** (*indecl.*)	enough
8	**nihil (nil)** (*indecl.*)	nothing
8	**Caesar -aris** *m.*	Caesar
9	**albus -a -um**	white
9	**almus -a -um**	nurturing
9	**cálidus -a -um**	warm, hot
9	**defessus -a -um**	tired, weary
9	**excelsus -a -um**	on high, lofty
9	**ferus -a -um**	wild, fierce
9	**foedus -a -um**	foul, ugly, hideous
9	**frígidus -a -um**	cold
9	**nefárius -a -um**	wicked
9	**stultus -a -um**	foolish, stupid
10	**solus -a -um**	alone, only, sole
10	**totus -a -um**	whole, entire
10	**ullus -a -um**	any (at all)
10	**nullus -a -um**	no, not any
10	**álius ália áliud**	other, another
10	**alter áltera álterum**	the other (of two), the second (of two)
10	**alter ... alter**	the one ... the other
10	**neuter -tra -trum**	neither (of two)
10	**uter -tra -trum**	which (of two)
11	**acer -cris -cre**	sharp, bitter
11	**álacer -cris -cre**	lively, spirited
11	**céleber -bris -bre**	famous
11	**celer céleris célere**	fast, swift
11	**audax -acis**	bold, rash
11	**díligens -entis**	careful, diligent
11	**felix -icis**	fortunate, lucky
11	**ingens -entis**	huge
11	**potens -entis**	powerful
11	**sápiens -entis**	wise, rational
11	**senex senis**	aged, old (person)
12	**cúpidus -a -um** (*w/ gen.*)	desirous (of), eager (for)
12	**plenus -a -um** (*w/ gen.*)	full (of)
12	**carus -a -um** (*w/ dat.*)	dear (to)
12	**finítimus -a -um** (*w/ dat.*)	neighboring, close (to)
12	**idóneus -a -um** (*w/ dat.*)	suitable, fit, proper (for)

Third Form Vocab Drill

#	Word	Meaning
12	**símilis -e** *(w/ dat.)*	similar (to)
12	**paratus -a -um** *(ad w/ acc.)*	prepared (for)
12	**útilis -e** *(ad w/ acc.)*	useful (for)
12	**tutus -a -um** *(w/ abl.)*	safe (from)
12	**vácuus -a -um** *(w/ abl.)*	empty (from or of)
13	**úndecim**	eleven
13	**duódecim**	twelve
13	**trédecim**	thirteen
13	**quattuórdecim**	fourteen
13	**quíndecim**	fifteen
13	**sédecim**	sixteen
13	**septéndecim**	seventeen
13	**duodeviginti**	eighteen
13	**undeviginti**	nineteen
13	**viginti**	twenty
13	**centum**	one hundred
13	**mille**	one thousand
14	**centúrio -onis** *m.*	centurion
14	**homo -inis** *m.*	man, human being
14	**léctio -onis** *f.*	lesson
14	**légio -onis** *f.*	legion
14	**leo -onis** *m.*	lion
14	**orátio -onis** *f.*	speech
14	**ordo -inis** *m.*	order, rank, line, row
14	**pássio -onis** *f.*	suffering
14	**tentátio -onis** *f.*	temptation
14	**virgo -inis** *f.*	virgin, maiden
15	**Athenae -arum** *f.*	Athens
15	**Británnia -ae** *f.*	Britain
15	**Caledónia -ae** *f.*	Scotland
15	**Carthago -inis** *f.*	Carthage
15	**Europa -ae** *f.*	Europe
15	**Germánia -ae** *f.*	Germany
15	**Gráecia -ae** *f.*	Greece
15	**Helvétia -ae** *f.*	Switzerland
15	**Hibérnia -ae** *f.*	Ireland
15	**is ea id**	he, she, it, him, her, they, their, them
15	**suus -a -um**	his (own), her (own), its (own), their (own)
16	**aestas -tatis** *f.*	summer

#	Word	Meaning
16	**auctóritas -tatis** *f.*	authority
16	**cáritas -tatis** *f.*	charity, love
16	**celéritas -tatis** *f.*	quickness, speed
16	**cívitas -tatis** *f.*	state
16	**libertas -tatis** *f.*	liberty, freedom
16	**pietas -tatis** *f.*	piety, duty
16	**tempestas -tatis** *f.*	thunderstorm
16	**véritas -tatis** *f.*	truth
16	**voluntas -tatis** *f.*	will
16	**hic haec hoc**	this, these
17	**amicítia -ae** *f.*	friendship
17	**fossa -ae** *f.*	ditch, trench
17	**fuga -ae** *f.*	flight, escape
17	**hasta -ae** *f.*	spear
17	**injúria -ae** *f.*	injury, injustice, wrong
17	**inópia -ae** *f.*	lack, scarcity, shortage
17	**memória -ae** *f.*	memory
17	**sagitta -ae** *f.*	arrow
17	**sapiéntia -ae** *f.*	wisdom
17	**sciéntia -ae** *f.*	knowledge
17	**ille illa illud**	he, she, it, they; that, those
17	**iste ista istud**	that, those (of yours)
17	**is ea id**	that, those
18	**agmen -inis** *n.*	army on the march, column
18	**carmen -inis** *n.*	song
18	**corpus -oris** *n.*	body
18	**genus -eris** *n.*	race, kind, class
18	**iter itíneris** *n.*	journey
18	**onus -eris** *n.*	burden
18	**opus -eris** *n.*	work
18	**tempus -oris** *n.*	time
18	**ver veris** *n.*	spring
18	**vulnus -eris** *n.*	wound
18	**ipse ipsa ipsum**	-self *(intensive)*
19	**-- sui sibi se se**	himself, herself, itself, themselves
20	**auxílium -i** *n.*	help, aid
20	**concílium -i** *n.*	council, meeting
20	**consílium -i** *n.*	counsel, advice, plan
20	**Evangélium -i** *n.*	Gospel
20	**impérium -i** *n.*	command, power
20	**ódium -i** *n.*	hate, hatred

Third Form Vocab Drill

#	Word	Meaning
20	**ovum -i** *n.*	egg
20	**perículum -i** *n.*	danger
20	**princípium -i** *n.*	beginning, origin
20	**vínculum -i** *n.*	chain, bond
21	**astrum -i** *n.*	heavenly body, heavens
21	**castellum -i** *n.*	fort
21	**exílium -i** *n.*	exile
21	**fatum -i** *n.*	destiny, fate
21	**inítium -i** *n.*	starting point
21	**pábulum -i** *n.*	fodder, nourishment
21	**praesídium -i** *n.*	protection, garrison
21	**prétium -i** *n.*	price
21	**spátium -i** *n.*	space, interval
21	**vestígium -i** *n.*	trace, footprint
22	**aedifícium -i** *n.*	building
22	**antrum -i** *n.*	cave
22	**letum -i** *n.*	death
22	**mandatum -i** *n.*	commandment, order
22	**ótium -i** *n.*	ease, leisure
22	**sepulchrum -i** *n.*	tomb
22	**theatrum -i** *n.*	theater
22	**tríduum -i** *n.*	three days
22	**vítium -i** *n.*	vice, blemish
22	**votum -i** *n.*	vow, prayer
23	**aer -is** *m.*	the air
23	**comes -itis** *m.*	companion
23	**flos floris** *m.*	flower
23	**grex gregis** *m.*	herd, flock
23	**hiems híemis** *f.*	winter
23	**júvenis -is** *m. or f.*	young person
23	**lapis -idis** *m.*	stone
23	**plebs plebis** *f.*	common people, plebeians
23	**obses -idis** *m.*	hostage
23	**uxor -oris** *f.*	wife
23	**ut** *(conj.)*	in order that, so that
24	**aequor -oris** *n.*	smooth surface, sea
24	**certamen -inis** *n.*	struggle, contest
24	**crus cruris** *n.*	leg
24	**latus -eris** *n.*	side, flank
24	**litus -oris** *n.*	shore, coast
24	**munus -eris** *n.*	office, duty
24	**os oris** *n.*	mouth

#	Word	Meaning
24	**os ossis** *n.*	bone
24	**rus ruris** *n.*	countryside
24	**scelus -eris** *n.*	crime, evil deed
25	**avis avis** *f.*	bird
25	**fames famis** *f.*	hunger, starvation
25	**fons fontis** *m.*	fountain, spring, source
25	**ignis ignis** *m.*	fire
25	**imber imbris** *m.*	rain
25	**nix nivis** *f.*	snow
25	**nox noctis** *f.*	night
25	**nubes nubis** *f.*	cloud
25	**ovis ovis** *f.*	sheep
25	**vestis vestis** *f.*	clothes
25	**ne**	so that … not, lest
26	**arcus -ūs** *m.*	bow
26	**currus -ūs** *m.*	chariot, cart, wagon
26	**cursus -ūs** *m.*	course, running
26	**equitatus -ūs** *m.*	cavalry
26	**éxitus -ūs** *m.*	end, outcome, exit
26	**ímpetus -ūs** *m.*	attack
26	**occasus -ūs** *m.*	falling, misfortune
26	**passus -ūs** *m.*	step, pace
26	**usus -ūs** *m.*	use, experience
26	**vultus -ūs** *m.*	countenance, expression
27	**alienus -a -um**	foreign, alien, strange, unfavorable
27	**angustus -a -um**	narrow, confined
27	**beatus -a -um**	blessed
27	**dúbius -a -um**	doubtful
27	**durus -a -um**	hard (not soft)
27	**pius -a -um**	pious, dutiful
27	**verus -a -um**	true
27	**citus -a -um**	rapid, quick
27	**clarus -a -um**	clear, bright, gleaming
27	**rústicus -a -um**	country (adj.), rural, unsophisticated, rustic
28	**agrestis -e**	boorish, crude
28	**civilis -e**	civil, of a citizen
28	**communis -e**	common
28	**crudelis -e**	cruel
28	**húmilis -e**	humble
28	**inanis -e**	vain, inane

Third Form Vocab Drill

28	**lenis -e**	mild, gentle
28	**mollis -e**	soft, yielding
28	**sublimis -e**	sublime, elevated
28	**tristis -e**	sad
28	**quam** *(adv.)*	than, as possible
30	**aequus -a -um**	equal to, even, level
30	**árduus -a -um**	steep, arduous
30	**ávidus -a -um**	avid, keen
30	**caecus -a -um**	blind
30	**cunctus -a -um**	all (in a group)
30	**dignus -a -um**	worthy
30	**mirus -a -um**	wondrous
30	**periculosus -a -um**	dangerous
30	**superbus -a -um**	proud
30	**tardus -a -um**	late, delayed

Second Form Vocab Drill

2	**vir viri** *m.*	man
2	**puer púeri** *m.*	boy, child
2	**vesper vésperi** *m.*	evening
2	**ager agri** *m.*	field, ground
2	**culter cultri** *m.*	knife
2	**liber libri** *m.*	book
2	**magister magistri** *m.*	teacher (male)
2	**magistra -ae** *f.*	teacher (female)
2	**líberi liberorum** *m.*	children
3	**dexter dextra dextrum**	right, right-hand
3	**sinister sinistra sinistrum**	left, left-hand
3	**ínteger íntegra íntegrum**	whole, uninjured
3	**pulcher pulchra pulchrum**	beautiful
3	**sacer sacra sacrum**	sacred
3	**aeger aegra aegrum**	sick, ill
3	**piger pigra pigrum**	lazy
3	**asper áspera ásperum**	sharp, harsh
3	**miser mísera míserum**	wretched
3	**liber líbera líberum**	free
5	**civis civis** *m./f.*	citizen
5	**hostis hostis** *m./f.*	enemy
5	**navis navis** *f.*	ship
5	**collis collis** *m.*	hill
5	**pons pontis** *m.*	bridge
5	**mons montis** *m.*	mountain
5	**pars partis** *f.*	part, region
5	**urbs urbis** *f.*	city
5	**gens gentis** *f.*	tribe
5	**mare maris** *n.*	sea
6	**brevis -e**	short, brief
6	**fácilis -e**	easy
6	**diffícilis -e**	difficult
6	**fortis -e**	strong, brave
6	**gravis -e**	heavy, serious, severe
6	**omnis -e**	each, every (s.); all (pl.)
6	**turpis -e**	shameful, disgraceful
6	**dulcis -e**	sweet, pleasant

6	**fidelis -e**	faithful
6	**nóbilis -e**	noble
7	**aquae -ae** *f.*	water
7	**culpa -ae** *f.*	fault, blame
7	**ira -ae** *f.*	anger
7	**luna -ae** *f.*	moon
7	**silva -ae** *f.*	forest
7	**stella -ae** *f.*	star
7	**umbra -ae** *f.*	shadow
7	**unda -ae** *f.*	wave
7	**ursa -ae** *f.*	bear (female)
7	**vita -ae** *f.*	life
7	**ego mei**	I, me
7	**nos nostri**	we, us
8	**fília -ae** *f.*	daughter
8	**Gállia -ae** *f.*	Gaul
8	**grátia -ae** *f.*	grace, favor; thanks (pl.)
8	**Hispánia -ae** *f.*	Spain
8	**Lúcia -ae** *f.*	Lucy
8	**pátria -ae** *f.*	fatherland, country
8	**pecúnia -ae** *f.*	money
8	**província -ae** *f.*	province
8	**via -ae** *f.*	road, way
8	**victória -ae** *f.*	victory
8	**tu tui**	you
8	**vos vestri**	you (pl.)
9	**áquila -ae** *f.*	eagle
9	**aurora -ae** *f.*	dawn
9	**corona -ae** *f.*	crown
9	**culina -ae** *f.*	kitchen
9	**fábula -ae** *f.*	story, tale
9	**fémina -ae** *f.*	woman
9	**fenestra -ae** *f.*	window
9	**fortuna -ae** *f.*	fortune
9	**ínsula -ae** *f.*	island
9	**jánua -ae** *f.*	door
9	**meus mea meum**	my
9	**tuus tua tuum**	your
9	**noster nostra nostrum**	our
9	**vester vestra vestrum**	your (pl.)

Second Form Vocab Drill

10	**a, ab** *(with abl.)*	by, from
10	**coram** *(with abl.)*	in the presence of
10	**cum** *(with abl.)*	with
10	**de** *(with abl.)*	about, down from
10	**e, ex** *(with abl.)*	out of, out from
10	**in** *(with abl.)*	in, on
10	**prae** *(with abl.)*	at the head of
10	**pro** *(with abl.)*	for, on behalf of, in front of
10	**sine** *(with abl.)*	without
10	**sub** *(with abl.)*	under, at the foot of
10	**tenus** *(with abl.)*	as far as
10	**ara -ae** *f.*	altar
10	**epístula -ae** *f.*	letter
10	**porta -ae** *f.*	gate
10	**sella -ae** *f.*	seat
10	**villa -ae** *f.*	farmhouse
11	**ad** *(with acc.)*	to, toward, at
11	**ante** *(with acc.)*	before (in time and place)
11	**apud** *(with acc.)*	among
11	**in** *(with acc.)*	into, onto
11	**inter** *(with acc.)*	between
11	**ob** *(with acc.)*	because of
11	**per** *(with acc.)*	through
11	**post** *(with acc.)*	after, behind
11	**propter** *(with acc.)*	on account of
11	**sub** *(with acc.)*	to the foot of
11	**trans** *(with acc.)*	across
11	**circum** *(with acc.)*	around
11	**contra** *(with acc.)*	against
11	**juxta** *(with acc.)*	near
11	**cena -ae** *f.*	dinner
11	**herba -ae** *f.*	green plant, grass
11	**tabella -ae** *f.*	writing tablet
11	**turba -ae** *f.*	crowd, turmoil
11	**vacca -ae** *f.*	cow
16	**altē**	highly, deeply
16	**latē**	widely
16	**líberē**	freely
16	**pulchrē**	beautifully
16	**ásperē**	roughly
16	**míserē**	unhappily

16	**multum**	much
16	**longē**	far, by far
16	**longus longa longum**	long
16	**laetē**	happily
16	**laetus laeta laetum**	happy
16	**lentē**	slowly
16	**lentus lenta lentum**	slow
16	**certē**	certainly
16	**certus certa certum**	certain
16	**bréviter**	shortly, briefly
16	**gráviter**	heavily, seriously
16	**fórtiter**	bravely
16	**fidéliter**	faithfully
16	**difficíliter**	with difficulty
16	**túrpiter**	shamefully
16	**fácile**	easily
13, 18	**rego régere rexi rectus**	to rule
13, 18	**dico dícere dixi dictus**	to say, speak
13, 18	**duco dúcere duxi ductus**	to lead
13, 18	**figo fígere fixi fixus**	to fix, fasten
13, 18	**jungo júngere junxi junctus**	to join, connect
13, 18	**struo strúre struxi structus**	to build, construct
13, 18	**traho tráhere traxi tractus**	to drag, haul
13, 18	**veho véhere vexi vectus**	to convey, transport
13, 18	**vivo vívere vixi victus**	to live, be alive
13, 18	**vinco víncere vici victus**	to conquer
14, 19	**áudio audire audivi auditus**	to hear
14, 19	**dórmio dormire dormivi dormitus**	to sleep
14, 19	**fínio finire finivi finitus**	to finish, limit
14, 19	**múnio munire munivi munitus**	to fortify, protect
14, 19	**scio scire scivi scitus**	to know

Second Form Vocab Drill

14, 19	**néscio nescire nescivi nescitus**	to not know
14, 19	**impédio -ire -ivi -itus**	to hinder, obstruct
14, 19	**vénio venire veni ventus**	to come
14, 19	**invénio invenire inveni inventus**	to discover, find out
14, 19	**séntio sentire sensi sensus**	to feel, perceive
15, 20	**cápio cápere cepi captus**	to take, capture
15, 20	**fácio fácere feci factus**	to make, do
15, 20	**jácio jácere jeci jactus**	to throw, hurl
15, 20	**fúgio fúgere fugi fúgitus**	to flee
15, 20	**cúpio cúpere cupivi cupitus**	to desire, long for
21	**quis?**	who?
21	**quid?**	what?
21	**quando?**	when?
21	**ubi?**	where? in what place?
21	**cur?**	why?
21	**quot?**	how many?
21	**quam diu?**	how long?
21	**quómodo?**	how (in what manner)?
21	**-ne**	*enclitic to form yes or no questions*
22	**campus -i** *m.*	field, plain
22	**cibus -i** *m.*	food
22	**hortus -i** *m.*	garden
22	**locus -i** *m.*	place
22	**ludus -i** *m.*	game, school
22	**lupus -i** *m.*	wolf
22	**nimbus -i** *m.*	cloud, storm cloud
22	**ventus -i** *m.*	wind
22	**Gallus -i** *m.*	a Gaul
22	**Marcus -i** *m.*	Mark
23	**ánimus -i** *m.*	mind, spirit
23	**bárbarus -i** *m.*	barbarian, foreigner
23	**Christianus -i** *m.*	a Christian
23	**discípulus -i** *m.*	student
23	**gládius -i** *m.*	sword

23	**legatus -i** *m.*	lieutenant
23	**óculus -i** *m.*	eye
23	**pópulus -i** *m.*	people
23	**Romanus -i** *m.*	a Roman
23	**sócius -i** *m.*	ally
24	**argentum -i** *n.*	silver
24	**aurum -i** *n.*	gold
24	**collum -i** *n.*	neck
24	**ferrum -i** *n.*	iron, iron tool
24	**lignum -i** *n.*	wood
24	**scutum -i** *n.*	shield
24	**telum -i** *n.*	missile (javelin, spear, dart)
24	**tergum -i** *n.*	back, rear
24	**vallum -i** *n.*	wall, rampart
24	**vinum -i** *n.*	wine
25	**brácchium -i** *n.*	arm (forearm)
25	**fólium -i** *n.*	leaf
25	**frumentum -i** *n.*	grain, corn
25	**gáudium -i** *n.*	joy
25	**peccatum -i** *n.*	sin, mistake
25	**praémium -i** *n.*	reward
25	**proélium -i** *n.*	battle
25	**saéculum -i** *n.*	age, time period
25	**signum -i** *n.*	sign
25	**stúdium -i** *n.*	zeal, enthusiasm, study
26	**arbor árboris** *f.*	tree
26	**amor amoris** *m.*	love, passion
26	**clamor clamoris** *m.*	shout, cry
26	**dolor doloris** *m.*	grief, pain
26	**imperator imperatoris** *m.*	general, commander
26	**labor laboris** *m.*	work, toil
26	**orator oratoris** *m.*	speaker, orator
26	**pastor pastoris** *m.*	shepherd, pastor
26	**piscator piscatoris** *m.*	fisherman
26	**senator senatoris** *m.*	senator

First Form Vocab Drill

1	**amo -are**	to love
1	**do dare dedi datus**	to give
1	**lavo lavare lavi lautus**	to wash
1	**nato -are**	to swim
1	**oro -are**	to speak, pray
1	**paro -are**	to prepare
1	**porto -are**	to carry
1	**servo -are**	to guard, keep
1	**sto stare steti status**	to stand
1	**voco -are**	to call
2	**aro -are**	to plow
2	**clamo -are**	to shout
2	**erro -are**	to err, wander
2	**juvo juvare juvi jutus**	to help
2	**laudo -are**	to praise
2	**narro -are**	to tell
2	**opto -are**	to desire, wish
2	**pugno -are**	to fight
2	**specto -are**	to look at
2	**tempto -are**	to tempt
3	**návigo -are**	to sail
3	**líbero -are**	to set free
3	**saluto -are**	to greet
3	**adoro -are**	to adore
3	**hábito -are**	to live in, dwell
3	**ámbulo -are**	to walk
3	**laboro -are**	to work
3	**júdico -are**	to judge, consider
3	**óccupo -are**	to seize
3	**súpero -are**	to overcome, surpass
5	**sum esse fui futurus**	to be
8	**non**	not
8	**hódie**	today
8	**heri**	yesterday
8	**cras**	tomorrow
8	**nunc**	now
8	**tum**	then, at that time
8	**numquam**	never
8	**umquam**	ever
8	**semper**	always
8	**saepe**	often

9	**puto -are**	to think
9	**muto -are**	to change
9	**celo -are**	to hide
9	**rogo -are**	to ask
9	**volo -are**	to fly
9	**spero -are**	to hope
9	**dúbito -are**	to doubt
9	**perturbo -are**	to disturb
9	**nego -are**	to deny
9	**accuso -are**	to accuse
10	**demonstro -are**	to show, point out
10	**núntio -are**	to report
10	**vúlnero -are**	to wound
10	**exploro -are**	to explore
10	**culpo -are**	to blame
10	**creo -are**	to create
10	**appello -are**	to address
10	**oppugno -are**	to attack
10	**exspecto -are**	to wait for, expect
10	**delecto -are**	to delight, give pleasure
14	**mensa -ae** *f.*	table
14	**puella -ae** *f.*	girl
14	**regina -ae** *f.*	queen
14	**terra -ae** *f.*	earth, land
14	**agrícola -ae** *m.*	farmer
14	**nauta -ae** *m.*	sailor
14	**poeta -ae** *m.*	poet
14	**Maria -ae** *f.*	Mary
14	**Roma -ae** *f.*	Rome
14	**Itália -ae** *f.*	Italy
15	**servus -i** *m.*	slave, servant
15	**amicus -i** *m.*	friend
15	**annus -i** *m.*	year
15	**Christus -i** *m.*	Christ
15	**agnus -i** *m.*	lamb
15	**dóminus -i** *m.*	lord, master
15	**equus -i** *m.*	horse
15	**fílius -i** *m.*	son
15	**deus -i** *m.*	god
15	**mundus -i** *m.*	world, mankind
16	**bellum -i** *n.*	war
16	**caelum -i** *n.*	sky, heaven

First Form Vocab Drill

16	**donum -i** *n.*	gift
16	**forum -i** *n.*	forum, marketplace
16	**óppidum -i** *n.*	town
16	**regnum -i** *n.*	kingdom
16	**saxum -i** *n.*	rock
16	**templum -i** *n.*	temple
16	**verbum -i** *n.*	word
16	**débitum -i** *n.*	debt, sin
18	**aeternus -a -um**	eternal, everlasting
18	**altus -a -um**	high, deep
18	**bonus -a -um**	good
18	**latus -a -um**	wide, broad
18	**magnus -a -um**	great, large
18	**malus -a -um**	bad
18	**multus -a -um**	much (pl. many)
18	**novus -a -um**	new
18	**parvus -a -um**	small
18	**sanctus -a -um**	sacred, holy
19	**unus -a -um**	one
19	**duo**	two
19	**tres**	three
19	**quattuor**	four
19	**quinque**	five
19	**sex**	six
19	**septem**	seven
19	**octo**	eight
19	**novem**	nine
19	**decem**	ten
19	**primus -a -um**	first
19	**secundus -a -um**	second
19	**tértius -a -um**	third
19	**quartus -a -um**	fourth
19	**quintus -a -um**	fifth
19	**sextus -a -um**	sixth
19	**séptimus -a -um**	seventh
19	**octavus -a -um**	eighth
19	**nonus -a -um**	ninth
19	**décimus -a -um**	tenth
21	**pater patris** *m.*	father
21	**frater fratris** *m.*	brother
21	**mater matris** *f.*	mother
21	**soror sororis** *f.*	sister

21	**rex regis** *m.*	king
21	**dux ducis** *m.*	leader
21	**miles mílitis** *m.*	soldier
22	**canis canis** *m./f.*	dog
22	**crux crucis** *f.*	cross
22	**lex legis** *f.*	law
22	**lux lucis** *f.*	light
22	**mos moris** *m.*	custom
22	**panis panis** *m.*	bread
22	**pax pacis** *f.*	peace
22	**pes pedis** *m.*	foot
22	**sol solis** *m.*	sun
22	**vox vocis** *f.*	voice
23	**caput cápitis** *n.*	head
23	**cor cordis** *n.*	heart
23	**flumen flúminis** *n.*	river
23	**lumen lúminis** *n.*	lamp
23	**nomen nóminis** *n.*	name
25	**adventus -ūs** *m.*	arrival
25	**domus -ūs** *f.*	house, home
25	**exércitus -ūs** *m.*	army
25	**fructus -ūs** *m.*	fruit
25	**manus -ūs** *f.*	hand
25	**metus -ūs** *m.*	fear
25	**portus -ūs** *m.*	harbor
25	**lacus -ūs** *m.*	lake
25	**senatus -ūs** *m.*	senate
25	**spíritus -ūs** *m.*	spirit
26	**dies diei** *m.*	day
26	**fácies faciei** *f.*	face
26	**fides fidei** *f.*	faith, trust
26	**res rei** *f.*	thing, matter, affair, business
26	**spes spei** *f.*	hope
29	**débeo -ēre**	to owe, ought
29	**dóceo -ēre -ui doctus**	to teach
29	**gáudeo -ēre -- --**	to rejoice
29	**hábeo -ēre**	to have
29	**móneo -ēre**	to warn
29	**móveo -ēre movi motus**	to move
29	**sédeo -ēre sedi sessus**	to sit

First Form Vocab Drill

29	táceo -ēre	to be silent
29	téneo -ēre -ui tentus	to hold
29	vídeo -ēre vidi, visus	to see
30	júbeo -ēre jussi jussus	to order, command
30	cáveo -ēre cavi cautus	to beware of, guard against
30	prohíbeo -ēre	to prevent
30	appáreo -ēre	to appear
30	váleo -ēre -ui --	to be strong, be well
30	respóndeo -ēre respondi, responsus	to respond, answer
30	máneo -ēre mansi, mansus	to remain, stay
30	árdeo -ēre arsi arsus	to burn, be on fire
30	térreo -ēre	to frighten
30	tímeo -ēre -ui --	to fear, be afraid of

Lesson 1 Quiz

Name_____ Date_____

A. Vocabulary
Give 1st principal part only.

1. think	puto		13. order	júbeo
2. point out	demonstro		14. wash	lavo
3. change	muto		15. remain	máneo
4. attack	oppugno		16. hope	spero
5. beware of	cáveo		17. hold	téneo
6. deny	nego		18. fly	volo
7. ask	rogo		19. blame	culpo
8. be silent	táceo		20. accuse	accuso
9. see	vídeo		21. doubt	dúbito
10. help	juvo		22. fear	tímeo
11. sit	sédeo		23. rejoice	gáudeo
12. hide	celo		24. owe	débeo

B. Vocabulary
Give all principal parts.

1. call	voco	vocare	vocavi	vocatus
2. stand	sto	stare	steti	status
3. help	juvo	juvare	juvi	jutus
4. wash	lavo	lavare	lavi	lautus
5. give	do	dare	dedi	datus
6. warn	móneo	monēre	mónui	mónitus
7. hold	téneo	tenēre	ténui	tentus
8. see	vídeo	vidēre	vidi	visus
9. move	móveo	movēre	movi	motus
10. sit	sédeo	sedēre	sedi	sessus

Quiz 1

Lesson 1 Quiz

C. Latin Sayings

1. I think, therefore I am. _Cógito ergo sum._
2. Docēre, delectare, movēre _To teach, to delight, to move_
3. In umbra, ígitur, pugnábimus. _Then we will fight in the shade._
4. Vídeo et táceo. _I see and am silent._
5. always faithful _semper fidelis_
6. Now or never _Nunc aut numquam_

D. Translate

Ablative of Agent

1. ambulabunt _they will walk_
2. manserunt _they remained_
3. yesterday, today, tomorrow _heri, hodie, cras_
4. Tu a Deo non temptáberis. _You will not be tempted by God._
5. Pastor a lupo videtur. _The shepherd is seen by the wolf._
6. Ab amicis juvatur. _Hsi is (being) helped by friends._
7. The Gauls were being attacked by the soldiers. _Galli a militibus oppugnabantur._

E. Grammar

1. In the active voice, the subject _performs the action of the verb_ .
2. In the passive voice, the subject _receives the action of the verb_ .
3. When the action of a passive verb is performed by a _living agent_ the construction is called the ablative of agent.
4. Verb families are called _conjugations_ , and noun families are called _declensions_ .
5. Give the three moods of Latin verbs.
   (1) _indicative_ (2) _imperative_ (3) _subjunctive_

Lesson 1 Quiz

F. Conjugate

Conjugate **porto** in the indicative active (6 tenses) and indicative passive (3 tenses).

Present Active	
porto	portamus
portas	portatis
portat	portant

Present Passive	
portor	portamur
portaris	portámini
portatur	portantur

Imperfect Active	
portabam	portabamus
portabas	portabatis
portabat	portabant

Imperfect Passive	
portabar	portabamur
portabaris	portabámini
portabatur	portabantur

Future Active	
portabo	portábimus
portabis	portábitis
portabit	portabunt

Future Passive	
portabor	portábimur
portáberis	portabímini
portábitur	portabuntur

Perfect Active	
portavi	portávimus
portavisti	portavistis
portavit	portaverunt

Perfect Passive	
-----	-----
-----	-----
-----	-----

Pluperfect Active	
portáveram	portaveramus
portáveras	portaveratis
portáverat	portáverant

Pluperfect Passive	
-----	-----
-----	-----
-----	-----

Future Perfect Active	
portávero	portavérimus
portáveris	portavéritis
portáverit	portáverint

Future Perfect Passive	
-----	-----
-----	-----
-----	-----

Name _____ Date _____

A. Vocabulary
Give 1st principal part only.

1. know _____ scio _____
2. convey _____ veho _____
3. finish _____ fínio _____
4. join _____ jungo _____
5. lead _____ duco _____
6. capture _____ cápio _____
7. build _____ struo _____
8. live _____ vivo _____
9. throw _____ jácio _____
10. not know _____ néscio _____
11. fasten _____ figo _____
12. say _____ dico _____
13. obstruct _____ impédio _____
14. feel _____ séntio _____
15. come _____ vénio _____
16. sleep _____ dórmio _____
17. hear _____ áudio _____
18. drag _____ traho _____
19. flee _____ fúgio _____
20. desire _____ cúpio _____
21. discover _____ invénio _____
22. fortify _____ múnio _____
23. rule _____ rego _____
24. conquer _____ vinco _____

B. Vocabulary
Fill in the 2nd, 3rd, and 4th principal parts.

Principal Part				Meaning
1st	2nd	3rd	4th	
pono	pónere	pósui	pósitus	to put, place
mitto	míttere	misi	missus	to send
claudo	cláudere	clausi	clausus	to close
gero	gérere	gessi	gestus	to wage, carry on
cedo	cédere	cessi	cessus	to yield, give way
premo	prémere	pressi	pressus	to press
scribo	scríbere	scripsi	scriptus	to write
áudio	audire	audivi	auditus	to hear
rego	régere	rexi	rectus	to rule
cápio	cápere	cepi	captus	to capture

Lesson 2 Quiz

C. Latin Sayings

1. Audi Ísrael! _____ Hear O Israel! _____
2. Aut viam invéniam aut fáciam. _____ I shall find a way or make one. _____
3. Cápitur urbs quae totum cepit orbem. _____
   The city which captured the whole world is (now) captured.
4. In hoc signo vinces. _____ In this sign you will conquer. _____
5. Magister dixit. _____ The master has spoken. _____
6. Nóscitur ex sóciis. _____ He is known by his companions. _____
7. Ferrum ferro exacúitur. _____ Iron is sharpened by iron. _____

D. Translate

1. fugerunt _____ they fled _____
2. struxit _____ hsi built, constructed _____
3. Amore junguntur. _____ They are joined by love. _____
4. Óppida vallo munientur. _____ The towns will be fortified by a wall. _____
5. Píscator ventis bonis véhitur. _____ The fisherman is transported by good winds. _____
6. Vos dolore impedímini. _____ You all are hindered by pain. _____

E. Grammar

1. In the active voice, the subject _____ performs the action of the verb _____.
2. In the passive voice, the subject _____ receives the action of the verb _____.
3. When the action of a passive verb is performed by a _____ non-living agent _____, the construction is called the ablative of means.
4. The conjugation a verb belongs to is determined by the _____ infinitive _____.
5. Give the three moods of Latin verbs.
   (1) _____ indicative _____ (2) _____ imperative _____ (3) _____ subjunctive _____

Lesson 2 Quiz

F. Conjugate

Conjugate **rego** in the indicative active (6 tenses) and indicative passive (3 tenses).

Present Active	
rego	régimus
regis	régitis
regit	regunt

Present Passive	
regor	régimur
régeris	regímini
régitur	reguntur

Imperfect Active	
regebam	regebamus
regebas	regebatis
regebat	regebant

Imperfect Passive	
regebar	regebamur
regebaris	regebámini
regebatur	regebantur

Future Active	
regam	regemus
reges	regetis
reget	regent

Future Passive	
regar	regemur
regēris	regémini
regetur	regentur

Perfect Active	
rexi	réximus
rexisti	rexistis
rexit	rexerunt

Perfect Passive	
-----	-----
-----	-----
-----	-----

Pluperfect Active	
réxeram	rexeramus
réxeras	rexeratis
réxerat	réxerant

Pluperfect Passive	
-----	-----
-----	-----
-----	-----

Future Perfect Active	
réxero	rexérimus
réxeris	rexéritis
réxerit	réxerint

Future Perfect Passive	
-----	-----
-----	-----
-----	-----

Lesson 3 Quiz

Name_____ Date_____

A. Imperatives

Complete chart with five model verbs and **sum**.

First two p.p.	Imperative Singular	Imperative Plural	Meaning
amo, amare	ama	amate	Love!
móneo, monēre	mone	monete	Warn!
rego, régere	rege	régite	Rule!
cápio, cápere	cape	cápite	Take!
áudio, audire	audi	audite	Hear!
sum, esse	es	este	Be!

Complete chart for Irregular Imperatives.

First two p.p.	Imperative Singular	Imperative Plural	Meaning
dico, dícere	dic	dícite	Speak!
duco, dúcere	duc	dúcite	Lead!
fácio, fácere	fac	fácite	Make!

B. Translate Imperatives

Latin	English
Da nobis hódie.	Give us today.
Cave canem.	Beware of the dog.
Festina lentē.	Make haste slowly.
Adeste fideles.	Come all ye faithful.
Carpe diem.	Seize the day.
Dimitte nobis débita nostra.	Forgive us our sins.

C. Vocabulary

Give all principal parts.

1. do, drive, act, treat, give ___ago___ ___ágere___ ___egi___ ___actus___

2. collect, force ___cogo___ ___cógere___ ___coegi___ ___coactus___

3. lift, raise ___tollo___ ___tóllere___ ___sústuli___ ___sublatus___

D. Conjugate

Conjugate **laudo** in the indicative active (6 tenses) and indicative passive (3 tenses).

Present Active	
laudo	laudamus
laudas	laudatis
laudat	laudant

Present Passive	
laudor	laudamur
laudaris	laudámini
laudatur	laudantur

Imperfect Active	
laudabam	laudabamus
laudabas	laudabatis
laudabat	laudabant

Imperfect Passive	
laudabar	laudabamur
laudabaris	laudabámini
laudabatur	laudabantur

Future Active	
laudabo	laudábimus
laudabis	laudábitis
laudabit	laudabunt

Future Passive	
laudabor	laudábimur
laudáberis	laudabímini
laudábitur	laudabuntur

Perfect Active	
laudavi	laudávimus
laudavisti	laudavistis
laudavit	laudaverunt

Perfect Passive	
-----	-----
-----	-----
-----	-----

Pluperfect Active	
laudáveram	laudaveramus
laudáveras	laudaveratis
laudáverat	laudáverant

Pluperfect Passive	
-----	-----
-----	-----
-----	-----

Future Perfect Active	
laudávero	laudavérimus
laudáveris	laudavéritis
laudáverit	laudáverint

Future Perfect Passive	
-----	-----
-----	-----
-----	-----

A. Review Vocabulary

Give all principal parts and meanings.

1. ago _____ ágere   egi   actus   to do, drive, act, treat
2. tollo _____ tóllere   sústuli   sublatus   to lift, raise up
3. cogo _____ cógere   coegi   coactus   to collect, force
4. pono_____ pónere   pósui   pósitus   to put, place
5. mitto_____ míttere   misi   missus   to send
6. scribo _____ scríbere   scripsi   scriptus   to write

B. Conjugate

In the first table, conjugate **laudo** in the perfect tense, passive voice.
Give meanings in the second table.

Person	Singular		Plural	
1st	laudatus -a -um	sum	laudati -ae -a	sumus
2nd	laudatus -a -um	es	laudati -ae -a	estis
3rd	laudatus -a -um	est	laudati -ae -a	sunt

Person	Singular	Plural
1st	I have been praised	we have been praised
2nd	you have been praised	you all have been praised
3rd	hsi has been praised	they have been praised

C. Translate

1. The die is cast. _____ Álea jacta est.
2. Lex servata est._____ The law has been kept.
3. Collis occupatus est. _____ The hill has been seized.
4. The city has been attacked._____ Urbs oppugnata est.
5. You have been sent. _____ (Tu) missus (-a) es.

D. Grammar

1. Give the two voices of Latin verbs. _____ active, passive
2. The 4th principal part is a _____ participle .
3. A participle is a _____ verbal adjective .

Lesson 4 Quiz

E. Conjugate

Conjugate **mitto** in the indicative active (6 tenses) and indicative passive (4 tenses).

Present Active	
mitto	míttimus
mittis	míttitis
mittit	mittunt

Present Passive	
mittor	míttimur
mítteris	mittímini
míttitur	mittuntur

Imperfect Active	
mittebam	mittebamus
mittebas	mittebatis
mittebat	mittebant

Imperfect Passive	
mittebar	mittebamur
mittebaris	mittebámini
mittebatur	mittebantur

Future Active	
mittam	mittemus
mittes	mittetis
mittet	mittent

Future Passive	
mittar	mittemur
mittēris	mittémini
mittetur	mittentur

Perfect Active	
misi	mísimus
misisti	misistis
misit	miserunt

Perfect Passive			
missus -a -um	sum	missi -ae -a	sumus
	es		estis
	est		sunt

Pluperfect Active	
míseram	miseramus
míseras	miseratis
míserat	míserant

Pluperfect Passive	
-----	-----
-----	-----
-----	-----

Future Perfect Active	
mísero	misérimus
míseris	miséritis
míserit	míserint

Future Perfect Passive	
-----	-----
-----	-----
-----	-----

Lesson 5 Quiz

Name_____ Date_____

A. Vocabulary

1. however (postp.)_____autem_____
2. either ... or _____aut ... aut_____
3. both ... and _____et ... et_____
4. therefore _____itaque_____
5. once, of old _____olim_____
6. and (enclitic conj.) _____-que_____
7. because _____quod_____
8. but _____sed_____
9. as _____sicut_____
10. for (postp.) _____enim_____

B. Conjugate

Conjugate **laudo** in the pluperfect tense, passive voice. Give meanings in the second table.

Person	Singular		Plural	
1st	laudatus -a -um	eram	laudati -ae -a	eramus
2nd	laudatus -a -um	eras	laudati -ae -a	eratis
3rd	laudatus -a -um	erat	laudati -ae -a	erant

Person	Singular	Plural
1st	I had been praised	we had been praised
2nd	you had been praised	you all had been praised
3rd	hsi had been praised	they had been praised

C. Translate

1. It is finished. _____Consummatum est._____
2. Discípuli a magistro coacti erant. _____The students had been collected by the teacher._____
3. equi vaccaéque _____horses and cows_____
4. Et imperator et mílites móniti sunt. _____Both the general and the soldiers have been warned._____
5. Good things had been done. _____Res bonae actae erant._____
6. The wolf had been captured. _____Lupus captus erat._____

D. Principal Parts Review

Give all four principal parts.

1. ago _____ago_____ágere_____egi_____actus_____
2. tollo _____tollo_____tóllere_____sústuli_____sublatus_____
3. cedo _____cedo_____cédere_____cessi_____cessus_____

Lesson 5 Quiz

E. Conjugate

Conjugate **móveo** in the indicative active (6 tenses) and indicative passive (5 tenses).

Present Active	
móveo	movemus
moves	movetis
movet	movent

Present Passive	
móveor	movemur
moveris	movémini
movetur	moventur

Imperfect Active	
movebam	movebamus
movebas	movebatis
movebat	movebant

Imperfect Passive	
movebar	movebamur
movebaris	movebámini
movebatur	movebantur

Future Active	
movebo	movébimus
movebis	movébitis
movebit	movebunt

Future Passive	
movebor	movébimur
movéberis	movebímini
movébitur	movebuntur

Perfect Active	
movi	móvimus
movisti	movistis
movit	moverunt

Perfect Passive			
motus -a -um	sum	moti -ae -a	sumus
	es		estis
	est		sunt

Pluperfect Active	
móveram	moveramus
móveras	moveratis
móverat	móverant

Pluperfect Passive			
motus -a -um	eram	moti -ae -a	eramus
	eras		eratis
	erat		erant

Future Perfect Active	
móvero	movérimus
móveris	movéritis
móverit	móverint

Future Perfect Passive	
-----	-----
-----	-----
-----	-----

Lesson 6 Quiz

Name_____ Date_____

A. Vocabulary

1. meanwhile __ínterim__
2. yes, so __ita__
3. also __étiam__
4. almost __fere__
5. nevertheless __tamen__

6. suddenly __súbito__
7. already, now __jam__
8. there, in that place __ibi__
9. afterwards __póstea__

B. Conjugate

In the first table, conjugate **laudo** in the future perfect tense, passive voice.
Give meanings in the second table.

Person	Singular		Plural	
1st	laudatus -a -um	ero	laudati -ae -a	érimus
2nd		eris		éritis
3rd		erit		erunt

Person	Singular	Plural
1st	I will have been praised	we will have been praised
2nd	you will have been praised	you all will have been praised
3rd	hsi will have been praised	they will have been praised

C. Translate

1. Do what you're doing. __Age quod agis.__
2. Tu ab imperatore mónitus eris. __You will have been warned by the general.__
3. Multae epístulae scriptae erunt. __Many letters will have been written.__
4. Shameful wars will have been waged. __Bella túrpia gesta erunt.__
5. He will have been sent. __Missus erit.__

D. Principal Parts Review

Give all four principal parts.

1. cogo __cogo   cógere   coegi   coactus__
2. tollo __tollo   tóllere   sústuli   sublatus__
3. gero __gero   gérere   gessi   gestus__

Lesson 6 Quiz

E. Conjugate

Conjugate <u>laudo</u> in the indicative active (6 tenses) and indicative passive (6 tenses).

Present Active	
laudo	laudamus
laudas	laudatis
laudat	laudant

Present Passive	
laudor	laudamur
laudaris	laudámini
laudatur	laudantur

Imperfect Active	
laudabam	laudabamus
laudabas	laudabatis
laudabat	laudabant

Imperfect Passive	
laudabar	laudabamur
laudabaris	laudabámini
laudabatur	laudabantur

Future Active	
laudabo	laudábimus
laudabis	laudábitis
laudabit	laudabunt

Future Passive	
laudabor	laudábimur
laudáberis	laudabímini
laudábitur	laudabuntur

Perfect Active	
laudavi	laudávimus
laudavisti	laudavistis
laudavit	laudaverunt

Perfect Passive			
laudatus -a -um	sum	laudati -ae -a	sumus
	es		estis
	est		sunt

Pluperfect Active	
laudáveram	laudaveramus
laudáveras	laudaveratis
laudáverat	laudáverant

Pluperfect Passive			
laudatus -a -um	eram	laudati -ae -a	eramus
	eras		eratis
	erat		erant

Future Perfect Active	
laudávero	laudavérimus
laudáveris	laudavéritis
laudáverit	laudáverint

Future Perfect Passive			
laudatus -a -um	ero	laudati -ae -a	érimus
	eris		éritis
	erit		erunt

Unit 1 Test

Name_____ Date_____

A. Vocabulary

Give principal parts and meanings.

1. ago _____ ágere __ egi _____ actus _____ to drive, act, treat, give
2. tollo _____ tóllere __ sústuli __ sublatus _____ to lift, raise up
3. cogo _____ cógere __ coegi _____ coactus _____ to collect, force
4. pono _____ pónere __ pósui _____ pósitus _____ to put, place
5. mitto _____ míttere __ misi _____ missus _____ to send
6. claudo _____ cláudere __ clausi _____ clausus _____ to close
7. gero _____ gérere __ gessi _____ gestus _____ to wage, carry on
8. cedo _____ cédere __ cessi _____ cessus _____ to yield, give way
9. scribo _____ scríbere __ scripsi __ scriptus _____ to write
10. premo _____ prémere __ pressi _____ pressus _____ to press

B. Vocabulary

1. meanwhile _____ ínterim
2. yes, so _____ ita
3. also _____ étiam
4. almost _____ fere
5. nevertheless _____ tamen
6. suddenly _____ súbito
7. already, now _____ jam
8. there, in that place _____ ibi
9. afterwards _____ póstea
10. however (postp.) _____ autem
11. either ... or _____ aut ... aut
12. both ... and _____ et ... et
13. therefore _____ ítaque
14. once, of old _____ olim
15. and (enclitic conj.) _____ -que
16. because _____ quod
17. but _____ sed
18. as _____ sicut
19. for (postp.) _____ enim

C. Sayings

1. Take up and read. ___Tolle, lege.___
2. It is finished. ___Consummatum est.___
3. Hear, O Israel! ___Audi Ísrael!___
4. I think, therefore I am. ___Cógito ergo sum.___
5. The die is cast. ___Álea jacta est.___
6. Do what you're doing. ___Age quod agis.___

D. Imperatives

Complete chart with five model verbs and **sum**.

First two p.p.	Imperative Singular	Imperative Plural	Meaning
amo, amare	ama	amate	Love!
móneo, monēre	mone	monete	Warn!
rego, régere	rege	régite	Rule!
cápio, cápere	cape	cápite	Take!
áudio, audire	audi	audite	Hear!
sum, esse	es	este	Be!

Complete chart for Irregular Imperatives.

First two p.p.	Imperative Singular	Imperative Plural	Meaning
dico, dícere	dic	dícite	Speak!
duco, dúcere	duc	dúcite	Lead!
fácio, fácere	fac	fácite	Make!

E. Translate Imperatives

Latin	English
Líbera nos a malo.	Deliver us from evil.
Cave canem.	Beware of the dog.
Festina lentē.	Make haste slowly.
Surge, súrgite.	Stand up.
Carpe diem.	Seize the day.
Benedíc Dómine nos.	Bless us O Lord.

F. Conjugate

Conjugate **amo** in the indicative active and passive.

1. principal parts ___amo   amare   amavi   amatus___
2. present stem ___ama-___

Present Active	
amo	amamus
amas	amatis
amat	amant

Present Passive	
amor	amamur
amaris	amámini
amatur	amantur

Imperfect Active	
amabam	amabamus
amabas	amabatis
amabat	amabant

Imperfect Passive	
amabar	amabamur
amabaris	amabámini
amabatur	amabantur

Future Active	
amabo	amábimus
amabis	amábitis
amabit	amabunt

Future Passive	
amabor	amábimur
amáberis	amabímini
amábitur	amabuntur

3. perfect stem ___amav-___
4. perfect passive participle ___amatus -a -um___

Perfect Active	
amavi	amávimus
amavisti	amavistis
amavit	amaverunt

Perfect Passive			
amatus -a -um	sum	amati -ae -a	sumus
	es		estis
	est		sunt

Pluperfect Active	
amáveram	amaveramus
amáveras	amaveratis
amáverat	amáverant

Pluperfect Passive			
amatus -a -um	eram	amati -ae -a	eramus
	eras		eratis
	erat		erant

Future Perfect Active	
amávero	amavérimus
amáveris	amavéritis
amáverit	amáverint

Future Perfect Passive			
amatus -a -um	ero	amati -ae -a	érimus
	eris		éritis
	erit		erunt

Unit 1 Test

G. Translate
Imperatives

1. Munite valla. _____ Fortify the walls. _____
2. Cape pecúniam. _____ Take the money. _____
3. Vive hódie. _____ Live today. _____
4. Find the soldier. _____ Inveni mílitem. _____
5. Come to the province. _ Veni ad provínciam. _
6. Make dinner now. _____ Fac nunc cenam. _____

H. Translate

1. Nos a Deo creati sumus. ___ We have been created by God. ___
2. Urbs viáque ab hóstibus tentae sunt. _____
   The city and the road have been held by the enemy (-ies).
3. Et sol et luna lucem dant. ___ Both the sun and the moon give light. ___
4. The knife has been hidden. ___ Culter celatus est. ___
5. We had been judged by the people. ___ A pópulo judicati (ae) eramus. ___
6. Are you swimming in the wide river? ___ Natásne in lato flúmine? ___

I. Fill in Blanks

1. The 4th principal part is a _____ participle _____ .
2. A participle is a _____ verbal adjective _____ .
3. In the active voice, the subject _____ performs the action of the verb _____ .
4. In the passive voice, the subject _____ receives the action of the verb _____ .
5. Give the three moods of Latin verbs.
   (1) _ indicative _ (2) _ imperative _ (3) _ subjunctive _
6. The indicative mood is used for _ statements _ and _ questions _ .
7. The imperative mood is used for _____ commands _____ .

Lesson 7 Quiz   Name_____ Date_____

A. Vocabulary
Give the dictionary form.

1. eye _ óculus -i m. _
2. reward _ praémium -i n. _
3. money _ pecúnia -ae f. _
4. mind _ ánimus -i m. _
5. woman _ fémina -ae f. _
6. neck _ collum -i n. _
7. ground _ ager agri m. _
8. land _ terra -ae f. _
9. garden _ hortus -i m. _
10. wood _ lignum -i n. _
11. back _ tergum -i n. _
12. children _ líberi -orum m. _
13. door _ jánua -ae f. _
14. gold _ aurum -i n. _
15. book _ liber libri m. _
16. island _ ínsula -ae f. _
17. iron _ ferrum -i n. _
18. knife _ culter cultri m. _
19. word _ verbum -i n. _
20. sailor _ nauta -ae m. _
21. horse _ equus -i m. _
22. daughter _ fília -ae f. _
23. shadow _ umbra -ae f. _
24. shield _ scutum -i n. _
25. boy _ puer púeri m. _
26. game _ ludus -i m. _
27. gate _ porta -ae f. _
28. year _ annus -i m. _
29. silver _ argentum -i n. _
30. evening _ vesper -peri m. _
31. life _ vita -ae f. _
32. man _ vir viri m. _
33. window _ fenestra -ae f. _
34. raincloud _ nimbus -i m. _
35. joy _ gáudium -i n. _
36. arm _ brácchium -i n. _
37. anger _ ira -ae f. _
38. wind _ ventus -i m. _
39. leaf _ fólium -i n. _
40. cow _ vacca -ae f. _
41. girl _ puella -ae f. _
42. dinner _ cena -ae f. _
43. god _ deus -i m. _
44. grain _ frumentum -i n. _
45. rock _ saxum -i n. _
46. wave _ unda -ae f. _
47. seat _ sella -ae f. _
48. place _ locus -i m. _
49. sign _ signum -i n. _
50. Italy _ Itália -ae f. _

B. Conjugate

Conjugate **pono** in the indicative active (6 tenses) and indicative passive (6 tenses).

Present Active	
pono	pónimus
ponis	pónitis
ponit	ponunt

Present Passive	
ponor	pónimur
póneris	ponimini
pónitur	ponuntur

Imperfect Active	
ponebam	ponebamus
ponebas	ponebatis
ponebat	ponebant

Imperfect Passive	
ponebar	ponebamur
ponebaris	ponebámini
ponebatur	ponebantur

Future Active	
ponam	ponemus
pones	ponetis
ponet	ponent

Future Passive	
ponar	ponemur
ponēris	ponémini
ponetur	ponentur

Perfect Active	
pósui	posúimus
posuisti	posuistis
pósuit	posuerunt

Perfect Passive			
pósitus -a -um	sum	pósiti -ae -a	sumus
	es		estis
	est		sunt

Pluperfect Active	
posúeram	posueramus
posúeras	posueratis
posúerat	posúerant

Pluperfect Passive			
pósitus -a -um	eram	pósiti -ae -a	eramus
	eras		eratis
	erat		erant

Future Perfect Active	
posúero	posuérimus
posúeris	posuéritis
posúerit	posúerint

Future Perfect Passive			
pósitus -a -um	ero	pósiti -ae -a	érimus
	eris		éritis
	erit		erunt

Lesson 7 Quiz

C. Latin Sayings

1. Quattuor anni témpora __The four seasons of the year__
2. Carpe diem. __Seize the day.__
3. Roma Aeterna __Eternal Rome__
4. Rex Regum __King of Kings__
5. Caput Mundi __Head of the World__

D. Decline

Case	Singular	Plural	Singular	Plural
nom.	culter	cultri	saxum	saxa
gen.	cultri	cultrorum	saxi	saxorum
dat.	cultro	cultris	saxo	saxis
acc.	cultrum	cultros	saxum	saxa
abl.	cultro	cultris	saxo	saxis

Case	Singular	Plural	Singular	Plural
nom.	puer	púeri	puella	puellae
gen.	púeri	puerorum	puellae	puellarum
dat.	púero	púeris	puellae	puellis
acc.	púerum	púeros	puellam	puellas
abl.	púero	púeris	puellā	puellis

E. Translate

1. capiuntur __they are being captured__
2. sciam __I will know__
3. Grátias tibi ago. __Thank you.__
4. Fili mi, da mihi cultrum. __My son, give me the knife.__
5. Fac, Marce, nunc cenam. __Mark, make dinner now.__
6. Pónite navem in lacum. __Put the ship in(to) the lake.__

F. Grammar

1. The dative and ablative plurals of **fília** and **dea** are __filiabus, deabus__ .

Lesson 8 Quiz

Name_____Date_____

A. Vocabulary
Give the dictionary form.

1. sun _____ sol solis m. _____
2. mountain _____ mons montis m. _____
3. face _____ fácies faciei f. _____
4. heart _____ cor cordis n. _____
5. hand _____ manus -ūs f. _____
6. foot _____ pes pedis m. _____
7. dog _____ canis canis m./f. _____
8. ship _____ navis navis f. _____
9. river _____ flumen flúminis n. _____
10. house _____ domus -ūs f. _____
11. hope _____ spes spei f. _____
12. brother _____ frater fratris m. _____
13. sister _____ soror -oris f. _____
14. head _____ caput cápitis n. _____
15. harbor _____ portus -ūs m. _____
16. city _____ urbs urbis f. _____
17. pain _____ dolor -oris m. _____

18. love _____ amor amoris m. _____
19. light _____ lux lucis f. _____
20. hill _____ collis collis m. _____
21. arrival _____ adventus -ūs m. _____
22. day _____ dies -ei m. _____
23. bread _____ panis panis m. _____
24. voice _____ vox vocis f. _____
25. lamp _____ lumen lúminis n. _____
26. fear _____ metus -ūs m. _____
27. shout _____ clamor -oris m. _____
28. citizen _____ civis civis m./f. _____
29. thing _____ res rei f. _____
30. custom _____ mos moris m. _____
31. faith _____ fides fídei f. _____
32. fruit _____ fructus -ūs m. _____
33. law _____ lex legis f. _____
34. work _____ labor -oris m. _____

B. Latin Sayings

1. Ego sum via et véritas et vita. _____ I am the way and the truth and the life. _____
2. Ad astra per áspera _____ To the stars through difficulties _____
3. Ars longa vita brevis. _____ Art is long and life is short. _____
4. Hánnibal ad portas _____ Hannibal at the gates _____

Lesson 8 Quiz

C. Conjugate
Conjugate **ago** in the indicative active (6 tenses) and indicative passive (6 tenses).

Present Active	
ago	ágimus
agis	ágitis
agit	agunt

Present Passive	
agor	ágimur
ágeris	agímini
ágitur	aguntur

Imperfect Active	
agebam	agebamus
agebas	agebatis
agebat	agebant

Imperfect Passive	
agebar	agebamur
agebaris	agebamini
agebatur	agebantur

Future Active	
agam	agemus
ages	agetis
aget	agent

Future Passive	
agar	agemur
agēris	agémini
agetur	agentur

Perfect Active	
egi	égimus
egisti	egistis
egit	egerunt

Perfect Passive			
actus -a -um	sum	acti -ae -a	sumus
	es		estis
	est		sunt

Pluperfect Active	
égeram	egeramus
égeras	egeratis
égerat	égerant

Pluperfect Passive			
actus -a -um	eram	acti -ae -a	eramus
	eras		eratis
	erat		erant

Future Perfect Active	
égero	egérimus
égeris	egéritis
égerit	égerint

Future Perfect Passive			
actus -a -um	ero	acti -ae -a	érimus
	eris		éritis
	erit		erunt

Lesson 8 Quiz

D. Decline

Case	Singular	Plural	Singular	Plural
nom.	dies	dies	urbs	urbes
gen.	diei	dierum	urbis	urbium
dat.	diei	diebus	urbi	urbibus
acc.	diem	dies	urbem	urbes
abl.	die	diebus	urbe	urbibus

Case	Singular	Plural	Singular	Plural
nom.	manus	manūs	pes	pedes
gen.	manūs	mánuum	pedis	pedum
dat.	mánui	mánibus	pedi	pédibus
acc.	manum	manūs	pedem	pedes
abl.	manu	mánibus	pede	pédibus

Case	Singular	Plural	Singular	Plural
nom.	cornu	córnua	caput	cápita
gen.	cornūs	córnuum	cápitis	cápitum
dat.	cornu	córnibus	cápiti	capítibus
acc.	cornu	córnua	caput	cápita
abl.	cornu	córnibus	cápite	capítibus

E. Grammar

1. An appositive is a noun that _____immediately follows_____ another noun and _____renames it_____ .

2. The accusative singular of **nihil** and **satis** are _____**nihil** and **satis**_____ .

3. The accusative singular of Jesus is _____**Jesum**_____ .

Lesson 9 Quiz

Name _____ Date _____

A. Vocabulary
Give the dictionary form.

1. sweet _____dulcis -e_____ 9. strong _____fortis -e_____
2. lazy _____piger -gra -grum_____ 10. shameful _____turpis -e_____
3. free _____liber -bera -berum_____ 11. new _____novus -a -um_____
4. heavy _____gravis -e_____ 12. noble _____nóbilis -e_____
5. easy _____fácilis -e_____ 13. harsh _____asper -era -erum_____
6. right _____dexter -tra -trum_____ 14. bad _____malus -a -um_____
7. sick _____aeger -gra -grum_____ 15. short _____brevis -e_____
8. wide _____latus -a -um_____ 16. much _____multus -a -um_____

B. Decline

M/F		Neuter	
omnis	omnes	omne	ómnia
omnis	ómnium	omnis	ómnium
omni	ómnibus	omni	ómnibus
omnem	omnes	omne	ómnia
omni	ómnibus	omni	ómnibus

C. New Vocabulary
Give the dictionary form.

1. tired _____defessus -a -um_____ 6. wild _____ferus -a -um_____
2. cold _____frígidus -a -um_____ 7. nurturing _____almus -a -um_____
3. foolish _____stultus -a -um_____ 8. ugly _____foedus -a -um_____
4. white _____albus -a -um_____ 9. wicked _____nefárius -a -um_____
5. lofty _____excelsus -a -um_____ 10. hot _____cálidus -a -um_____

D. Translate

1. Amor vincit ómnia. _____Love conquers all things._____
2. Ómnia erant nova. _____All things were new._____
3. Multi non sunt líberi. _____Many (people) are not free._____
4. Nostri oppugnantur. _____Our men are being attacked._____

Lesson 9 Quiz

E. Conjugate

Conjugate <u>cogo</u> in the indicative active (6 tenses) and indicative passive (6 tenses).

Present Active	
cogo	cógimus
cogis	cógitis
cogit	cogunt

Present Passive	
cogor	cógimur
cógeris	cogímini
cógitur	coguntur

Imperfect Active	
cogebam	cogebamus
cogebas	cogebatis
cogebat	cogebant

Imperfect Passive	
cogebar	cogebamur
cogebaris	cogebámini
cogebatur	cogebantur

Future Active	
cogam	cogemus
coges	cogetis
coget	cogent

Future Passive	
cogar	cogemur
cogĕris	cogémini
cogetur	cogentur

Perfect Active	
coegi	coégimus
coegisti	coegistis
coegit	coegerunt

Perfect Passive			
coactus -a -um	sum	coacti -ae -a	sumus
	es		estis
	est		sunt

Pluperfect Active	
coégeram	coegeramus
coégeras	coegeratis
coégerat	coégerant

Pluperfect Passive			
coactus -a -um	eram	coacti -ae -a	eramus
	eras		eratis
	erat		erant

Future Perfect Active	
coégero	coegérimus
coégeris	coegéritis
coégerit	coégerint

Future Perfect Passive			
coactus -a -um	ero	coacti -ae -a	érimus
	eris		éritis
	erit		erunt

Lesson 10 Quiz   Name_____ Date_____

A. New Vocabulary

Give the dictionary form.

1. other _____ álius ália áliud _____
2. whole _____ totus -a -um _____
3. which _____ uter utra utrum _____
4. one _____ unus -a -um _____
5. not any _____ nullus -a -um _____
6. the one … the other _____ alter … alter _____
7. neither _____ neuter -tra -trum _____
8. only _____ solus -a -um _____
9. any at all _____ ullus -a -um _____
10. second (of two) _____ alter áltera álterum _____

B. Decline

Singular			Plural		
nullus	nulla	nullum	nulli	nullae	nulla
nullíus	nullíus	nullíus	nullorum	nullarum	nullorum
nulli	nulli	nulli	nullis	nullis	nullis
nullum	nullam	nullum	nullos	nullas	nulla
nullo	nullā	nullo	nullis	nullis	nullis

C. Translate

1. alter ego _____ another self _____
2. Neuter exércitus vincet. _____ Neither army will conquer. _____
3. Solum unum scutum novum hábeo. _____ I have only one new shield. _____
4. Scribe álterā manu. _____ Write with the other hand. _____
5. Praémium álteri míliti dedit. _____ He gave a reward to the other soldier. _____
6. Dux totíus exércitūs est. _____ He is the leader of the whole army. _____
7. Nullam pecúniam habent. _____ They have no money. _____
8. Ullam pecúniam non habent. _____ They do not have any money. _____

D. Grammar

1. The Naughty Nine have exceptional forms in the _____ genitive and dative singular _____ .
2. Latin often uses the masculine or neuter plural adjective to designate_____ a class of people or things _____ .
3. A noun that immediately follows another noun and renames it is an _____ appositive _____ .

Lesson 10 Quiz

E. Conjugate

Conjugate **premo** in the indicative active (6 tenses) and indicative passive (6 tenses).

Present Active	
premo	prémimus
premis	prémitis
premit	premunt

Present Passive	
premor	prémimur
prémeris	premímini
prémitur	premuntur

Imperfect Active	
premebam	premebamus
premebas	premebatis
premebat	premebant

Imperfect Passive	
premebar	premebamur
premebaris	premebámini
premebatur	premebantur

Future Active	
premam	prememus
premes	premetis
premet	prement

Future Passive	
premar	prememur
premēris	premémini
premetur	prementur

Perfect Active	
pressi	préssimus
pressisti	pressistis
pressit	presserunt

Perfect Passive			
pressus -a -um	sum	pressi -ae -a	sumus
	es		estis
	est		sunt

Pluperfect Active	
présseram	presseramus
présseras	presseratis
présserat	présserant

Pluperfect Passive			
pressus -a -um	eram	pressi -ae -a	eramus
	eras		eratis
	erat		erant

Future Perfect Active	
préssero	pressérimus
présseris	presséritis
présserit	présserint

Future Perfect Passive			
pressus -a -um	ero	pressi -ae -a	érimus
	eris		éritis
	erit		erunt

Page 2

Lesson 11 Quiz

Name_____ Date_____

A. New Vocabulary

Give the dictionary form.

1. powerful _____potens potentis_____
2. aged _____senex senis_____
3. sharp _____acer -cris -cre_____
4. huge _____ingens ingentis_____
5. lively _____álacer -cris -cre_____
6. bold _____audax audacis_____
7. swift _____celer céleris célere_____
8. wise _____sápiens sapientis_____
9. famous _____céleber -bris -bre_____
10. careful _____diligens diligentis_____
11. lucky _____felix felicis_____

B. Decline

M/F		Neuter	
felix	felices	felix	felícia
felicis	felícium	felicis	felícium
felici	felícibus	felici	felícibus
felicem	felices	felix	felícia
felici	felícibus	felici	felícibus

C. Translate

1. Erat regina sápiens. _____She was a wise queen._____
2. Terram duci potenti dederunt. _____They gave land to the powerful leader._____
3. Vacca cornua ingentia habet. _____The cow has huge horns._____
4. Senes erant felices. _____The old people were fortunate._____
5. homo sápiens _____rational man_____
6. munitur _____it is fortified_____

D. Grammar

1. Give the two kinds of Latin adjectives.
   (1) _____1st/2nd-declension adjectives_____ (2) _____3rd-declension adjectives_____

2. Give the three kinds of 1st/2nd-declension adjectives.
   (1) _____regular_____ (2) _____-er_____ (3) _____Naughty Nine_____

3. Give the three kinds of 3rd-declension adjectives.
   (1) _____one termination_____ (2) _____two terminations_____ (3) _____three terminations_____

Page 1

Lesson 11 Quiz

E. Conjugate

Conjugate **claudo** in the indicative active (6 tenses) and indicative passive (6 tenses).

Present Active	
claudo	cláudimus
claudis	clauditis
claudit	claudunt

Present Passive	
claudor	cláudimur
cláuderis	claudímini
cláuditur	clauduntur

Imperfect Active	
claudebam	claudebamus
claudebas	claudebatis
claudebat	claudebant

Imperfect Passive	
claudebar	claudebamur
claudebaris	claudebámini
claudebatur	claudebantur

Future Active	
claudam	claudemus
claudes	claudetis
claudet	claudent

Future Passive	
claudar	claudemur
claudēris	claudémini
claudetur	claudentur

Perfect Active	
clausi	cláusimus
clausisti	clausistis
clausit	clauserunt

Perfect Passive			
clausus -a -um	sum	clausi -ae -a	sumus
	es		estis
	est		sunt

Pluperfect Active	
cláuseram	clauseramus
cláuseras	clauseratis
cláuserat	cláuserant

Pluperfect Passive			
clausus -a -um	eram	clausi -ae -a	eramus
	eras		eratis
	erat		erant

Future Perfect Active	
cláusero	clausérimus
cláuseris	clauséritis
cláuserit	cláuserint

Future Perfect Passive			
clausus -a -um	ero	clausi -ae -a	érimus
	eris		éritis
	erit		erunt

Lesson 12 Quiz

Name_____ Date_____

A. Prepositions

Translate and give the case required for the object.

1. through ___per___ acc.
2. without ___sine___ abl.
3. before ___ante___ acc.
4. with ___cum___ abl.
5. for ___pro___ abl.
6. around ___circum___ acc.
7. after ___post___ acc.
8. out of ___e, ex___ abl.
9. into ___in___ acc.
10. toward ___ad___ acc.

B. New Vocabulary

Give the dictionary form and the case and/or preposition it takes.

1. full ___plenus -a -um___ gen.
2. dear ___carus -a -um___ dat.
3. empty ___vácuus -a -um___ abl.
4. suitable ___idóneus -a -um___ dat.
5. similar ___símilis -e___ dat.
6. neighboring ___finítimus -a -um___ dat.
7. useful ___útilis -e___ ad w/acc.
8. safe ___tutus -a -um___ abl.
9. desirous ___cúpidus -a -um___ gen.
10. prepared ___paratus -a -um___ ad w/acc.

C. Translate

1. aquae plenus ___full of water___
2. paratus ad bellum ___prepared for war___
3. útilis ad laborem ___useful for work___
4. návibus idóneus ___suitable for ships___
5. pecúniae cúpidus ___eager for money___
6. matri carus ___dear to the mother___
7. cívibus vácuus ___empty of citizens___
8. frumento símilis ___similar to grain___

D. Translate

1. trans flumen ___across the river___
2. in urbem ___into the city___
3. in domu ___in the house___
4. pro rege ___for (on behalf of) the king___
5. ad provínciam ___to the province___
6. inter vias ___between the roads___

Lesson 12 Quiz

E. Conjugate

Conjugate **vénio** in the indicative active (6 tenses).

Present Active	
vénio	venimus
venis	venitis
venit	véniunt

Present Passive	
-----	-----
-----	-----
-----	-----

Imperfect Active	
veniebam	veniebamus
veniebas	veniebatis
veniebat	veniebant

Imperfect Passive	
-----	-----
-----	-----
-----	-----

Future Active	
véniam	veniemus
vénies	venietis
véniet	vénient

Future Passive	
-----	-----
-----	-----
-----	-----

Perfect Active	
veni	vēnimus
venisti	venistis
vēnit	venerunt

Perfect Passive	
-----	-----
-----	-----
-----	-----

Pluperfect Active	
véneram	veneramus
véneras	veneratis
vénerat	vénerant

Pluperfect Passive	
-----	-----
-----	-----
-----	-----

Future Perfect Active	
vénero	venérimus
véneris	venéritis
vénerit	vénerint

Future Perfect Passive	
-----	-----
-----	-----
-----	-----

Lesson 13 Quiz

Name_____ Date_____

A. Vocabulary

1. ever _____ umquam
2. certainly _____ certē
3. tomorrow _____ cras
4. easily _____ fácile
5. today _____ hódie
6. yesterday _____ heri
7. by far _____ longē
8. much _____ multum
9. now _____ nunc
10. then _____ tum
11. slowly _____ lentē
12. bravely _____ fórtiter
13. never _____ numquam
14. often _____ saepe
15. with difficulty _____ difficiliter
16. hundred _____ centum
17. thousand _____ mille
18. faithfully _____ fidéliter
19. roughly _____ ásperē
20. briefly _____ bréviter

B. Numbers

1. ten _____ decem
2. seventeen _____ septéndecim
3. fifth _____ quintus -a -um
4. twenty _____ viginti
5. eight _____ octo
6. nineteen _____ undeviginti
7. eleven _____ úndecim
8. second _____ secundus -a -um
9. fifteen _____ quíndecim
10. fourth _____ quartus -a -um
11. one hundred _____ centum
12. twelve _____ duódecim
13. fourteen _____ quattuórdecim
14. ninth _____ nonus -a -um
15. sixteen _____ sédecim
16. eighteen _____ duodeviginti
17. three _____ tres tria
18. tenth _____ décimus -a -um
19. thirteen _____ trédecim
20. two _____ duo -ae -o
21. first _____ primus -a -um
22. one thousand _____ mille

Lesson 13 Quiz

C. Decline

Case	Masculine	Feminine	Neuter
nom.	duo	duae	duo
gen.	duorum	duarum	duorum
dat.	duobus	duabus	duobus
acc.	duo / duos	duas	duo
abl.	duobus	duabus	duobus

D. Conjugate

Conjugate **dórmio** in the indicative active (6 tenses).

Present Active	
dórmio	dormimus
dormis	dormitis
dormit	dórmiunt

Present Passive	
-----	-----
-----	-----
-----	-----

Imperfect Active	
dormiebam	dormiebamus
dormiebas	dormiebatis
dormiebat	dormiebant

Imperfect Passive	
-----	-----
-----	-----
-----	-----

Future Active	
dórmiam	dormiemus
dórmies	dormietis
dórmiet	dórmient

Future Passive	
-----	-----
-----	-----
-----	-----

Perfect Active	
dormivi	dormívimus
dormivisti	dormivistis
dormivit	dormiverunt

Perfect Passive	
-----	-----
-----	-----
-----	-----

Pluperfect Active	
dormíveram	dormiveramus
dormíveras	dormiveratis
dormíverat	dormíverant

Pluperfect Passive	
-----	-----
-----	-----
-----	-----

Future Perfect Active	
dormívero	dormivérimus
dormíveris	dormivéritis
dormíverit	dormíverint

Future Perfect Passive	
-----	-----
-----	-----
-----	-----

Unit 2 Test

Name _____ Date _____

A. Vocabulary

Give the dictionary form.

1. weary _defessus -a -um_
2. cold _frígidus -a -um_
3. huge _ingens ingentis_
4. which _uter utra utrum_
5. powerful _potens potentis_
6. dear _carus -a -um_
7. the other _alter áltera álterum_
8. swift _celer céleris célere_
9. wild _ferus -a -um_
10. nothing _nihil (nil)_
11. only _solus -a -um_
12. whole _totus -a -um_
13. knee _genu -ūs n._
14. fortunate _felix felicis_
15. other _álius ália áliud_
16. wicked _nefárius -a -um_
17. similar _símilis -e_
18. any at all _ullus -a -um_
19. suitable _idóneus -a -um_
20. hot _cálidus -a -um_
21. lively _álacer -cris -cre_
22. full _plenus -a -um_
23. enough _satis_
24. safe _tutus -a -um_
25. ugly _foedus -a -um_
26. bold _audax audacis_
27. horn _cornu -ūs n._
28. not any _nullus -a -um_
29. aged _senex senis_
30. useful _útilis -e_
31. careful _díligens diligentis_
32. empty _vácuus -a -um_
33. white _albus -a -um_
34. famous _céleber -bris -bre_
35. neighboring _finítimus -a -um_
36. neither _neuter -tra -trum_
37. sharp _acer -cris -cre_
38. the one … the other _alter … alter_
39. lofty _excelsus -a -um_
40. prepared _paratus -a -um_

B. Give the Vocative

1. my son _fili mi_
2. Claudius _Claudi_
3. servus _serve_

C. Latin Sayings

1. Rational man _____ Homo sápiens _____
2. Love conquers all things. _____ Amor vincit ómnia. _____
3. another self _____ alter ego _____
4. O the times, O the customs. _____ O témpora, O mores _____

D. Decline

M/F		N	
Singular	Plural	Singular	Plural
celer / céleris	céleres	célere	celéria
céleris	celérium	céleris	celérium
céleri	celéribus	céleri	celéribus
célerem	céleres	célere	celéria
céleri	celéribus	céleri	celéribus

M/F		N	
Singular	Plural	Singular	Plural
audax	audaces	audax	audácia
audacis	audácium	audacis	audácium
audaci	audácibus	audaci	audácibus
audacem	audáces	audax	audácia
audaci	audácibus	audaci	audácibus

Singular			Plural		
M	F	N	M	F	N
álius	ália	áliud	álii	áliae	ália
alíus	alíus	alíus	aliorum	aliarum	aliorum
álii	alii	alii	áliis	áliis	áliis
álium	áliam	áliud	álios	álias	ália
álio	áliã	álio	áliis	áliis	áliis

Singular	Plural
genu	génua
genūs	génuum
genu	génibus
genu	génua
genu	génibus

M/N	F
duo	duae
duorum	duarum
duobus	duabus
duo / duos	duas
duobus	duabus

Jesus
Jesu
Jesu
Jesum
Jesu

E. Numbers

	Cardinal	Ordinal
I	unus -a -um	primus -a -um
II	duo -ae -o	secundus -a -um
III	tres tria	tértius -a -um
IV	quattuor	quartus -a -um
V	quinque	quintus -a -um
VI	sex	sextus -a -um
VII	septem	séptimus -a -um
VIII	octo	octavus -a -um
IX	novem	nonus -a -um
X	decem	décimus -a -um
XI	úndecim	
XII	duódecim	
XIII	trédecim	
XIV	quattuórdecim	
XV	quíndecim	
XVI	sédecim	
XVII	septéndecim	
XVIII	duodeviginti	
XIX	undeviginti	
XX	viginti	
C	centum	
M	mille	

Unit 2 Test

F. Grammar

1. Give two examples of adjectives used as nouns in English. _the poor, good, bad, ugly, tired, etc._

2. Latin uses the masculine or neuter plural adjective as a noun to designate _____
   a class of people or things .

3. Give two examples of the above. **multa**, **fortes**, **multi**, etc.

4. Give three cardinal numbers that are declined in Latin. **unus -a -um, duo -ae -o, tres tria**

5. Give two nouns that do not decline. **satis**, **nihil**

6. A noun that directly follows another noun and renames it is called an _____ appositive _____ .

7. Give the Vocative Rule and an example. _____
   The vocative is the same as the nominative except in the m.s.nom. where **-us** changes to **-e**
   and **-ius** to **-i**. **Et tu Brute?**, **Christe eleison**, **fili mi**, **Benedíc Dómine nos**

8. The vocative is the case of _____ direct address _____ .

9. Give the two major kinds of adjectives. _1st/2nd and 3rd declension_

10. The Naughty Nine are irregular in what cases? _genitive and dative_

G. Translate

1. Est domus alíus civis. _____ It is the house of another citizen.

2. Totum frumentum mittam. _____ I will send all the grain.

3. Nullam aquam habent. _____ They have no water.

4. Mitte epístulam uni magistro. _____ Send a letter to one teacher.

5. Multi sunt pacis cúpidi. _____ Many people are eager for peace.

6. Multa sunt urbi finítima. _____ Many things are close to the city.

7. Marcus, senator, est in templo. _____ Mark, the senator, is in the temple.

8. Epístulam Marco, senatori, mittam. _____ I will send a letter to Mark, the senator.

9. Ágite vaccas trans viam. _____ Drive the cows across the road.

H. Conjugate

Conjugate **mitto** in the indicative active (6 tenses) and indicative passive (6 tenses).

Present Active	
mitto	míttimus
mittis	míttitis
mittit	mittunt

Present Passive	
mittor	míttimur
mítteris	mittímini
míttitur	mittuntur

Imperfect Active	
mittebam	mittebamus
mittebas	mittebatis
mittebat	mittebant

Imperfect Passive	
mittebar	mittebamur
mittebaris	mittebámini
mittebatur	mittebantur

Future Active	
mittam	mittemus
mittes	mittetis
mittet	mittent

Future Passive	
mittar	mittemur
mittēris	mittémini
mittetur	mittentur

Perfect Active	
misi	mísimus
misisti	misistis
misit	miserunt

Perfect Passive			
missus -a -um	sum	missi -ae -a	sumus
	es		estis
	est		sunt

Pluperfect Active	
míseram	miseramus
míseras	miseratis
míserat	míserant

Pluperfect Passive			
missus -a -um	eram	missi -ae -a	eramus
	eras		eratis
	erat		erant

Future Perfect Active	
mísero	misérimus
míseris	miséritis
míserit	míserint

Future Perfect Passive			
missus -a -um	ero	missi -ae -a	érimus
	eris		éritis
	erit		erunt

Name_____ Date_____

A. Vocabulary

Give the dictionary form.

1. temptation _tentátio -onis f._
2. lion _leo -onis m._
3. maiden _virgo -inis f._
4. legion _légio -onis f._
5. centurion _centúrio -onis m._

6. lesson _léctio -onis f._
7. human being _homo -inis m._
8. speech _orátio -onis f._
9. suffering _pássio -onis f._
10. line, row _ordo -inis m._

B. Decline

1st and 2nd Person Personal Pronouns

Case	1st Person		2nd Person	
	Singular	Plural	Singular	Plural
nom.	ego	nos	tu	vos
gen.	mei	nostri, nostrum	tui	vestri, vestrum
dat.	mihi	nobis	tibi	vobis
acc.	me	nos	te	vos
abl.	me	nobis	te	vobis

C. Translate

1. I love my mother. _Matrem amo. (meam is not needed)_
2. Vos audívimus. _We heard you._
3. Magistra librum mihi dedit. _The teacher gave me a book._
4. Epístula a te scripta est. _The letter has been written by you._
5. fear of you all _metus vestri_
6. part of us _pars nostrum_
7. with us _nobiscum_
8. Tecum ambulábimus. _We will walk with you._

D. Grammar

1. The genitive forms of 1st and 2nd person pronouns **are / ~~are not~~** used to express possession.

2. Possession in the 1st and 2nd persons is expressed with the adjectives _____ **meus, tuus, noster, vester** .

E. Conjugate

Conjugate **pono** in the indicative active (6 tenses) and the indicative passive (6 tenses).

Present Active	
pono	pónimus
ponis	pónitis
ponit	ponunt

Present Passive	
ponor	pónimur
póneris	ponímini
pónitur	ponuntur

Imperfect Active	
ponebam	ponebamus
ponebas	ponebatis
ponebat	ponebant

Imperfect Passive	
ponebar	ponebamur
ponebaris	ponebámini
ponebatur	ponebantur

Future Active	
ponam	ponemus
pones	ponetis
ponet	ponent

Future Passive	
ponar	ponemur
ponĕris	ponémini
ponetur	ponentur

Perfect Active	
pósui	posúimus
posuisti	posuistis
pósuit	posuerunt

Perfect Passive			
pósitus -a -um	sum	pósiti -ae -a	sumus
	es		estis
	est		sunt

Pluperfect Active	
posúeram	posueramus
posúeras	posueratis
posúerat	posúerant

Pluperfect Passive			
pósitus -a -um	eram	pósiti -ae -a	eramus
	eras		eratis
	erat		erant

Future Perfect Active	
posúero	posuérimus
posúeris	posuéritis
posúerit	posúerint

Future Perfect Passive			
pósitus -a -um	ero	pósiti -ae -a	érimus
	eris		éritis
	erit		erunt

Lesson 15 Quiz

Name_____ Date_____

A. Vocabulary

Give the dictionary form.

1. Ireland _____Hibérnia -ae f._____
2. Switzerland _____Helvétia -ae f._____
3. Britain _____Británnia -ae f._____
4. Scotland _____Caledónia -ae f._____
5. Germany _____Germánia -ae f._____
6. Carthage _____Carthago -inis f._____
7. Europe _____Europa -ae f._____
8. Greece _____Graécia -ae f._____
9. Athens _____Athenae -arum f._____

B. Decline

3rd Person Personal Pronouns

Case	Singular			Plural		
	M	F	N	M	F	N
nom.	is	ea	id	ei	eae	ea
gen.	ejus	ejus	ejus	eorum	earum	eorum
dat.	ei	ei	ei	eis	eis	eis
acc.	eum	eam	id	eos	eas	ea
abl.	eo	eā	eo	eis	eis	eis

C. Translate

1. Caesar mílites suos appellavit. _____Caesar addressed his own soldiers._____
2. Caesar ejus mílites appellavit. _____Caesar addressed his soldiers._____
3. Galli in portum suum navigaverunt. _____The Gauls sailed into their own harbor._____
4. Galli in eorum portum navigaverunt. _____The Gauls sailed into their harbor._____

D. Grammar

1. **Meus, tuus, noster,** and **vester** function as possessive _____adjectives_____ .
   Ejus, eorum, and **earum** function as possessive _____pronouns_____ .
2. **Is** and **ea** mean *he* and *she* when referring to_____persons or animals_____ .
3. **Is** and **ea** mean *it* when referring to _____non-living things with grammatical gender_____ .
4. The 3rd person possessive pronoun adjective (reflexive) is _____suus -a -um_____ .

Lesson 15 Quiz

E. Conjugate

Conjugate **téneo** in the indicative active (6 tenses) and the indicative passive (6 tenses).

Present Active	
téneo	tenemus
tenes	tenetis
tenet	tenent

Present Passive	
teneor	tenemur
teneris	tenemini
tenetur	tenentur

Imperfect Active	
tenebam	tenebamus
tenebas	tenebatis
tenebat	tenebant

Imperfect Passive	
tenebar	tenebamur
tenebaris	tenebamini
tenebatur	tenebantur

Future Active	
tenebo	tenébimus
tenebis	tenébitis
tenebit	tenebunt

Future Passive	
tenebor	tenébimur
tenéberis	tenebímini
tenébitur	tenebuntur

Perfect Active	
ténui	tenúimus
tenuisti	tenuistis
ténuit	tenuerunt

Perfect Passive			
tentus -a -um	sum	tenti -ae -a	sumus
	es		estis
	est		sunt

Pluperfect Active	
tenúeram	tenueramus
tenúeras	tenueratis
tenúerat	tenúerant

Pluperfect Passive			
tentus -a -um	eram	tenti -ae -a	eramus
	eras		eratis
	erat		erant

Future Perfect Active	
tenúero	tenúérimus
tenúeris	tenúéritis
tenúerit	tenúerint

Future Perfect Passive			
tentus -a -um	ero	tenti -ae -a	érimus
	eris		éritis
	erit		erunt

Name_____ Date_____

A. Vocabulary

Give the dictionary form.

1. charity _____ cáritas -atis f.
2. freedom _____ libertas -atis f.
3. will _____ voluntas -atis f.
4. truth _____ véritas -atis f.
5. summer _____ aestas -atis f.
6. state _____ cívitas -atis f.
7. storm _____ tempestas -atis f.
8. authority _____ auctóritas -atis f.
9. speed _____ celéritas -atis f.
10. sense of duty _____ píetas -atis f.

B. Decline

hic haec hoc

Case	Singular			Plural		
	M	F	N	M	F	N
nom.	hic	haec	hoc	hi	hae	haec
gen.	hujus	hujus	hujus	horum	harum	horum
dat.	huic	huic	huic	his	his	his
acc.	hunc	hanc	hoc	hos	has	haec
abl.	hoc	hac	hoc	his	his	his

C. Translate

1. Faith, hope, and love, these three _____ Fides, spes, cáritas, tria haec
2. Hoc signum tollo._____ I lift up this standard.
3. Haec terra mea est. _____ This is my land.
4. In hac viā ámbulo. _____ I am walking in this road.
5. Hoc gládio pugno. _____ I am fighting with this sword.
6. the truth of this story _____ veritas hujus fábulae
7. soldiers of these armies _____ mílites horum exercítuum
8. Haec sunt utília. _____ These things are useful.

D. Grammar

1. **Hic haec hoc** is both an _____ adjective _____ and a _____ pronoun _____ .
2. Nouns ending in **-tas -tatis** are always _____ feminine _____ .
3. _____ Demonstrative _____ pronouns point out persons or things.
4. **Hic haec hoc** points out things _____ (close to / far from _____ the speaker.

E. Conjugate

Conjugate **jácio** in the indicative active (6 tenses) and the indicative passive (6 tenses).

Present Active	
jácio	jácimus
jacis	jácitis
jacit	jáciunt

Present Passive	
jácior	jácimur
jáceris	jacímini
jácitur	jaciuntur

Imperfect Active	
jaciebam	jaciebamus
jaciebas	jaciebatis
jaciebat	jaciebant

Imperfect Passive	
jaciebar	jaciebamur
jaciebaris	jaciebámini
jaciebatur	jaciebantur

Future Active	
jáciam	jaciemus
jácies	jacietis
jáciet	jácient

Future Passive	
jáciar	jaciemur
jacieris	jaciémini
jacietur	jacientur

Perfect Active	
jeci	jécimus
jecisti	jecistis
jecit	jecerunt

Perfect Passive			
jactus -a -um	sum	jacti -ae -a	sumus
	es		estis
	est		sunt

Pluperfect Active	
jéceram	jeceramus
jéceras	jeceratis
jécerat	jecerant

Pluperfect Passive			
jactus -a -um	eram	jacti -ae -a	eramus
	eras		eratis
	erat		erant

Future Perfect Active	
jécero	jecérimus
jéceris	jecéritis
jécerit	jecerint

Future Perfect Passive			
jactus -a -um	ero	jacti -ae -a	érimus
	eris		éritis
	erit		erunt

Lesson 17 Quiz

Name_____ Date_____

A. Vocabulary

Give the dictionary form.

1. lack _____inópia -ae f._____
2. knowledge _____sciéntia -ae f._____
3. ditch _____fossa -ae f._____
4. memory _____memória -ae f._____
5. flight _____fuga -ae f._____

6. injury _____injúria -ae f._____
7. friendship _____amicítia -ae f._____
8. spear _____hasta -ae f._____
9. arrow _____sagitta -ae f._____
10. wisdom _____sapiéntia -ae f._____

B. Decline

ille illa illud

Case	Singular			Plural		
	M	F	N	M	F	N
nom.	ille	illa	illud	illi	illae	illa
gen.	illíus	illíus	illíus	illorum	illarum	illorum
dat.	illi	illi	illi	illis	illis	illis
acc.	illum	illam	illud	illos	illas	illa
abl.	illo	illā	illo	illis	illis	illis

C. Translate

1. A day of wrath, that day _____Dies irae, dies illa_____
2. illíus urbis portus _____the harbor of that city_____
3. Quid in illā fossā celas? _____What are you hiding in that ditch?_____
4. Illi non sunt amici nostri. _____Those are not our friends._____
5. Illae sunt senatoris fíliae. _____Those are the daughters of the senator._____
6. Saxum in illud flumen jáciam. _____I will throw a rock into that river._____

D. Grammar

1. When used together, **hic** means _____the latter_____, and **ille** means _____the former_____.
2. List the four demonstratives with their meanings:
   (1) _____hic haec hoc_____ this, these
   (2) _____ille illa illud_____ that, those
   (3) _____iste ista istud_____ that, those near to the 2nd person, in contempt
   (4) _____is ea id_____ that, those (non-specific)

E. Conjugate

Conjugate **séntio** in the indicative active (6 tenses) and the indicative passive (6 tenses).

Present Active	
séntio	sentimus
sentis	sentitis
sentit	séntiunt

Present Passive	
séntior	sentimur
sentiris	sentímini
sentitur	sentiuntur

Imperfect Active	
sentiebam	sentiebamus
sentiebas	sentiebatis
sentiebat	sentiebant

Imperfect Passive	
sentiebar	sentiebamur
sentiebaris	sentiebámini
sentiebatur	sentiebantur

Future Active	
séntiam	sentiemus
sénties	sentietis
séntiet	séntient

Future Passive	
séntiar	sentiemur
sentieris	sentiémini
sentietur	sentientur

Perfect Active	
sensi	sénsimus
sensisti	sensistis
sensit	senserunt

Perfect Passive			
sensus -a -um	sum	sensi -ae -a	sumus
	es		estis
	est		sunt

Pluperfect Active	
sénseram	senseramus
sénseras	senseratis
sénserat	sénserant

Pluperfect Passive			
sensus -a -um	eram	sensi -ae -a	eramus
	eras		eratis
	erat		erant

Future Perfect Active	
sénsero	sensérimus
sénseris	senséritis
sénserit	sénserint

Future Perfect Passive			
sensus -a -um	ero	sensi -ae -a	érimus
	eris		éritis
	erit		erunt

Lesson 18 Quiz

Name_____ Date_____

A. Vocabulary

Give the dictionary form.

1. kind _____genus -eris n._____
2. work_____opus -eris n._____
3. wound _____vulnus -eris n._____
4. column_____agmen -inis n._____
5. burden _____onus -eris n._____

6. song _____carmen -inis n._____
7. journey _____iter itíneris n._____
8. body_____corpus -oris n._____
9. time _____tempus -oris n._____
10. spring_____ver veris n._____

B. Decline

ipse ipsa ipsum

Case	Singular			Plural		
	M	F	N	M	F	N
nom.	ipse	ipsa	ipsum	ipsi	ipsae	ipsa
gen.	ipsíus	ipsíus	ipsíus	ipsorum	ipsarum	ipsorum
dat.	ipsi	ipsi	ipsi	ipsis	ipsis	ipsis
acc.	ipsum	ipsam	ipsum	ipsos	ipsas	ipsa
abl.	ipso	ipsã	ipso	ipsis	ipsis	ipsis

C. Translate

1. Knowledge itself is power. _____Ipsa sciéntia potestas est._____
2. Ipse senator in foro orat. _____The senator himself is speaking in the forum._____
3. Ipsa in saxo sedet. _____She herself is sitting on a rock._____
4. Epístulam ipsi regi scripsi. _____I wrote a letter to the king himself._____
5. Ipsam urbem oppugnaverunt._____They have attacked the city itself._____
6. The town itself is burning. _____Ipsum óppidum ardet._____
7. He himself ordered the journey. _____Ipse iter jussit._____

D. Grammar

1. The reflexive pronoun refers _____back to the subject_____ .
2. The intensive pronoun or adjective_____emphasizes_____ another word in the sentence.
3. The intensive and reflexive pronouns have the _____same_____ forms in English, but _____different_____ forms in Latin.
4. In English, reflexive and intensive pronouns end in _____*-self* or *-selves*_____ .

Lesson 18 Quiz

E. Conjugate

Conjugate **júbeo** in the indicative active (6 tenses) and the indicative passive (6 tenses).

Present Active	
júbeo	jubemus
jubes	jubetis
jubet	jubent

Present Passive	
jubeor	jubemur
juberis	jubémini
jubetur	jubentur

Imperfect Active	
jubebam	jubebamus
jubebas	jubebatis
jubebat	jubebant

Imperfect Passive	
jubebar	jubebamur
jubebaris	jubebámini
jubebatur	jubebantur

Future Active	
jubebo	jubébimus
jubebis	jubébitis
jubebit	jubebunt

Future Passive	
jubebor	jubébimur
jubéberis	jubébímini
jubébitur	jubebuntur

Perfect Active	
jussi	jússimus
jussisti	jussistis
jussit	jusserunt

Perfect Passive			
jussus -a -um	sum	jussi -ae -a	sumus
	es		estis
	est		sunt

Pluperfect Active	
jússeram	jusseramus
jússeras	jusseratis
jússerat	jússerant

Pluperfect Passive			
jussus -a -um	eram	jussi -ae -a	eramus
	eras		eratis
	erat		erant

Future Perfect Active	
jússero	jussérimus
jússeris	jusséritis
jússerit	jússerint

Future Perfect Passive			
jussus -a -um	ero	jussi -ae -a	érimus
	eris		éritis
	erit		erunt

Lesson 19 Quiz

Name_____ Date_____

A. Translate

1. in itself _____ per se _____
2. Miles se celavit. _____ The soldier hid himself. _____
3. Me audivi. _____ I heard myself. _____
4. We wounded ourselves. _____ Nos vulnerávimus. _____
5. Cultro me vulneravi. _____ I wounded myself with a knife. _____
6. Canis in flumen se jecit. _____ The dog threw himself into the river. ___

B. Grammar

1. Give the four demonstrative pronouns.
   (1) _____ is ea id _____
   (2) _____ hic haec hoc _____
   (3) _____ ille illa illud _____
   (4) _____ iste ista istud _____

2. The reflexive pronouns have no _____ nominative _____ forms because they refer back to the _____ subject _____, are always in the _____ predicate _____, and function as _____ objects _____ .

3. An intensive pronoun or adjective _____ emphasizes _____ another word in the sentence.

4. The 1st and 2nd person reflexive pronouns have the same forms as the corresponding _____ personal pronouns _____ .

5. The 3rd person reflexive pronouns are _____ sui, sibi, se, se _____ .

6. The 3rd person reflexive pronoun adjective is _____ suus -a -um _____ .

7. Give the 1st person reflexive/intensive pronouns in English.
   myself, ourselves

8. Give the 2nd person reflexive/intensive pronouns in English.
   yourself, yourselves

9. Give the 3rd person reflexive/intensive pronouns in English.
   himself, herself, itself, themselves

C. Vocabulary
Give the dictionary form.

1. row _____ ordo -inis m. _____
2. spear _____ hasta -ae f. _____
3. Scotland _____ Caledónia -ae f. _____
4. journey _____ iter itíneris n. _____
5. storm _____ tempestas -atis f. _____
6. kind _____ genus -eris n. _____
7. lack _____ inópia -ae f. _____
8. lesson _____ léctio -onis f. _____
9. sense of duty _____ píetas -atis f. _____
10. song _____ carmen -inis n. _____
11. Britain _____ Británnia -ae f. _____
12. lion _____ leo leonis m. _____
13. knowledge _____ sciéntia -ae f. _____
14. this, these _____ hic haec hoc _____
15. injury _____ injúria -ae f. _____
16. column _____ agmen -inis n. _____
17. -self, -selves _____ ipse -a -um _____
18. spring _____ ver veris n. _____
19. Switzerland _____ Helvétia -ae f. _____
20. memory _____ memória -ae f. _____
21. summer _____ aestas -atis f. _____
22. centurion _____ centúrio -onis m. _____
23. ditch _____ fossa -ae f. _____
24. body _____ corpus -oris n. _____
25. speed _____ celéritas -atis f. _____
26. speech _____ orátio -onis f. _____
27. himself, herself, itself _____ sui, sibi, se, se _____
28. truth _____ véritas -atis f. _____
29. wound _____ vulnus -eris n. _____
30. human being _____ homo -inis m. _____
31. flight _____ fuga -ae f. _____
32. that, those _____ ille illa illud _____
33. charity _____ cáritas -atis f. _____
34. friendship _____ amicítia -ae f. _____
35. Greece _____ Graécia -ae f. _____
36. time _____ tempus -oris n. _____
37. liberty _____ libertas -atis f. _____
38. that, those (of yours) _____ iste ista istud _____
39. legion _____ légio -onis f. _____
40. Athens _____ Athenae -arum f. _____
41. arrow _____ sagitta -ae f. _____
42. Germany _____ Germánia -ae f. _____
43. authority _____ auctóritas -atis f. _____
44. Carthage _____ Carthago -inis f. _____
45. work _____ opus -eris n. _____
46. wisdom _____ sapiéntia -ae f. _____
47. temptation _____ tentátio -onis f. _____
48. Ireland _____ Hibérnia -ae f. _____

Lesson 19 Quiz

49. own _____ suus -a -um _____

50. will _____ voluntas -atis f. _____

51. state _____ cívitas -atis f. _____

52. maiden _____ virgo -inis f. _____

53. Europe _____ Europa -ae f. _____

54. burden _____ onus -eris n. _____

55. suffering _____ pássio -onis f. _____

Unit 3 Test

Name _____ Date _____

A. Vocabulary
Give the dictionary form.

1. row _____ ordo -inis m. _____

2. spear _____ hasta -ae f. _____

3. Scotland _____ Caledónia -ae f. _____

4. journey _____ iter itíneris n. _____

5. storm _____ tempestas -atis f. _____

6. kind _____ genus -eris n. _____

7. lack _____ inópia -ae f. _____

8. lesson _____ léctio -onis f. _____

9. sense of duty _____ píetas -atis f. _____

10. song _____ carmen -inis n. _____

11. Britain _____ Británnia -ae f. _____

12. lion _____ leo leonis m. _____

13. knowledge _____ sciéntia -ae f. _____

14. this, these _____ hic haec hoc _____

15. injury _____ injúria -ae f. _____

16. column _____ agmen -inis n. _____

17. -self, -selves _____ ipse -a -um _____

18. spring _____ ver veris n. _____

19. Switzerland _____ Helvétia -ae f. _____

20. memory _____ memória -ae f. _____

21. summer _____ aestas -atis f. _____

22. centurion _____ centúrio -onis m. _____

23. ditch _____ fossa -ae f. _____

24. body _____ corpus -oris n. _____

25. speed _____ celéritas -atis f. _____

26. speech _____ orátio -onis f. _____

27. himself, herself, itself _____ sui, sibi, se, se _____

28. truth _____ véritas -atis f. _____

29. wound _____ vulnus -eris n. _____

30. human being _____ homo -inis m. _____

31. flight _____ fuga -ae f. _____

32. that, those _____ ille illa illud _____

33. charity _____ cáritas -atis f. _____

34. friendship _____ amicítia -ae f. _____

35. Greece _____ Graécia -ae f. _____

36. time _____ tempus -oris n. _____

37. liberty _____ libertas -atis f. _____

38. that, those (of yours) _____ iste ista istud _____

39. legion _____ légio -onis f. _____

40. Athens _____ Athenae -arum f. _____

41. arrow _____ sagitta -ae f. _____

42. Germany _____ Germánia -ae f. _____

43. authority _____ auctóritas -atis f. _____

44. Carthage _____ Carthago -inis f. _____

45. work _____ opus -eris n. _____

46. wisdom _____ sapiéntia -ae f. _____

47. temptation _____ tentátio -onis f. _____

48. Ireland _____ Hibérnia -ae f. _____

Unit 3 Test

49. own ___suus -a -um___
50. will ___voluntas -atis f..___
51. state ___cívitas -atis f.___
52. maiden ___virgo -inis f.___
53. Europe ___Europa -ae f.___
54. burden ___onus -eris n.___
55. suffering ___pássio -onis f.___

B. Decline

Case	Singular	Plural	Singular	Plural
nom.	ego	nos	tu	vos
gen.	mei	nostri, nostrum	tui	vestri, vestrum
dat.	mihi	nobis	tibi	vobis
acc.	me	nos	te	vos
abl.	me	nobis	te	vobis

Case	Singular			Plural		
	M	F	N	M	F	N
nom.	is	ea	id	ei	eae	ea
gen.	ejus	ejus	ejus	eorum	earum	eorum
dat.	ei	ei	ei	eis	eis	eis
acc.	eum	eam	id	eos	eas	ea
abl.	eo	eā	eo	eis	eis	eis

Case	Singular			Plural		
	M	F	N	M	F	N
nom.	hic	haec	hoc	hi	hae	haec
gen.	hujus	hujus	hujus	horum	harum	horum
dat.	huic	huic	huic	his	his	his
acc.	hunc	hanc	hoc	hos	has	haec
abl.	hoc	hac	hoc	his	his	his

Case	Singular			Plural		
	M	F	N	M	F	N
nom.	ille	illa	illud	illi	illae	illa
gen.	illíus	illíus	illíus	illorum	illarum	illorum
dat.	illi	illi	illi	illis	illis	illis
acc.	illum	illam	illud	illos	illas	illa
abl.	illo	illā	illo	illis	illis	illis

Unit 3 Test

Case	Singular			Plural		
	M	F	N	M	F	N
nom.	ipse	ipsa	ipsum	ipsi	ipsae	ipsa
gen.	ipsíus	ipsíus	ipsíus	ipsorum	ipsarum	ipsorum
dat.	ipsi	ipsi	ipsi	ipsis	ipsis	ipsis
acc.	ipsum	ipsam	ipsum	ipsos	ipsas	ipsa
abl.	ipso	ipsā	ipso	ipsis	ipsis	ipsis

Case	Singular	Plural	Singular	Plural
nom.	ordo	órdines	légio	legiones
gen.	órdinis	órdinum	legionis	legionum
dat.	órdini	ordínibus	legioni	legiónibus
acc.	órdinem	órdines	legionem	legiones
abl.	órdine	ordínibus	legione	legiónibus

Case	Singular	Plural	Singular	Plural
nom.	aestas	aestates	cívitas	civitates
gen.	aestatis	aestatum	civitatis	civitatum
dat.	aestati	aestátibus	civitati	civitátibus
acc.	aestatem	aestates	civitatem	civitates
abl.	aestate	aestátibus	civitate	civitátibus

Case	Singular	Plural	Singular	Plural
nom.	carmen	cármina	genus	génera
gen.	cárminis	cárminum	géneris	génerum
dat.	cármini	carmínibus	géneri	genéribus
acc.	carmen	cármina	genus	génera
abl.	cármine	carmínibus	génere	genéribus

C. Latin Sayings

1. Faith, hope, and love, these three ___Fides, spes, cáritas, tria haec___
2. A day of wrath, that day ___Dies irae, dies illa___
3. Knowledge itself is power. ___Ipsa sciéntia potestas est.___
4. in itself ___per se___

D. Grammar

1. **Meus**, **tuus**, **noster**, and **vester** obeys the _____Adjective Agreement Rule_____ .

2. Most 3rd-declension nouns ending in **o** are _____feminine_____ .

3. **Is ea id** obeys the _____Pronoun Agreement Rule_____ .

4. The genitives of **is ea id** are used to show _____possession_____ .

5. Forms of **is ea id** mean *he* and *she* when referring to _____persons or animals_____ .

6. Forms of **is ea id** mean *it* when referring to _____non-living things with grammatical gender_____ .

7. **Hic**, **ille**, **iste**, and **ipse** are both _____adjectives_____ and _____pronouns_____ .

8. Third-declension nouns ending in **-tas -tatis** are always _____feminine_____ .

9. When used together, **hic** means _____the latter_____ , and **ille** means _____the former_____ .

10. Reflexive pronouns and adjectives refer_____back to the subject_____ .

E. Translate

1. with me _____mecum_____

2. with you all _____vobiscum_____

3. Puer suam domum spectat. _____The boy is looking at his own house._____

4. Puella in aquā se vidit. _____The girl saw herself in the water._____

5. Debetis vos juvare. _____You all should help yourselves._____

6. His ságittis pugnábimus. _____We will fight with these arrows._____

7. Illud onus tollam. _____I will lift up that burden._____

8. Donum ipsi senatori dabo. _____I will give a gift to the senator himself._____

9. Istud opus non amo. _____I do not like that work (of yours)._____

10. Exércitum in eorum provínciam mittemus. _____We will send an army into their province._____

F. Conjugate

Conjugate **<u>tollo</u>** in the indicative active (6 tenses) and the indicative passive (6 tenses).

Present Active	
tollo	tóllimus
tollis	tóllitis
tollit	tollunt

Present Passive	
tollor	tóllimur
tólleris	tollímini
tóllitur	tolluntur

Imperfect Active	
tollebam	tollebamus
tollebas	tollebatis
tollebat	tollebant

Imperfect Passive	
tollebar	tollebamur
tollebaris	tollebámini
tollebatur	tollebantur

Future Active	
tollam	tollemus
tolles	tolletis
tollet	tollent

Future Passive	
tollar	tollemur
tollēris	tollémini
tolletur	tollentur

Perfect Active	
sústuli	sustúlimus
sustulisti	sustulistis
sústulit	sustulerunt

Perfect Passive			
sublatus -a -um	sum	sublati -ae -a	sumus
	es		estis
	est		sunt

Pluperfect Active	
sustúleram	sustuleramus
sustúleras	sustuleratis
sustúlerat	sustúlerant

Pluperfect Passive			
sublatus -a -um	eram	sublati -ae -a	eramus
	eras		eratis
	erat		erant

Future Perfect Active	
sustúlero	sustulérimus
sustúleris	sustuléritis
sustúlerit	sustúlerint

Future Perfect Passive			
sublatus -a -um	ero	sublati -ae -a	érimus
	eris		éritis
	erit		erunt

Lesson 20 Quiz

Name_____ Date_____

A. Vocabulary

Give the dictionary form.

1. egg _____ ovum -i n.
2. aid _____ auxílium -i n.
3. power _____ impérium -i n.
4. beginning _____ princípium -i n.
5. Gospel _____ Evangélium -i n.
6. advice _____ consílium -i n.
7. danger _____ perículum -i n.
8. chain _____ vínculum -i n.
9. hatred _____ ódium -i n.
10. meeting _____ concílium -i n.

B. Conjugate

Present Subjunctive Active

1st (amo)	2nd (móneo)	3rd (rego)	3rd io (cápio)	4th (áudio)
amem	móneam	regam	cápiam	áudiam
ames	móneas	regas	cápias	áudias
amet	móneat	regat	cápiat	áudiat
amemus	moneamus	regamus	capiamus	audiamus
ametis	moneatis	regatis	capiatis	audiatis
ament	móneant	regant	cápiant	áudiant

C. Translate

1. Let the buyer beware. _____ Cáveat emptor.
2. mittamus _____ let us send
3. téneat _____ let him (her) hold
4. laborent _____ let them work
5. dórmias _____ may you sleep
6. jáciat _____ let him (her) throw
7. Let us build a city. _____ Urbem struamus.

D. Give the subjunctive vowel change for each conjugation

1st _____ substitute e for a

2nd _____ add a

3rd _____ substitute a for vowels i, o, u

3rd io _____ add a

4th _____ add a

Lesson 20 Quiz

E. Conjugate

Conjugate **muto** in the indicative active (6 tenses) and the indicative passive (6 tenses).

Present Active	
muto	mutamus
mutas	mutatis
mutat	mutant

Present Passive	
mutor	mutamur
mutaris	mutámini
mutatur	mutantur

Imperfect Active	
mutabam	mutabamus
mutabas	mutabatis
mutabat	mutabant

Imperfect Passive	
mutabar	mutabamur
mutabaris	mutabámini
mutabatur	mutabantur

Future Active	
mutabo	mutábimus
mutabis	mutábitis
mutabit	mutabunt

Future Passive	
mutabor	mutábimur
mutáberis	mutabímini
mutábitur	mutabuntur

Perfect Active	
mutavi	mutávimus
mutavisti	mutavistis
mutavit	mutaverunt

Perfect Passive			
mutatus -a -um	sum	mutati -ae -a	sumus
	es		estis
	est		sunt

Pluperfect Active	
mutáveram	mutaveramus
mutáveras	mutaveratis
mutáverat	mutáverant

Pluperfect Passive			
mutatus -a -um	eram	mutati -ae -a	eramus
	eras		eratis
	erat		erant

Future Perfect Active	
mutávero	mutavérimus
mutáveris	mutavéritis
mutáverit	mutáverint

Future Perfect Passive			
mutatus -a -um	ero	mutati -ae -a	érimus
	eris		éritis
	erit		erunt

Name_____ Date_____

A. Vocabulary

Give the dictionary form.

1. garrison _____praesídium -i n._____
2. trace _____vestígium -i n._____
3. heavenly body _____astrum -i n._____
4. starting point _____inítium -i n._____
5. exile _____exílium -i n._____

6. space _____spátium -i n._____
7. destiny _____fatum -i n._____
8. fort _____castellum -i n._____
9. fodder _____pábulum -i n._____
10. price _____prétium -i n._____

B. Translate

1. Hallowed be thy name. _____Sanctificetur nomen tuum._____

2. Advéniat regnum tuum. _____(may) Thy kingdom come._____

3. Ne fugiamus. _____Let us not flee._____

4. Urbem muniamus? _____Should we fortify the city?_____

5. Quis ducat? _____Who should lead?_____

6. Let us pray. _____Oremus._____

7. Let us rejoice. _____Gaudeamus._____

C. Grammar

1. A _____deliberative_____ question is asked in doubt or indignation, uses the subjunctive, and is expressed in English by the verbal helper _____should_____ .

2. The hortatory subjunctive expresses _____exhortation, indirect command, strong wish_____ , and uses the verbal helpers _____let and may_____ .

3. The two tenses missing from the subjunctive are _____future and future perfect_____ .

4. Give six English words that express the subjunctive.
   (1) _____let_____   (4) _____may_____
   (2) _____might_____   (5) _____should_____
   (3) _____could_____   (6) _____would_____

5. The subjunctive is used primarily in _____subordinate_____ clauses, but also has some uses in _____independent_____ clauses.

D. Conjugate

Conjugate five model verbs in the present subjunctive active and passive.

Present Subjunctive Active				
1st (amo)	2nd (móneo)	3rd (rego)	3rd io (cápio)	4th (áudio)
amem	móneam	regam	cápiam	áudiam
ames	móneas	regas	cápias	áudias
amet	móneat	regat	cápiat	áudiat
amemus	moneamus	regamus	capiamus	audiamus
ametis	moneatis	regatis	capiatis	audiatis
ament	móneant	regant	cápiant	áudiant

Present Subjunctive Passive				
1st (amo)	2nd (móneo)	3rd (rego)	3rd io (cápio)	4th (áudio)
amer	mónear	regar	cápiar	áudiar
ameris	monearis	regaris	capiaris	audiaris
ametur	moneatur	regatur	capiatur	audiatur
amemur	moneamur	regamur	capiamur	audiamur
amémini	moneámini	regámini	capiámini	audiámini
amentur	moneantur	regantur	capiantur	audiantur

Lesson 22 Quiz

Name_____Date_____

A. Vocabulary
Give the dictionary form.

1. cave _____antrum -i n._____   6. leisure _____ótium -i n._____
2. three days _____tríduum -i n._____   7. theater _____theatrum -i n._____
3. vow _____votum -i n._____   8. vice_____vítium -i n._____
4. death _____letum -i n._____   9. tomb_____sepulchrum -i n._____
5. building_____aedifícium -i n._____   10. commandment_____mandatum -i n._____

B. Conjugate

Imperfect Subjunctive Active				
1st (amo)	2nd (móneo)	3rd (rego)	3rd io (cápio)	4th (áudio)
amarem	monerem	régerem	cáperem	audirem
amares	moneres	régeres	cáperes	audires
amaret	moneret	régeret	cáperet	audiret
amaremus	moneremus	regeremus	caperemus	audiremus
amaretis	moneretis	regeretis	caperetis	audiretis
amarent	monerent	régerent	cáperent	audirent

Imperfect Subjunctive Passive				
1st (amo)	2nd (móneo)	3rd (rego)	3rd io (cápio)	4th (áudio)
amarer	monerer	régerer	cáperer	audirer
amareris	monereris	regereris	capereris	audireris
amaretur	moneretur	regeretur	caperetur	audiretur
amaremur	moneremur	regeremur	caperemur	audiremur
amarémini	monerémini	regerémini	caperémini	audirémini
amarentur	monerentur	regerentur	caperentur	audirentur

C. Translate

1. May he rest in peace._____Requiescat in pace._____
2. Quid fácerem? _____What should I have done?_____
3. Quid fáciam? _____What should I do?_____
4. Fugiamus?_____Should we flee?_____
5. Fugeremus?_____Should we have fled?_____

Lesson 22 Quiz

D. Conjugate
Conjugate five model verbs in the present subjunctive active and passive.

Present Subjunctive Active				
1st (amo)	2nd (móneo)	3rd (rego)	3rd io (cápio)	4th (áudio)
amem	móneam	regam	cápiam	áudiam
ames	móneas	regas	cápias	áudias
amet	móneat	regat	cápiat	áudiat
amemus	moneamus	regamus	capiamus	audiamus
ametis	moneatis	regatis	capiatis	audiatis
ament	móneant	regant	cápiant	áudiant

Present Subjunctive Passive				
1st (amo)	2nd (móneo)	3rd (rego)	3rd io (cápio)	4th (áudio)
amer	mónear	regar	cápiar	áudiar
ameris	monearis	regaris	capiaris	audiaris
ametur	moneatur	regatur	capiatur	audiatur
amemur	moneamur	regamur	capiamur	audiamur
amémini	moneámini	regámini	capiámini	audiámini
amentur	moneantur	regantur	capiantur	audiantur

E. Grammar

1. A deliberative question uses the _____present_____ subjunctive for present time and the _____imperfect_____ subjunctive for past time.

2. A sentence to help you remember the vowel changes in the present subjunctive is: We beat a liar.

3. A deliberative question is expressed in English with the verbal helper _____should_____ .

4. Hortatory expressions may be translated into English using the verbal helpers_____let_____ or _____may_____ .

5. A subjunctive is made negative by using the conjunction _____ne_____ .

Name_____ Date_____

A. Vocabulary
Give the dictionary form.

1. stone _____lapis -idis m._____
2. winter _____hiems híemis f._____
3. the air _____aer áeris m._____
4. wife _____uxor -is f._____
5. hostage _____obses -idis m._____

6. flock _____grex gregis m._____
7. companion _____comes -itis m._____
8. young person _____júvenis -is m./f._____
9. flower _____flos floris m._____
10. common people _____plebs -is f._____

B. Conjugate
sum

Present Subjunctive		Imperfect Subjunctive	
sim	simus	essem	essemus
sis	sitis	esses	essetis
sit	sint	esset	essent

C. Translate

1. I believe in order that I may understand. _____Credo ut intéllegam._____
2. you all might be _____essetis_____
3. we may be _____simus_____
4. Laboro ut vivam. _____I work in order to (that I may) live._____
5. Clamo ut áudiar. _____I am shouting in order to (that I may) be heard._____
6. Pugnant ut vincant. _____They are fighting to (that they may) win (conquer)._____

D. Grammar

1. Something that is exceptionally bad is _____egregious_____ .
2. To express purpose with the conjunction **ut**, the main clause is in the _____indicative_____ , and the subordinate clause is in the _____subjunctive_____ .
3. A deliberative question uses the _____present_____ subjunctive for present time and the _____imperfect_____ subjunctive for past time.
4. Hortatory expressions may be translated into English using the verbal helpers _____let_____ or _____may_____ .

E. Conjugate
Conjugate five model verbs in the present and imperfect subjunctive active and passive.

Present Subjunctive Active				
1st (amo)	2nd (móneo)	3rd (rego)	3rd **io** (cápio)	4th (áudio)
amem	móneam	regam	cápiam	áudiam
ames	móneas	regas	cápias	áudias
amet	móneat	regat	cápiat	áudiat
amemus	moneamus	regamus	capiamus	audiamus
ametis	moneatis	regatis	capiatis	audiatis
ament	móneant	regant	cápiant	áudiant

Imperfect Subjunctive Active				
1st (amo)	2nd (móneo)	3rd (rego)	3rd **io** (cápio)	4th (áudio)
amarem	monerem	régerem	cáperem	audirem
amares	moneres	régeres	cáperes	audires
amaret	moneret	régeret	cáperet	audiret
amaremus	moneremus	regeremus	caperemus	audiremus
amaretis	moneretis	regeretis	caperetis	audiretis
amarent	monerent	régerent	cáperent	audirent

Present Subjunctive Passive				
1st (amo)	2nd (móneo)	3rd (rego)	3rd **io** (cápio)	4th (áudio)
amer	mónear	regar	cápiar	áudiar
ameris	monearis	regaris	capiaris	audiaris
ametur	moneatur	regatur	capiatur	audiatur
amemur	moneamur	regamur	capiamur	audiamur
amémini	moneámini	regámini	capiámini	audiámini
amentur	moneantur	regantur	capiantur	audiantur

Imperfect Subjunctive Passive				
1st (amo)	2nd (móneo)	3rd (rego)	3rd **io** (cápio)	4th (áudio)
amarer	monerer	régerer	cáperer	audirer
amareris	monereris	regereris	capereris	audireris
amaretur	moneretur	regeretur	caperetur	audiretur
amaremur	moneremur	regeremur	caperemur	audiremur
amarémini	monerémini	regerémini	caperémini	audirémini
amarentur	monerentur	regerentur	caperentur	audirentur

Lesson 24 Quiz

Name_____ Date_____

A. Vocabulary
Give the dictionary form.

1. mouth — os oris n.
2. side — latus -eris n.
3. shore — litus -oris n.
4. level plain — aequor -oris n.
5. crime — scelus -eris n.
6. bone — os ossis n.
7. duty — munus -eris n.
8. leg — crus cruris n.
9. countryside — rus ruris n.
10. contest — certamen -inis n.

B. Conjugate

Perfect Subjunctive Active

1st (amo)	2nd (móneo)	3rd (rego)	3rd io (cápio)	4th (áudio)
amáverim	monúerim	réxerim	céperim	audíverim
amáveris	monúeris	réxeris	céperis	audíveris
amáverit	monúerit	réxerit	céperit	audíverit
amavérimus	monuérimus	rexérimus	cepérimus	audivérimus
amavéritis	monuéritis	rexéritis	cepéritis	audivéritis
amáverint	monúerint	réxerint	céperint	audíverint

Perfect Subjunctive Passive

1st (amo)	2nd (móneo)	3rd (rego)	3rd io (cápio)	4th (áudio)
amatus -a -um sim	mónitus -a -um sim	rectus -a -um sim	captus -a -um sim	auditus -a -um sim
sis	sis	sis	sis	sis
sit	sit	sit	sit	sit
amati -ae -a simus	móniti -ae -a simus	recti -ae -a simus	capti -ae -a simus	auditi -ae -a simus
sitis	sitis	sitis	sitis	sitis
sint	sint	sint	sint	sint

C. Translate or Answer

1. Hábeas corpus. — You may have the body.
2. scíveris — you may have known
3. factum sit — it may have been done
4. posúerint — they may have placed
5. visa sint — they may have been seen
6. Something that turns to bone or becomes rigid is said to ____ossify____ .

Lesson 24 Quiz

D. Conjugate
Conjugate five model verbs in the present and imperfect subjunctive active and passive.

Present Subjunctive Active

1st (amo)	2nd (móneo)	3rd (rego)	3rd io (cápio)	4th (áudio)
amem	móneam	regam	cápiam	áudiam
ames	móneas	regas	cápias	áudias
amet	móneat	regat	cápiat	áudiat
amemus	moneamus	regamus	capiamus	audiamus
ametis	moneatis	regatis	capiatis	audiatis
ament	móneant	regant	cápiant	áudiant

Imperfect Subjunctive Active

1st (amo)	2nd (móneo)	3rd (rego)	3rd io (cápio)	4th (áudio)
amarem	monerem	régerem	cáperem	audirem
amares	moneres	régeres	cáperes	audires
amaret	moneret	régeret	cáperet	audiret
amaremus	moneremus	regeremus	caperemus	audiremus
amaretis	moneretis	regeretis	caperetis	audiretis
amarent	monerent	régerent	cáperent	audirent

Present Subjunctive Passive

1st (amo)	2nd (móneo)	3rd (rego)	3rd io (cápio)	4th (áudio)
amer	mónear	regar	cápiar	áudiar
ameris	monearis	regaris	capiaris	audiaris
ametur	moneatur	regatur	capiatur	audiatur
amemur	moneamur	regamur	capiamur	audiamur
amémini	moneámini	regámini	capiámini	audiámini
amentur	moneantur	regantur	capiantur	audiantur

Imperfect Subjunctive Passive

1st (amo)	2nd (móneo)	3rd (rego)	3rd io (cápio)	4th (áudio)
amarer	monerer	régerer	cáperer	audirer
amareris	monereris	regereris	capereris	audireris
amaretur	moneretur	regeretur	caperetur	audiretur
amaremur	moneremur	regeremur	caperemur	audiremur
amarémini	monerémini	regerémini	caperémini	audirémini
amarentur	monerentur	regerentur	caperentur	audirentur

Name_____Date_____

A. Vocabulary

Give the dictionary form.

1. snow _____nix nivis f._____
2. sheep _____ovis ovis f._____
3. fountain_____fons fontis m._____
4. bird_____avis avis f._____
5. night_____nox noctis f._____

6. rain_____imber imbris m._____
7. hunger_____fames famis f._____
8. fire _____ignis ignis m._____
9. cloud _____nubes nubis f._____
10. clothes _____vestis vestis f._____

B. Conjugate

Pluperfect Subjunctive Active

1st (amo)	2nd (móneo)	3rd (rego)	3rd **io** (cápio)	4th (áudio)
amavissem	monuissem	rexissem	cepissem	audivissem
amavisses	monuisses	rexisses	cepisses	audivisses
amavisset	monuisset	rexisset	cepisset	audivisset
amavissemus	monuissemus	rexissemus	cepissemus	audivissemus
amavissetis	monuissetis	rexissetis	cepissetis	audivissetis
amavissent	monuissent	rexissent	cepissent	audivissent

Pluperfect Subjunctive Passive

1st (amo)	2nd (móneo)	3rd (rego)	3rd **io** (cápio)	4th (áudio)
amatus -a -um essem	mónitus -a -um essem	rectus -a -um essem	captus -a -um essem	auditus -a -um essem
esses	esses	esses	esses	esses
esset	esset	esset	esset	esset
amati -ae -a essemus	móniti -ae -a essemus	recti -ae -a essemus	capti -ae -a essemus	auditi -ae -a essemus
essetis	essetis	essetis	essetis	essetis
essent	essent	essent	essent	essent

C. Translate

1. Dum vívimus, vivamus. _____While we live, let us live._____
2. negavissemus _____we might have denied_____
3. visus esses_____you might have been seen_____
4. egissent _____they might have driven_____
5. victi essent _____they might have been conquered_____

Lesson 25 Quiz

D. Conjugate

Conjugate five model verbs in the present, imperfect, and perfect subjunctive active.

Present Subjunctive Active

1st (amo)	2nd (móneo)	3rd (rego)	3rd **io** (cápio)	4th (áudio)
amem	móneam	regam	cápiam	áudiam
ames	móneas	regas	cápias	áudias
amet	móneat	regat	cápiat	áudiat
amemus	moneamus	regamus	capiamus	audiamus
ametis	moneatis	regatis	capiatis	audiatis
ament	móneant	regant	cápiant	áudiant

Imperfect Subjunctive Active

1st (amo)	2nd (móneo)	3rd (rego)	3rd **io** (cápio)	4th (áudio)
amarem	monerem	régerem	cáperem	audirem
amares	moneres	régeres	cáperes	audires
amaret	moneret	régeret	cáperet	audiret
amaremus	moneremus	regeremus	caperemus	audiremus
amaretis	moneretis	regeretis	caperetis	audiretis
amarent	monerent	régerent	cáperent	audirent

Perfect Subjunctive Active

1st (amo)	2nd (móneo)	3rd (rego)	3rd **io** (cápio)	4th (áudio)
amáverim	monúerim	réxerim	céperim	audíverim
amáveris	monúeris	réxeris	céperis	audíveris
amáverit	monúerit	réxerit	céperit	audíverit
amavérimus	monuérimus	rexérimus	cepérimus	audivérimus
amavéritis	monuéritis	rexéritis	cepéritis	audivéritis
amáverint	monúerint	réxerint	céperint	audíverint

E. Grammar

1. A negative clause of purpose uses the conjunction __ne__ in place of the conjunction__ut__ .
2. An animal that is active at night instead of the day is_____nocturnal_____ .
3. A____hortatory____ subjunctive expresses an exhortation, indirect command, or a strong wish.

Lesson 26 Quiz

Name_____Date_____

A. Vocabulary

Give the dictionary form.

1. bow _____arcus -ūs m._____
2. falling _____occasus -ūs m._____
3. step_____passus -ūs m._____
4. exit _____éxitus -ūs m._____
5. cart_____currus -ūs m._____

6. use _____usus -ūs m._____
7. cavalry_____equitatus -ūs m._____
8. attack _____ímpetus -ūs m._____
9. expression _____vultus -ūs m._____
10. course _____cursus -ūs m._____

B. Conjugate

sum

Perfect Subjunctive		Pluperfect Subjunctive	
fúerim	fuérimus	fuissem	fuissemus
fúeris	fuéritis	fuisses	fuissetis
fúerit	fúerint	fuisset	fuissent

C. Translate

1. Cedant arma togae. _____Let arms yield to the toga._____
2. they may have been_____fúerint_____
3. she might have been _____fuisset_____
4. I may have been _____fúerim_____
5. we might have been_____fuissemus_____
6. Pugnaverunt ut víncerent. _____They fought in order that they might conquer._____

D. Grammar

1. The two common feminine nouns of the 4th declension are _____**domus** and **manus**_____ .
2. The two common neuter nouns of the 4th declension are_____**cornu** and **genu**_____ .
3. The perfect subjunctive active is the same as the _____future perfect active indicative_____ except for the 1st person singular.
4. An _____impetuous_____ person acts without thinking.

Lesson 26 Quiz

E. Conjugate

Conjugate five model verbs in the four tenses of the subjunctive <u>active</u>.

Present Subjunctive Active				
1st (amo)	2nd (móneo)	3rd (rego)	3rd **io** (cápio)	4th (áudio)
amem	móneam	regam	cápiam	áudiam
ames	móneas	regas	cápias	áudias
amet	móneat	regat	cápiat	áudiat
amemus	moneamus	regamus	capiamus	audiamus
ametis	moneatis	regatis	capiatis	audiatis
ament	móneant	regant	cápiant	áudiant

Imperfect Subjunctive Active				
1st (amo)	2nd (móneo)	3rd (rego)	3rd **io** (cápio)	4th (áudio)
amarem	monerem	régerem	cáperem	audirem
amares	moneres	régeres	cáperes	audires
amaret	moneret	régeret	cáperet	audiret
amaremus	moneremus	regeremus	caperemus	audiremus
amaretis	moneretis	regeretis	caperetis	audiretis
amarent	monerent	régerent	cáperent	audirent

Perfect Subjunctive Active				
1st (amo)	2nd (móneo)	3rd (rego)	3rd **io** (cápio)	4th (áudio)
amáverim	monúerim	réxerim	céperim	audíverim
amáveris	monúeris	réxeris	céperis	audíveris
amáverit	monúerit	réxerit	céperit	audíverit
amavérimus	monuérimus	rexérimus	cepérimus	audivérimus
amavéritis	monuéritis	rexéritis	cepéritis	audivéritis
amáverint	monúerint	réxerint	céperint	audíverint

Pluperfect Subjunctive Active				
1st (amo)	2nd (móneo)	3rd (rego)	3rd **io** (cápio)	4th (áudio)
amavissem	monuissem	rexissem	cepissem	audivissem
amavisses	monuisses	rexisses	cepisses	audivisses
amavisset	monuisset	rexisset	cepisset	audivisset
amavissemus	monuissemus	rexissemus	cepissemus	audivissemus
amavissetis	monuissetis	rexissetis	cepissetis	audivissetis
amavissent	monuissent	rexissent	cepissent	audivissent

Name _____ Date _____

A. Vocabulary
Give the dictionary form.

1. exile _____ exílium -i n. _____
2. commandment _____ mandatum -i n. _____
3. smooth surface _____ aequor -oris n. _____
4. tomb _____ sepulchrum -i n. _____
5. night _____ nox noctis f. _____
6. leisure _____ ótium -i n. _____
7. cavalry _____ equitatus -ūs m. _____
8. course _____ cursus -ūs m. _____
9. advice _____ consílium -i n. _____
10. starting point _____ inítium -i n. _____
11. winter _____ hiems híemis f. _____
12. common people _____ plebs -is f. _____
13. fountain _____ fons fontis m. _____
14. wife _____ uxor -is f. _____
15. countenance _____ vultus -ūs m. _____
16. heavenly body _____ astrum -i n. _____
17. destiny _____ fatum -i n. _____
18. rain _____ imber imbris m. _____
19. duty _____ munus -eris n. _____
20. origin _____ princípium -i n. _____
21. egg _____ ovum -i n. _____
22. theater _____ theatrum -i n. _____
23. companion _____ comes -itis m. _____
24. hatred _____ ódium -i n. _____

25. power _____ impérium -i n. _____
26. garrison _____ praesídium -i n. _____
27. step _____ passus -ūs m. _____
28. blemish _____ vítium -i n. _____
29. cart _____ currus -ūs m. _____
30. flock _____ grex gregis m. _____
31. snow _____ nix nivis f. _____
32. sheep _____ ovis ovis f. _____
33. price _____ prétium -i n. _____
34. in order that _____ ut _____
35. contest _____ certamen -inis n. _____
36. help _____ auxílium -i n. _____
37. building _____ aedifícium -i n. _____
38. fire _____ ignis ignis m. _____
39. mouth _____ os oris n. _____
40. crime _____ scelus -eris n. _____
41. three days _____ tríduum -i n. _____
42. hostage _____ obses -idis m. _____
43. exit _____ éxitus -ūs m. _____
44. meeting _____ concílium -i n. _____
45. bow _____ arcus ūs m. _____
46. leg _____ crus cruris n. _____
47. stone _____ lapis -idis m. _____
48. attack _____ ímpetus -ūs m. _____

49. countryside _____ rus ruris n. _____
50. young person _____ júvenis júvenis m./f.
51. shore _____ litus -oris n. _____
52. bone _____ os ossis n. _____
53. hunger _____ fames famis f. _____
54. flower _____ flos floris m. _____
55. bird _____ avis avis f. _____
56. space _____ spátium -i n. _____
57. use _____ usus -ūs m. _____
58. cloud _____ nubes nubis f. _____
59. the air _____ aer -is m. _____
60. Gospel _____ Evangélium -i n. _____

61. side _____ latus -eris n. _____
62. fodder _____ pábulum -i n. _____
63. death _____ letum -i n. _____
64. falling _____ occasus -ūs m. _____
65. danger _____ perículum -i n. _____
66. trace _____ vestígium -i n. _____
67. chain _____ vínculum -i n. _____
68. cave _____ antrum -i n. _____
69. vow _____ votum -i n. _____
70. fort _____ castellum -i n. _____
71. clothes _____ vestis vestis f. _____

B. Latin Sayings

1. While we live, let us live. _____ Dum vívimus, vivamus.
2. I believe in order that I may understand. _____ Credo ut intéllegam.
3. Let the buyer beware. _____ Cáveat emptor.
4. Hallowed be thy name. _____ Sanctificetur nomen tuum.
5. You may have the body. _____ Hábeas corpus.
6. Let arms yield to the toga. _____ Cedant arma togae.
7. May he rest in peace. _____ Requiescat in pace.

Unit 4 Test

C. Grammar

1. Give the three moods of the Latin verb.
   (1) __indicative__
   (2) __imperative__
   (3) __subjunctive__

2. Give the six English words that may be used to express the subjunctive mood.
   (1) __let__   (4) __may__
   (2) __might__   (5) __should__
   (3) __could__   (6) __would__

3. The indicative mood describes action that is __actual, real__, and the subjunctive mood describes action that is __potential__.

4. The subjunctive is used mainly in __subordinate__ clauses.

5. Two uses of the subjunctive in independent clauses are __hortatory and deliberative questions__.

D. Translate

1. Inítium faciamus. __Let us make a beginning.__

2. Aves volant ne capiantur. __Birds fly lest they be captured.__

3. Quis viam servet? __Who should guard the road?__

4. Fúgio ne vulnerer. __I am fleeing lest I be wounded.__

5. Portas claudamus ut simus tuti. __Let us close the gates in order to be safe.__

Unit 4 Test

E. Conjugate

Conjugate five model verbs in the four tenses of the subjunctive <u>active</u>.

Present Subjunctive Active

1st (amo)	2nd (móneo)	3rd (rego)	3rd **io** (cápio)	4th (áudio)
amem	móneam	regam	cápiam	áudiam
ames	móneas	regas	cápias	áudias
amet	móneat	regat	cápiat	áudiat
amemus	moneamus	regamus	capiamus	audiamus
ametis	moneatis	regatis	capiatis	audiatis
ament	móneant	regant	cápiant	áudiant

Imperfect Subjunctive Active

1st (amo)	2nd (móneo)	3rd (rego)	3rd **io** (cápio)	4th (áudio)
amarem	monerem	régerem	cáperem	audirem
amares	moneres	régeres	cáperes	audires
amaret	moneret	régeret	cáperet	audiret
amaremus	moneremus	regeremus	caperemus	audiremus
amaretis	moneretis	regeretis	caperetis	audiretis
amarent	monerent	régerent	cáperent	audirent

Perfect Subjunctive Active

1st (amo)	2nd (móneo)	3rd (rego)	3rd **io** (cápio)	4th (áudio)
amáverim	monúerim	réxerim	céperim	audíverim
amáveris	monúeris	réxeris	céperis	audíveris
amáverit	monúerit	réxerit	céperit	audíverit
amavérimus	monuérimus	rexérimus	cepérimus	audivérimus
amavéritis	monuéritis	rexéritis	cepéritis	audivéritis
amáverint	monúerint	réxerint	céperint	audíverint

Pluperfect Subjunctive Active

1st (amo)	2nd (móneo)	3rd (rego)	3rd **io** (cápio)	4th (áudio)
amavissem	monuissem	rexissem	cepissem	audivissem
amavisses	monuisses	rexisses	cepisses	audivisses
amavisset	monuisset	rexisset	cepisset	audivisset
amavissemus	monuissemus	rexissemus	cepissemus	audivissemus
amavissetis	monuissetis	rexissetis	cepissetis	audivissetis
amavissent	monuissent	rexissent	cepissent	audivissent

F. Conjugate

Conjugate five model verbs in the four tenses of the subjunctive <u>passive</u>.

Present Subjunctive Passive

1st (amo)	2nd (móneo)	3rd (rego)	3rd io (cápio)	4th (áudio)
amer	mónear	regar	cápiar	áudiar
ameris	monearis	regaris	capiaris	audiaris
ametur	moneatur	regatur	capiatur	audiatur
amemur	moneamur	regamur	capiamur	audiamur
amémini	moneámini	regámini	capiámini	audiámini
amentur	moneantur	regantur	capiantur	audiantur

Imperfect Subjunctive Passive

1st (amo)	2nd (móneo)	3rd (rego)	3rd io (cápio)	4th (áudio)
amarer	monerer	régerer	cáperer	audirer
amareris	monereris	regereris	capereris	audireris
amaretur	moneretur	regeretur	caperetur	audiretur
amaremur	moneremur	regeremur	caperemur	audiremur
amarémini	monerémini	regerémini	caperémini	audirémini
amarentur	monerentur	regerentur	caperentur	audirentur

Perfect Subjunctive Passive

1st (amo)	2nd (móneo)	3rd (rego)	3rd io (cápio)	4th (áudio)
amatus -a -um sim	mónitus -a -um sim	rectus -a -um sim	captus -a -um sim	auditus -a -um sim
sis	sis	sis	sis	sis
sit	sit	sit	sit	sit
amati -ae -a simus	móniti -ae -a simus	recti -ae -a simus	capti -ae -a simus	auditi -ae -a simus
sitis	sitis	sitis	sitis	sitis
sint	sint	sint	sint	sint

Pluperfect Subjunctive Passive

1st (amo)	2nd (móneo)	3rd (rego)	3rd io (cápio)	4th (áudio)
amatus -a -um essem	mónitus -a -um essem	rectus -a -um essem	captus -a -um essem	auditus -a -um essem
esses	esses	esses	esses	esses
esset	esset	esset	esset	esset
amati -ae -a essemus	móniti -ae -a essemus	recti -ae -a essemus	capti -ae -a essemus	auditi -ae -a essemus
essetis	essetis	essetis	essetis	essetis
essent	essent	essent	essent	essent

G. Sum - Present Subjunctive

Person	Singular		Plural	
	Latin	Meaning	Latin	Meaning
1st	sim	I may be	simus	we may be
2nd	sis	you may be	sitis	you all may be
3rd	sit	hsi may be	sint	they may be

H. Sum - Imperfect Subjunctive

Person	Singular		Plural	
	Latin	Meaning	Latin	Meaning
1st	essem	I might be	essemus	we might be
2nd	esses	you might be	essetis	you all might be
3rd	esset	hsi might be	essent	they might be

Lesson 27 Quiz   Name_____ Date_____

A. Vocabulary
Give the dictionary form.

1. hard ___durus -a -um___
2. rustic ___rústicus -a -um___
3. foreign ___alienus -a -um___
4. blessed ___beatus -a -um___
5. true ___verus -a -um___
6. rapid ___citus -a -um___
7. doubtful ___dúbius -a -um___
8. narrow ___angustus -a -um___
9. dutiful ___pius -a -um___
10. bright ___clarus -a -um___

B. Decline
Decline the comparative of **citus**.

M/F		N	
cítior	citiores	cítius	citiora
citioris	citiorum	citioris	citiorum
citiori	citióribus	citiori	citióribus
citiorem	citiores	cítius	citiora
citiore	citióribus	citiore	citióribus

C. Translate or Answer

1. Faster, Higher, Stronger ___Cítius, Áltius, Fórtius___
2. Exércitum potentíssimum habemus. ___We have the most powerful army.___
3. Pone saxum grávius in fossam. ___Place the heavier rock in the ditch.___
4. This rock is the hardest. ___Hoc saxum est duríssimum.___
5. An ___alien___ is someone from a foreign country.

D. Give the comparative and superlative forms, with meanings

Positive	Comparative	Superlative
certus -a -um *certain*	cértior cértius / *more certain*	certíssimus -a -um / *most certain*
fortis -e *brave*	fórtior fórtius / *braver*	fortíssimus -a -um / *bravest*
potens, potentis *powerful*	poténtior poténtius / *more powerful*	potentíssimus -a -um / *most powerful*

E. Conjugate
Conjugate **paro** in the indicative active (6 tenses) and the indicative passive (6 tenses).

Present Active	
paro	paramus
paras	paratis
parat	parant

Present Passive	
paror	paramur
pararis	parámini
paratur	parantur

Imperfect Active	
parabam	parabamus
parabas	parabatis
parabat	parabant

Imperfect Passive	
parabar	parabamur
parabaris	parabámini
parabatur	parabantur

Future Active	
parabo	parábimus
parabis	parábitis
parabit	parabunt

Future Passive	
parabor	parábimur
paráberis	parabímini
parábitur	parabuntur

Perfect Active	
paravi	parávimus
paravisti	paravistis
paravit	paraverunt

Perfect Passive			
paratus -a -um	sum	parati -ae -a	sumus
	es		estis
	est		sunt

Pluperfect Active	
paráveram	paraveramus
paráveras	paraveratis
paráverat	paráverant

Pluperfect Passive			
paratus -a -um	eram	parati -ae -a	eramus
	eras		eratis
	erat		erant

Future Perfect Active	
parávero	paravérimus
paráveris	paravéritis
paráverit	paráverint

Future Perfect Passive			
paratus -a -um	ero	parati -ae -a	érimus
	eris		éritis
	erit		erunt

Lesson 27 Quiz

F. Conjugate
Conjugate **paro** in the subjunctive active and passive.

Present Active	
parem	paremus
pares	paretis
paret	parent

Present Passive	
parer	paremur
pareris	parémini
paretur	parentur

Imperfect Active	
pararem	pararemus
parares	pararetis
pararet	pararent

Imperfect Passive	
pararer	pararemur
parareris	pararémini
pararetur	pararentur

Perfect Active	
paráverim	paravérimus
paráveris	paravéritis
paráverit	paráverint

Perfect Passive			
paratus -a -um	sim	parati -ae -a	simus
	sis		sitis
	sit		sint

Pluperfect Active	
paravissem	paravissemus
paravisses	paravissetis
paravisset	paravissent

Pluperfect Passive			
paratus -a -um	essem	parati -ae -a	essemus
	esses		essetis
	esset		essent

Lesson 28 Quiz

Name_____ Date_____

A. Vocabulary
Give the dictionary form.

1. humble____húmilis -e____
2. common____communis -e____
3. sublime____sublimis -e____
4. vain____inanis -e____
5. sad____tristis -e____
6. cruel____crudelis -e____
7. soft____mollis -e____
8. civil____civilis -e____
9. mild____lenis -e____
10. boorish____agrestis -e____

B. Decline
Decline the comparative of **pulcher**.

M/F		N	
púlchrior	pulchriores	púlchrius	pulchriora
pulchrioris	pulchriorum	pulchrioris	pulchriorum
pulchriori	pulchrióribus	pulchriori	pulchrióribus
pulchriorem	pulchriores	púlchrius	pulchriora
pulchriore	pulchrióribus	pulchriore	pulchrióribus

C. Translate

1. New order of the ages ____Novus ordo seclorum____
2. Currum celeriorem vidi.____I have seen a faster cart.____
3. Currus celérrimus est longíssimus.____The fastest cart is the longest.____
4. Leo est crudélior quam ovis.____The lion is more cruel than the sheep.____
5. The queen is rather humble.____Regina est humílior.____

D. Give the comparative and superlative forms, with meanings

Positive	Comparative	Superlative
miser -era -erum *wretched*	misérior misérius / *more wretched*	misérrimus -a -um / *most wretched*
pulcher -chra -chrum *beautiful*	púlchrior púlchrius / *more beautiful*	pulchérrimus -a -um / *most beautiful*
acer acris acre *sharp*	ácrior ácrius / *sharper*	acérrimus -a -um / *sharpest*
fidelis -e *faithful*	fidélior fidélius / *more faithful*	fidelíssimus -a -um / *most faithful*
fácilis -e *easy*	facílior facílius / *easier*	facíllimus -a -um / *easiest*

Lesson 28 Quiz

E. Conjugate

Conjugate **júbeo** in the indicative active (6 tenses) and the indicative passive (6 tenses).

Present Active	
júbeo	jubemus
jubes	jubetis
jubet	jubent

Present Passive	
júbeor	jubemur
juberis	jubémini
jubetur	jubentur

Imperfect Active	
jubebam	jubebamus
jubebas	jubebatis
jubebat	jubebant

Imperfect Passive	
jubebar	jubebamur
jubebaris	jubebámini
jubebatur	jubebantur

Future Active	
jubebo	jubébimus
jubebis	jubébitis
jubebit	jubebunt

Future Passive	
jubebor	jubébimur
jubéberis	jubebímini
jubébitur	jubebuntur

Perfect Active	
jussi	jússimus
jussisti	jussistis
jussit	jusserunt

Perfect Passive			
jussus -a -um	sum	jussi -ae -a	sumus
	es		estis
	est		sunt

Pluperfect Active	
jússeram	jusseramus
jússeras	jusseratis
jússerat	jússerant

Pluperfect Passive			
jussus -a -um	eram	jussi -ae -a	eramus
	eras		eratis
	erat		erant

Future Perfect Active	
jússero	jussérimus
jússeris	jusséritis
jússerit	jússerint

Future Perfect Passive			
jussus -a -um	ero	jussi -ae -a	érimus
	eris		éritis
	erit		erunt

Lesson 28 Quiz

F. Conjugate

Conjugate **jubeo** in the subjunctive active and passive.

Present Active	
júbeam	jubeamus
júbeas	jubeatis
júbeat	júbeant

Present Passive	
júbear	jubeamur
jubearis	jubeámini
jubeatur	jubeantur

Imperfect Active	
juberem	juberemus
juberes	juberetis
juberet	juberent

Imperfect Passive	
juberer	juberemur
jubereris	juberémini
juberetur	juberentur

Perfect Active	
jússerim	jussérimus
jússeris	jusséritis
jússerit	jússerint

Perfect Passive			
jussus -a -um	sim	jussi -ae -a	simus
	sis		sitis
	sit		sint

Pluperfect Active	
jussissem	jussissemus
jussisses	jussissetis
jussisset	jussissent

Pluperfect Passive			
jussus -a -um	essem	jussi -ae -a	essemus
	esses		essetis
	esset		essent

A. Give the comparative and superlative forms, with meanings

positive	comparative	superlative
bonus -a -um	mélior mélius / *better*	óptimus -a -um / *best*
malus -a -um	pejor pejus / *worse*	péssimus -a -um / *worst*
magnus -a -um	major majus / *greater*	máximus -a -um / *greatest*
parvus -a -um	minor minus / *smaller*	mínimus -a -um / *smallest*
multus -a -um	plus pluris n. / *more*	plúrimus -a -um / *most*
multi -ae -a	plures plura / *more*	plúrimi -ae -a / *most*
senex, senis	sénior sénius / *older*	máximus natu / *oldest*
júvenis -is	júnior június / *younger*	mínimus natu / *youngest*
dúbius -a -um	magis dúbius / *more doubtful*	máximē dúbius / *most doubtful*
idóneus -a -um	magis idóneus / *more suitable*	máximē idóneus / *most suitable*

B. Translate

1. One out of many _____ E plúribus unum _____
2. Galli naves óptimas habent. _____ The Gauls have very good ships. _____
3. A mílitibus óptimis servamur. _____ We are being guarded by the best soldiers. _____
4. Éxitus est magis dúbius. _____ The outcome is more doubtful. _____
5. Canis mínimus vocem máximam habet. _____ The smallest dog has the biggest voice. _____

C. Grammar

1. The superlative adjective is used more in Latin than in English and is thus _____ weaker _____ .
2. The absolute superlative can be expressed by using _____ ómnium _____ .
3. Adjective with stems ending in a vowel are usually compared using the adverbs _____ magis and máximē _____ .

D. Conjugate

Conjugate **pono** in the indicative active (6 tenses) and the indicative passive (6 tenses).

Present Active	
pono	pónimus
ponis	pónitis
ponit	ponunt

Present Passive	
ponor	pónimur
póneris	ponímini
pónitur	ponuntur

Imperfect Active	
ponebam	ponebamus
ponebas	ponebatis
ponebat	ponebant

Imperfect Passive	
ponebar	ponebamur
ponebaris	ponebámini
ponebatur	ponebantur

Future Active	
ponam	ponemus
pones	ponetis
ponet	ponent

Future Passive	
ponar	ponemur
ponēris	ponémini
ponetur	ponentur

Perfect Active	
pósui	posúimus
posuisti	posuistis
pósuit	posuerunt

Perfect Passive			
pósitus -a -um	sum	pósiti -ae -a	sumus
	es		estis
	est		sunt

Pluperfect Active	
posúeram	posueramus
posúeras	posueratis
posúerat	posúerant

Pluperfect Passive			
pósitus -a -um	eram	pósiti -ae -a	eramus
	eras		eratis
	erat		erant

Future Perfect Active	
posúero	posuérimus
posúeris	posuéritis
posúerit	posúerint

Future Perfect Passive			
pósitus -a -um	ero	pósiti -ae -a	érimus
	eris		éritis
	erit		erunt

Quiz 29

Lesson 29 Quiz

E. Conjugate

Conjugate **pono** in the subjunctive active and passive.

Present Active	
ponam	ponamus
ponas	ponatis
ponat	ponant

Present Passive	
ponar	ponamur
ponaris	ponámini
ponatur	ponantur

Imperfect Active	
pónerem	poneremus
póneres	poneretis
póneret	pónerent

Imperfect Passive	
pónerer	poneremur
ponereris	ponerémini
poneretur	ponerentur

Perfect Active	
posúerim	posuérimus
posúeris	posuéritis
posúerit	posúerint

Perfect Passive			
pósitus -a -um	sim	pósiti -ae -a	simus
	sis		sitis
	sit		sint

Pluperfect Active	
posuissem	posuissemus
posuisses	posuissetis
posuisset	posuissent

Pluperfect Passive			
pósitus -a -um essem		pósiti -ae -a	essemus
	esses		essetis
	esset		essent

Lesson 30 Quiz

Name _____ Date _____

A. Vocabulary

Give the dictionary form.

1. level _____aequus -a -um_____
2. avid _____ávidus -a -um_____
3. all (group) _____cunctus -a -um_____
4. dangerous _____periculosus -a -um_____
5. steep _____árduus -a -um_____
6. wondrous _____mirus -a -um_____
7. late _____tardus -a -um_____
8. blind _____caecus -a -um_____
9. worthy _____dignus -a -um_____
10. proud _____superbus -a -um_____

B. Give the comparative and superlative forms, with meanings

positive	comparative	superlative
latus -a -um *wide*	látior látius / *wider*	latíssimus -a -um / *widest*
latē *widely*	látius / *more widely*	latíssimē / *most widely*
gravis -e *serious*	grávior grávius / *more serious*	gravíssimus -a -um / *most serious*
gráviter *seriously*	grávius / *more seriously*	gravíssimē / *most seriously*

C. Translate

1. He has favored our undertaking. _____Ánnuit coeptis._____
2. Is celérius quam ego ambulabat. _____He was walking faster than I._____
3. Haec navis iter celeríssimē faciet. _____This ship will make the journey very quickly._____
4. Difficíllimē laborant. _____They are working with great difficulty._____

D. Grammar

1. Adverbs stand _____before_____ the verbs they modify.
2. Like adjectives, the comparative and superlative adverbs are _____weaker_____ than their English equivalents.
3. The superlative of regular adverbs is formed by changing the **-us** of the superlative adjective to _____-ē_____.

E. Conjugate

Conjugate **fínio** in the indicative active (6 tenses) and the indicative passive (6 tenses).

Present Active	
fínio	finimus
finis	finitis
finit	fíniunt

Present Passive	
finior	finimur
finiris	finímini
finitur	finiuntur

Imperfect Active	
finiebam	finiebamus
finiebas	finiebatis
finiebat	finiebant

Imperfect Passive	
finiebar	finiebamur
finiebaris	finiebámini
finiebatur	finiebantur

Future Active	
fíniam	finiemus
fínies	finietis
fíniet	fínient

Future Passive	
fíniar	finiemur
finieris	finiemini
finietur	finientur

Perfect Active	
finivi	finívimus
finivisti	finivistis
finivit	finiverunt

Perfect Passive			
finitus -a -um	sum	finiti -ae -a	sumus
	es		estis
	est		sunt

Pluperfect Active	
finíveram	finiveramus
finíveras	finiveratis
finíverat	finíverant

Pluperfect Passive			
finitus -a -um	eram	finiti -ae -a	eramus
	eras		eratis
	erat		erant

Future Perfect Active	
finívero	finivérimus
finíveris	finivéritis
finíverit	finíverint

Future Perfect Passive			
finitus -a -um	ero	finiti -ae -a	érimus
	eris		éritis
	erit		erunt

F. Conjugate

Conjugate **fínio** in the subjunctive active and passive.

Present Active	
fíniam	finiamus
fínias	finiatis
fíniat	fíniant

Present Passive	
fíniar	finiamur
finiaris	finiámini
finiatur	finiantur

Imperfect Active	
finirem	finiremus
finires	finiretis
finiret	finirent

Imperfect Passive	
finirer	finiremur
finireris	finirémini
finiretur	finirentur

Perfect Active	
finíverim	finivérimus
finíveris	finivéritis
finíverit	finíverint

Perfect Passive			
finitus -a -um	sim	finiti -ae -a	simus
	sis		sitis
	sit		sint

Pluperfect Active	
finivissem	finivissemus
finivisses	finivissetis
finivisset	finivissent

Pluperfect Passive			
finitus -a -um	essem	finiti -ae -a	essemus
	esses		essetis
	esset		essent

Quiz 30

Lesson 31 Quiz

Name_____ Date_____

A. Give the comparative and superlative forms, with meanings

Positive	Comparative	Superlative
bene	mélius / *better*	óptimē / *best*
parum	minus / *less*	mínimē / *least*
diu	diútius / *longer (time)*	diutíssimē / *longest (time)*
male	pejus / *worse*	péssimē / *worst*
saepe	saépius / *more often*	saepíssimē / *most often*
magnópere	magis / *more*	máximē / *most*
prope	própius / *nearer*	próximē / *next*
multum	plus / *more*	plúrimum / *most*

B. Translate

1. much in little _____ multum in parvo
2. Epístulas saépius mittam. _____ I will send letters more often.
3. Diutíssimē dormivit. _____ Hsi slept for a very long time.
4. Is mélius quam tu natat. _____ He swims better than you.
5. Quis grátias plúrimum agit? _____ Who gives thanks the most?
6. Romani bellum minus quam Galli gerunt. _____ Romans wage war less than the Gauls.
7. Post cenam péssimē laboramus. _____ We work worst after dinner.
8. Stay longer! _____ Mane(te) diútius!

C. Grammar

1. Besides its meaning as a comparison, the superlative adverb can mean _____ very _____ .
2. Besides its meaning as a comparison, the comparative adverb can mean _____ rather, too _____ .

Lesson 31 Quiz

D. Conjugate

Conjugate **cúpio** in the indicative active (6 tenses) and the indicative passive (6 tenses).

Present Active	
cúpio	cúpimus
cupis	cúpitis
cupit	cúpiunt

Present Passive	
cúpior	cúpimur
cúperis	cupímini
cúpitur	cupiuntur

Imperfect Active	
cupiebam	cupiebamus
cupiebas	cupiebatis
cupiebat	cupiebant

Imperfect Passive	
cupiebar	cupiebamur
cupiebaris	cupiébamini
cupiebatur	cupiebantur

Future Active	
cúpiam	cupiemus
cúpies	cupietis
cúpiet	cúpient

Future Passive	
cúpiar	cupiemur
cupieris	cupiémini
cupietur	cupientur

Perfect Active	
cupivi	cupívimus
cupivisti	cupivistis
cupivit	cupiverunt

Perfect Passive			
cupitus -a -um	sum	cupiti -ae -a	sumus
	es		estis
	est		sunt

Pluperfect Active	
cupíveram	cupiveramus
cupíveras	cupiveratis
cupíverat	cupíverant

Pluperfect Passive			
cupitus -a -um	eram	cupiti -ae -a	eramus
	eras		eratis
	erat		erant

Future Perfect Active	
cupívero	cupivérimus
cupíveris	cupivéritis
cupíverit	cupíverint

Future Perfect Passive			
cupitus -a -um	ero	cupiti -ae -a	érimus
	eris		éritis
	erit		erunt

E. Conjugate

Conjugate **cúpio** in the subjunctive active and passive.

Present Active	
cúpiam	cupiamus
cúpias	cupiatis
cúpiat	cúpiant

Present Passive	
cúpiar	cupiamur
cupiaris	cupiámini
cupiatur	cupiantur

Imperfect Active	
cúperem	cuperemus
cúperes	cuperetis
cúperet	cúperent

Imperfect Passive	
cúperer	cuperemur
cupereris	cuperémini
cuperetur	cuperentur

Perfect Active	
cupíverim	cupivérimus
cupíveris	cupivéritis
cupíverit	cupíverint

Perfect Passive			
cupitus -a -um	sim	cupiti -ae -a	simus
	sis		sitis
	sit		sint

Pluperfect Active	
cupivissem	cupivissemus
cupivisses	cupivissetis
cupivisset	cupivissent

Pluperfect Passive			
cupitus -a -um	essem	cupiti -ae -a	essemus
	esses		essetis
	esset		essent

A. Vocabulary

Give the dictionary form.

1. sublime ___sublimis -e___
2. mild ___lenis -e___
3. narrow ___angustus -a -um___
4. common ___communis -e___
5. all (group) ___cunctus -a -um___
6. soft ___mollis -e___
7. humble ___húmilis -e___
8. blind ___caecus -a -um___
9. doubtful ___dúbius -a -um___
10. wondrous ___mirus -a -um___
11. sad ___tristis -e___
12. vain ___inanis -e___
13. steep ___árduus -a -um___
14. level ___aequus -a -um___
15. civil ___civilis -e___
16. worthy ___dignus -a -um___
17. than (adv.) ___quam___
18. hard ___durus -a -um___
19. blessed ___beatus -a -um___
20. foreign ___alienus -a -um___
21. dangerous ___periculosus -a -um___
22. true ___verus -a -um___
23. cruel ___crudelis -e___
24. rapid ___citus -a -um___
25. dutiful ___pius -a -um___
26. clear ___clarus -a -um___
27. late ___tardus -a -um___
28. rustic ___rústicus -a -um___
29. proud ___superbus -a -um___
30. boorish ___agrestis -e___
31. avid ___ávidus -a -um___

Unit 5 Test

B. Latin Sayings

1. New order of the ages ___Novus ordo seclorum___
2. He has favored our undertaking. ___Ánnuit coeptis.___
3. much in little ___multum in parvo___
4. One out of many ___E plúribus unum___
5. Faster, Higher, Stronger ___Cítius, Áltius, Fórtius___

C. Grammar

1. The three degrees of comparison are:
   (1) ___positive___ (2) ___comparative___ (3) ___superlative___
2. In English, many positive adjectives can be changed into comparatives by adding ___-er___ , and changed into superlatives by adding ___-est___ .
3. In Latin, the comparative adjective is formed by adding ___-ior___ and ___-ius___ to the stem.
4. The comparative adjective is declined like ___a regular M/F or a neuter noun___ , but does not show the ___i-stem pattern___ .
5. In Latin, the superlative is formed by adding ___-issimus -a -um (also -rimus or -limus)___ to the stem.
6. The superlative adjective is declined like ___a 1st/2nd-declension adjective___ .
7. Nouns compared by **quam** must be ___in the same case___ .
8. Adjectives with stems ending in a vowel are usually compared using the Latin adverbs ___**magis** and **máximē**___ .
9. The comparative adverb is the ___neuter nominative singular___ of the adjective.
10. The superlative adverb is formed by adding ___-ē___ to the superlative adjective stem.

Unit 5 Test
Unit 5 Test

D. Decline

Decline the comparative of **lenis**.

M/F		N	
lénior	leniores	lénius	leniora
lenioris	leniorum	lenioris	leniorum
leniori	lenióribus	leniori	lenióribus
leniorem	leniores	lénius	leniora
leniore	lenióribus	leniore	lenióribus

E. Adjective Forms

Give the comparative and superlative adjective forms, and translate.

Positive	Comparative	Superlative
verus -a -um	vérior -ius / *truer*	veríssimus -a -um / *truest*
mollis -e	móllior -ius / *softer*	mollíssimus -a -um / *softest*
céleber -bris -bre	celébrior -ius / *more famous*	celebérrimus -a -um / *most famous*
multus -a -um	plus pluris / *more*	plúrimus -a -um / *most*
bonus -a -um	mélior -ius / *better*	óptimus -a -um / *best*
parvus -a -um	minor minus / *smaller*	mínimus -a -um / *smallest*
multi -ae -a	plures plura / *more*	plúrimi -ae -a / *most*
malus -a -um	pejor pejus / *worse*	péssimus -a -um / *worst*
magnus -a -um	major majus / *greater*	máximus -a -um / *greatest*
senex senis	sénior sénius / *older*	máximus natu / *oldest*
júvenis -is	júnior június / *younger*	mínimus natu / *youngest*
símilis -e	simílior -ius / *more similar*	simíllimus -a -um / *most similar*

F. Adverb Forms

Give the comparative and superlative adverb forms, and translate.

Positive	Comparative	Superlative
laetē	laétius / *more happily*	laetíssimē / *most happily*
ácriter	ácrius / *more sharply*	acérrimē / *most sharply*
fácile	facílius / *more easily*	facíllimē / *most easily*
bene	mélius / *better*	óptimē / *best*
parum	minus / *less*	mínimē / *least*
saepe	saépius / *more often*	saepíssimē / *most often*
multum	plus / *more*	plúrimum / *most*
magnópere	magis / *more*	máximē / *most*
male	pejus / *worse*	péssimē / *worst*
diu	diútius / *longer (time)*	diutíssimē / *longest (time)*
prope	própius / *nearer*	próximē / *next*
potenter	poténtius / *more powerfully*	potentíssimē / *most powerfully*

G. Conjugate

Conjugate **ago** in the indicative active (6 tenses) and the indicative passive (6 tenses).

Present Active	
ago	ágimus
agis	ágitis
agit	agunt

Present Passive	
agor	ágimur
ágeris	agímini
ágitur	aguntur

Imperfect Active	
agebam	agebamus
agebas	agebatis
agebat	agebant

Imperfect Passive	
agebar	agebamur
agebaris	agebámini
agebatur	agebantur

Future Active	
agam	agemus
ages	agetis
aget	agent

Future Passive	
agar	agemur
agēris	agémini
agetur	agentur

Perfect Active	
egi	égimus
egisti	egistis
egit	egerunt

Perfect Passive			
actus -a -um	sum	acti -ae -a	sumus
	es		estis
	est		sunt

Pluperfect Active	
égeram	egeramus
égeras	egeratis
égerat	égerant

Pluperfect Passive			
actus -a -um	eram	acti -ae -a	eramus
	eras		eratis
	erat		erant

Future Perfect Active	
égero	egérimus
égeris	egéritis
égerit	égerint

Future Perfect Passive			
actus -a -um	ero	acti -ae -a	érimus
	eris		éritis
	erit		erunt

Unit 5 Test

H. Conjugate

Conjugate **ago** in the subjunctive active and passive.

Present Active	
agam	agamus
agas	agatis
agat	agant

Present Passive	
agar	agamur
agaris	agámini
agatur	agantur

Imperfect Active	
ágerem	ageremus
ágeres	ageretis
ágeret	ágerent

Imperfect Passive	
agerer	ageremur
agereris	agerémini
ageretur	agerentur

Perfect Active	
égerim	egérimus
égeris	egéritis
égerit	égerint

Perfect Passive			
actus -a -um	sim	acti -ae -a	simus
	sis		sitis
	sit		sint

Pluperfect Active	
egissem	egissemus
egisses	egissetis
egisset	egissent

Pluperfect Passive			
actus -a -um	essem	acti -ae -a	essemus
	esses		essetis
	esset		essent

In-Class Review for Final   Name_____ Date_____

A. Grammar

1. Give the three moods of Latin verbs.
   (1) ____indicative____ (2) ____imperative____ (3) ____subjunctive____

2. The indicative mood is used for ____statements and questions____ .

3. The imperative mood is used for____commands____ .

4. The subjunctive mood is used for ____potential action (opinions, purpose, wishes, etc.)____ .

5. The Naughty Nine have irregular forms in what cases? ____genitive, dative____

6. Forms of **is** and **ea** mean *he* and *she* when referring to ____persons, animals____
   and *it* when referring to ____things with grammatical gender____ .

7. Give two ways to use the subjunctive in an independent clause.
   (1) ____hortatory subjunctive____
   (2) ____deliberative questions____

8. The present subjunctive is formed by____adding____ or ____changing____ these vowels
   before the personal ending:
   1st conj. ____substitue **e** for **a**____
   2nd conj. ____add **a**____
   3rd conj.____substitute **a** for **i, o, u**____
   3rd conj. **io** ____add **a**____
   4th conj.____add **a**____

9. In a sentence with a purpose clause, the main verb is in the ____indicative mood____ , and
   the purpose clause is in the ____subjunctive mood____ .

10. If the verb of the main clause is in the present or future, the verb of the purpose clause is in the
    ____present subjunctive____ .

11. If the verb of the main clause is in the past, the verb of the purpose clause is in the
    ____imperfect subjunctive____ .

12. Give the degrees of comparison for adjectives and adverbs.
    (1) ____positive____ (2) ____comparative____ (3) ____superlative____

13. The ____positive____ is descriptive.

14. The ____comparative____ implies a comparison between two persons or things.

15. The ____superlative____ implies a comparison among more than two persons or things.

A. Vocabulary

Nouns: Check the correct gender, and give the genitive form and meaning.

Nom. Sg.	M	F	N	Genitive Form	Meaning
1. onus			x	óneris	burden
2. perículum			x	perículi	danger
3. ímpetus	x			ímpetūs	attack
4. ótium			x	ótii	ease, leisure
5. iter			x	itíneris	journey
6. sagitta		x		sagittae	arrow
7. currus	x			currūs	chariot, cart, wagon
8. lapis	x			lápidis	stone
9. aedifícium			x	aedifícii	building
10. ver			x	veris	spring
11. genu			x	genūs	knee
12. ordo	x			órdinis	line, row, order, rank
13. uxor		x		uxoris	wife
14. auctóritas		x		auctoritatis	authority
15. equitatus	x			equitatūs	cavalry
16. imber	x			imbris	rain, rainstorm
17. astrum			x	astri	heavenly body, heavens
18. sapiéntia		x		sapiéntiae	wisdom
19. litus			x	litoris	shore, coast
20. rus			x	ruris	countryside
21. vestis		x		vestis	clothes
22. scelus			x	scéleris	crime

Verbs: Give the remaining principal parts and meaning.

	Principal Part			Meaning
1st	2nd	3rd	4th	
1. cedo	cédere	cessi	cessus	to yield, give way
2. cogo	cógere	coegi	coactus	to collect, force
3. pono	pónere	pósui	pósitus	to put, place
4. claudo	cláudere	clausi	clausus	to close
5. ago	ágere	egi	actus	to do, drive, act, treat
6. scribo	scríbere	scripsi	scriptus	to write
7. gero	gérere	gessi	gestus	to wage, carry on
8. tollo	tóllere	sústuli	sublatus	to lift up, raise
9. premo	prémere	pressi	pressus	to press
10. mitto	míttere	misi	missus	to send

Third Form Final Exam

Adjectives: Give the rest of the dictionary form and meaning.

Adjective	Rest of dictionary form and meaning	
1. uter	-tra -trum	which (of two)
2. defessus	-a -um	weary, tired
3. potens	potentis	powerful
4. útilis	-e	useful
5. plenus	-a -um	full
6. álius	ália áliud	other, another
7. foedus	-a -um	foul, ugly, hideous
8. ingens	ingentis	huge
9. celer	céleris célere	fast, swift
10. felix	felicis	fortunate, lucky
11. idóneus	-a -um	suitable, fit, proper
12. álacer	-cris -cre	lively, spirited
13. nullus	-a -um	no, not any

Comparison of Adjectives and Adverbs: Complete the chart.

	Positive	Comparative	Superlative
adjective	latus -a -um	látior -ius	latíssimus -a -um
adverb	latē	látius	latíssimē
adjective	gravis -e	grávior -ius	gravíssimus -a -um
adverb	gráviter	grávius	gravíssimē

Comparison of Adjectives: Give the comparative and superlative forms.

Positive	Comparative	Superlative
1. potens	poténtior -ius	potentíssimus -a -um
2. miser	misérior -ius	misérrimus -a -um
3. pulcher	púlchrior -ius	pulchérrimus -a -um
4. acer	ácrior -ius	acérrimus -a -um
5. fidelis	fidélior -ius	fidelíssimus -a -um
6. fácilis	facílior -ius	facíllimus -a -um

Third Form Final Exam

B. Decline: fórtior fórtius

Case	M/F		N	
nom.	fórtior	fortiores	fórtius	fortióra
gen.	fortioris	fortiorum	fortioris	fortiorum
dat.	fortiori	fortióribus	fortiori	fortióribus
acc.	fortiorem	fortiores	fórtius	fortióra
abl.	fortiore	fortióribus	fortiore	fortióribus

C. Conjugate: Móneo in the indicative active (6 tenses) with meanings as shown.

Present Active (Latin)	
móneo	monemus
mones	monetis
monet	monent

Present Active Meanings, Sing. only
I warn, am warning, do warn
you warn, are warning, do warn
hsi warns, is warning, does warn

Imperfect Active (Latin)	
monebam	monebamus
monebas	monebatis
monebat	monebant

Imperfect Active Meanings, Sing. only
I was warning
you were warning
hsi was warning

Future Active (Latin)	
monebo	monébimus
monebis	monébitis
monebit	monebunt

Future Active Meanings, Sing. only
I will warn
you will warn
hsi will warn

Perfect Active (Latin)	
mónui	monúimus
monuisti	monuistis
mónuit	monuerunt

Perfect Active Meanings, Sing. only
I warned, have warned, did warn
you warned, have warned, did warn
hsi warned, has warned, did warn

Pluperfect Active (Latin)	
monúeram	monueramus
monúeras	monueratis
monúerat	monúerant

Pluperfect Active Meanings, Sing. only
I had warned
you had warned
hsi had warned

Future Perfect Active (Latin)	
monúero	monuérimus
monúeris	monuéritis
monúerit	monúerint

Future Perfect Active Meanings, Sing. only
I will have warned
you will have warned
hsi will have warned

D. Conjugate: <u>Móneo</u> in the indicative passive (6 tenses) with meanings as shown.

Present Passive (Latin)	
móneor	monemur
moneris	monémini
monetur	monentur

Present Passive Meanings, Sing. only
I am (being) warned
you are (being) warned
hsi is (being) warned

Imperfect Passive (Latin)	
monebar	monebamur
monebaris	monebámini
monebatur	monebantur

Imperfect Passive Meanings, Sing. only
I was (being) warned
you were (being) warned
hsi was (being) warned

Future Passive (Latin)	
monebor	monébimur
monéberis	monebímini
monébitur	monebuntur

Future Passive Meanings, Sing. only
I will be warned
you will be warned
hsi will be warned

Perfect Passive (Latin)			
mónitus -a -um	sum	móniti -ae -a	sumus
	es		estis
	est		sunt

Perfect Passive Meanings, Sing. only
I have been warned
you have been warned
hsi has been warned

Pluperfect Passive (Latin)			
mónitus -a -um	eram	móniti -ae -a	eramus
	eras		eratis
	erat		erant

Pluperfect Passive Meanings, Sing. only
I had been warned
you had been warned
hsi had been warned

Future Perfect Passive (Latin)			
mónitus -a -um	ero	móniti -ae -a	érimus
	eris		éritis
	erit		erunt

Future Perfect Passive Meanings, Sing. only
I will have been warned
you will have been warned
hsi will have been warned

E. Conjugate: <u>Móneo</u> in the subjunctive active (4 tenses) and passive (4 tenses).

Present Active	
móneam	moneamus
móneas	moneatis
móneat	móneant

Present Passive	
mónear	moneamur
monearis	moneámini
moneatur	moneantur

Imperfect Active	
monerem	moneremus
moneres	moneretis
moneret	monerent

Imperfect Passive	
monerer	moneremur
monereris	monerémini
moneretur	monerentur

Perfect Active	
monúerim	monuérimus
monúeris	monuéritis
monúerit	monúerint

Perfect Passive			
mónitus -a -um	sim	móniti -ae -a	simus
	sis		sitis
	sit		sint

Pluperfect Active	
monuissem	monuissemus
monuisses	monuissetis
monuisset	monuissent

Pluperfect Passive			
mónitus -a -um	essem	móniti -ae -a	essemus
	esses		essetis
	esset		essent

F. Conjugate: <u>Cápio</u> in the subjunctive active (4 tenses) and passive (4 tenses).

Present Active	
cápiam	capiamus
cápias	capiatis
cápiat	cápiant

Present Passive	
cápiar	capiamur
capiaris	capiámini
capiatur	capiantur

Imperfect Active	
cáperem	caperemus
cáperes	caperetis
cáperet	cáperent

Imperfect Passive	
cáperer	caperemur
capereris	caperémini
caperetur	caperentur

Perfect Active	
céperim	cepérimus
céperis	cepéritis
céperit	céperint

Perfect Passive			
captus -a -um	sim	capti -ae -a	simus
	sis		sitis
	sit		sint

Pluperfect Active	
cepissem	cepissemus
cepisses	cepissetis
cepisset	cepissent

Pluperfect Passive			
captus -a -um	essem	capti -ae -a	essemus
	esses		essetis
	esset		essent

Third Form Final Exam

G. Conjugate: <u>Sum</u> in the indicative with meanings (6 tenses), and in the subjunctive (4 tenses).

Present Indicative (Latin)	
sum	sumus
es	estis
est	sunt

Present Indicative Meanings, Sing. only
I am
you are
hsi was

Imperfect Indicative (Latin)	
eram	eramus
eras	eratis
erat	erant

Imperfect Indicative Meanings, Sing. only
I was
you were
hsi was

Future Indicative (Latin)	
ero	érimus
eris	éritis
erit	erunt

Future Indicative Meanings, Sing. only
I will be
you will be
hsi will be

Perfect Indicative (Latin)	
fui	fúimus
fuisti	fuistis
fuit	fuerunt

Perfect Indicative Meanings, Sing. only
I have been
you have been
hsi has been

Pluperfect Indicative (Latin)	
fúeram	fueramus
fúeras	fueratis
fúerat	fúerant

Pluperfect Indicative Meanings, Sing. only
I had been
you had been
hsi had been

Future Perfect Indicative (Latin)	
fúero	fuérimus
fúeris	fuéritis
fúerit	fúerint

Future Perfect Indicative Meanings, Sing. only
I will have been
you will have been
hsi will have been

Present Subjunctive	
sim	simus
sis	sitis
sit	sint

Perfect Subjunctive	
fúerim	fuérimus
fúeris	fuéritis
fúerit	fúerint

Imperfect Subjunctive	
essem	essemus
esses	essetis
esset	essent

Pluperfect Subjunctive	
fuissem	fuissemus
fuisses	fuissetis
fuisset	fuissent

Third Form Final Exam

H. Declensions

Singular	Plural
cornu	córnua
cornūs	córnuum
cornu	córnibus
cornu	córnua
cornu	córnibus

Singular	Plural
agmen	ágmina
ágminis	ágminum
ágmini	agmínibus
agmen	ágmina
ágmine	agmínibus

Singular			Plural		
M	F	N	M	F	N
solus	sola	solum	soli	solae	sola
solíus	solíus	solíus	solorum	solarum	solorum
soli	soli	soli	solis	solis	solis
solum	solam	solum	solos	solas	sola
solo	solā	solo	solis	solis	solis

Singular			Plural		
M/F		N	M/F		N
acer	acris	acre	acres		ácria
acris		acris	ácrium		ácrium
acri		acri	ácribus		ácribus
acrem		acre	acres		ácria
acri		acri	ácribus		ácribus

I. Pronouns: Decline the 3rd person personal pronoun <u>is</u> and the demonstrative pronoun <u>hic</u>.

Singular			Plural		
M	F	N	M	F	N
is	ea	id	ei	eae	ea
ejus	ejus	ejus	eorum	earum	eorum
ei	ei	ei	eis	eis	eis
eum	eam	eum	eos	eas	ea
eo	eā	eo	eis	eis	eis

Singular			Plural		
M	F	N	M	F	N
hic	haec	hoc	hi	hae	haec
hujus	hujus	hujus	horum	harum	horum
huic	huic	huic	his	his	his
hunc	hanc	hoc	hos	has	haec
hoc	hac	hoc	his	his	his

J. Latin Sayings

1. The die is cast. _Álea jacta est._
2. O the times, O the customs _O témpora, O mores_
3. Faster, Higher, Stronger _Cítius, Áltius, Fórtius_
4. I believe in order that I may understand. _Credo ut intéllegam._
5. Love conquers all things. _Amor vincit ómnia._
6. You may have the body. _Hábeas corpus._
7. Let arms yield to the toga. _Cedant arma togae._
8. It is finished. _Consummatum est._
9. in itself _per se_
10. Let the buyer beware. _Cáveat emptor_

K. Form Drill A

1. scribatur _it may be written_
2. claudet _hsi will close_
3. posúerant _they had placed_
4. acta sint _they may have been driven_
5. mítteres _you might send_
6. sustúlimus _we have lifted up_
7. premantur _they may be pressed_
8. céderet _hsi might yield_
9. gestum est _it has been waged_
10. cogunt _they collect_

L. Form Drill B: hb = had been (#2), mh = might have (#3), whb = will have been (#7)

1. I may send _mittam_
2. they hb written _scripti (-ae -a) erant_
3. we mh placed _posuissemus_
4. she will collect _coget_
5. we may yield _cedamus_
6. it may be driven _agatur_
7. it whb waged _gestum erit_
8. I might lift up _tóllerem_
9. it might be closed _clauderetur_
10. let them be pressed _premantur_

M. Translation

1. Pro se diligenter laborent. _Let them work diligently for themselves._
2. Ab hóstibus fugiamus? _Should we flee from the enemies?_
3. Quis mittetur in provínciam? _Who will be sent into the province?_
4. Hic equus est cítior quam illo. _This horse is quicker than that one._
5. Urbs mea forum pulchérrimum habet. _My city has the most beautiful forum._
6. Senator oravit ut urbem móneret. _The senator has spoken in order to warn the city._
7. Ipse imperator mínimē laborabat. _The general himself was working least._
8. Graéciae litus a nautis exploratum erat. _The shore of Greece had been explored by the sailors._
9. Aurum celábitis ne id inveniatur. _You all will hide the gold lest it be discovered._
10. Claude, Marce, pede jánuam. _Mark, close the door with your foot._